TEACHER'S GUIDE 6A

Consultant and author
Dr Fong Ho Kheong

Authors
Gan Kee Soon and Chelvi Ramakrishnan

UK consultants
Carole Skinner, Simon d'Angelo and Elizabeth Gibbs

OXFORD
UNIVERSITY PRESS

Published by Marshall Cavendish Education
Times Centre, 1 New Industrial Road, Singapore 536196
Customer Service Hotline: (65) 6213 9444
Email: tmesales@mceducation.com
Website: www.mceducation.com

Distributed by
Oxford University Press
Great Clarendon Street, Oxford,
OX2 6DP, United Kingdom
www.oxfordprimary.co.uk
www.oxfordowl.co.uk

First published 2015

ISBN 978-981-01-8910-5

Printed in the United Kingdom

Acknowledgements
Written by Dr Fong Ho Kheong, Gan Kee Soon and Chelvi Ramakrishnan

UK consultants: Carole Skinner, Simon d'Angelo and Elizabeth Gibbs

Cover artwork by Daron Parton

The authors and publisher would like to thank all schools and individuals who helped to trial and review Inspire Maths resources.

Contents

The background to *Inspire Maths*

A letter from Dr Fong Ho Kheong

Dear Colleague,

I am both humbled and proud to see that my work has now been adapted for use in many countries. *My Pals are Here!*, the series from which *Inspire Maths* is adapted, has been translated into languages including Spanish, Indonesian, Dutch and Arabic, and the books are used by millions of children all over the world.

International surveys show that children taught with the series score higher than their peers in standardised tests, and also that it helps young children to become more confident with maths. The 2012 PISA survey again placed Singapore's children at the top of international rankings for mathematics; the country also had the highest percentage of top achievers. In the USA, it was reported in 2013 that schools in the Fayette County, West Virginia who had adopted the programme had made impressive progress in their mathematics results, including a 12 per cent improvement among third graders in one school and a 20 per cent improvement among fourth graders in another.

Why does *Inspire Maths* work? A major strength of *Inspire Maths* is its robust structure, based on best-practice principles and methods of teaching and learning mathematics, including the concrete-pictorial-abstract (CPA) and scaffolding approaches, and a systematic teaching pathway. This comprehensive pathway emphasises mastery – with continuous, active reinforcement of concepts to help children assimilate and accommodate their learning – followed by extension, challenging children to develop and practise the thinking skills that will enable them to become confident, critically aware and independent learners. The textbooks from which *Inspire Maths* is adapted have also been informed by continuous evaluation of their success in the classroom, through a process of school visits, classroom observation and programme review. Because of this, *Inspire Maths* gives you a proven framework for supporting children of all abilities to achieve success.

Inspire Maths is based on well-established constructivist ideas of learning, and the views of internationally-renowned educationalists including Jerome Bruner, Jean Piaget, Lev Vygotsky, Richard Skemp and David Ausubel. Constructivism underpins the programme's approach to learning mathematical concepts and skills through assimilation and accommodation, and their reinforcement through reflective activities such as journal writing and error correction. This perspective is also reflected in the programme's emphasis on mastery learning and building children's confidence.

More particularly, Bruner's three modes of representation are mirrored by the concrete–pictorial–abstract learning progression which is central to *Inspire Maths*. Bruner's ideas parallel Piaget's stages of development; essentially, children's understanding of mathematical concepts depends on their stage of development. Learning in the early stages is achieved through concrete representation. Then, when ready, children can move on to pictorial representations – such as the bar model – which in turn provide them with a bridge to the abstract stage, and a flexible, fully independent understanding of the abstract, symbolic language of maths. Though it cannot be used to tackle every problem, the bar model has a particularly significant role in helping children at the concrete and semi-concrete operational stage (Piaget's developmental theory) to approach and solve problems successfully.

Skemp's ideas about instrumental and relational understanding are also an important part of the pedagogy underpinning *Inspire Maths*. Skemp suggests that learning mathematics by relating ideas to each other (relational understanding) is more meaningful, and therefore more effective, than memorising facts and procedures (instrumental understanding). Building on these ideas, *Inspire Maths* is designed to develop children's lasting and profound mathematical understanding which they will continue to extend and apply.

I would like to congratulate the UK schools and teachers who have made the choice to use *Inspire Maths*. I am confident that your children will experience similar success to that seen in other countries who have adopted this approach.

Dr Fong achieved a PhD in Mathematics Education from King's College London before teaching mathematics in the National Institute of Education, Nanyang Technological University, for over 24 years. He is currently a senior Mathematics Specialist with the Regional Centre for Education in Science and Mathematics (RECSAM) in Penang, Malaysia. He has published more than 100 journal articles, research reports, and primary and secondary mathematics books, and his research work includes diagnosing children with mathematical difficulties and teaching thinking skills to solve mathematical problems.

What is *Inspire Maths*?

Inspire Maths is the UK edition of *My Pals are Here!*, the internationally renowned approach used to teach maths in Singapore, which was heavily influenced by the Cockroft report of 1982[1]. Singapore's Ministry of Education drew on leading international research on effective teaching and learning of mathematics to meet the challenge of raising primary mathematics attainment within Singapore's schools.

The approach to mathematics teaching and learning that was developed was further refined over subsequent decades and it is this approach that is central to *My Pals are Here!* Authored by Dr Fong Ho Kheong and first published in 2001, *My Pals are Here!* is used by almost 100% of State Primary schools and over 80% of Primary schools in Singapore.

Dr Fong's overarching aim in developing *My Pals are Here!* was to help all children understand and use mathematics confidently and competently, and to support non-specialist maths teachers to deliver this. The programme's success in achieving this aim is reflected in the high levels of mathematics attainment by Singapore's pupils, who are consistently ranked among the very top in international comparison studies such as PISA and TIMSS. It is also reflected in the results of schools outside Singapore that have adopted the series, for example, in the USA and South Africa.

Inspire Maths provides a highly scaffolded learning framework with problem solving at its heart. It is built on a focused, coherent and cumulative spiral curriculum that continuously builds and consolidates knowledge to reach deep understanding. The programme encourages extensive practice to develop fluency and mastery, so that every child – across all abilities – can succeed at mathematics.

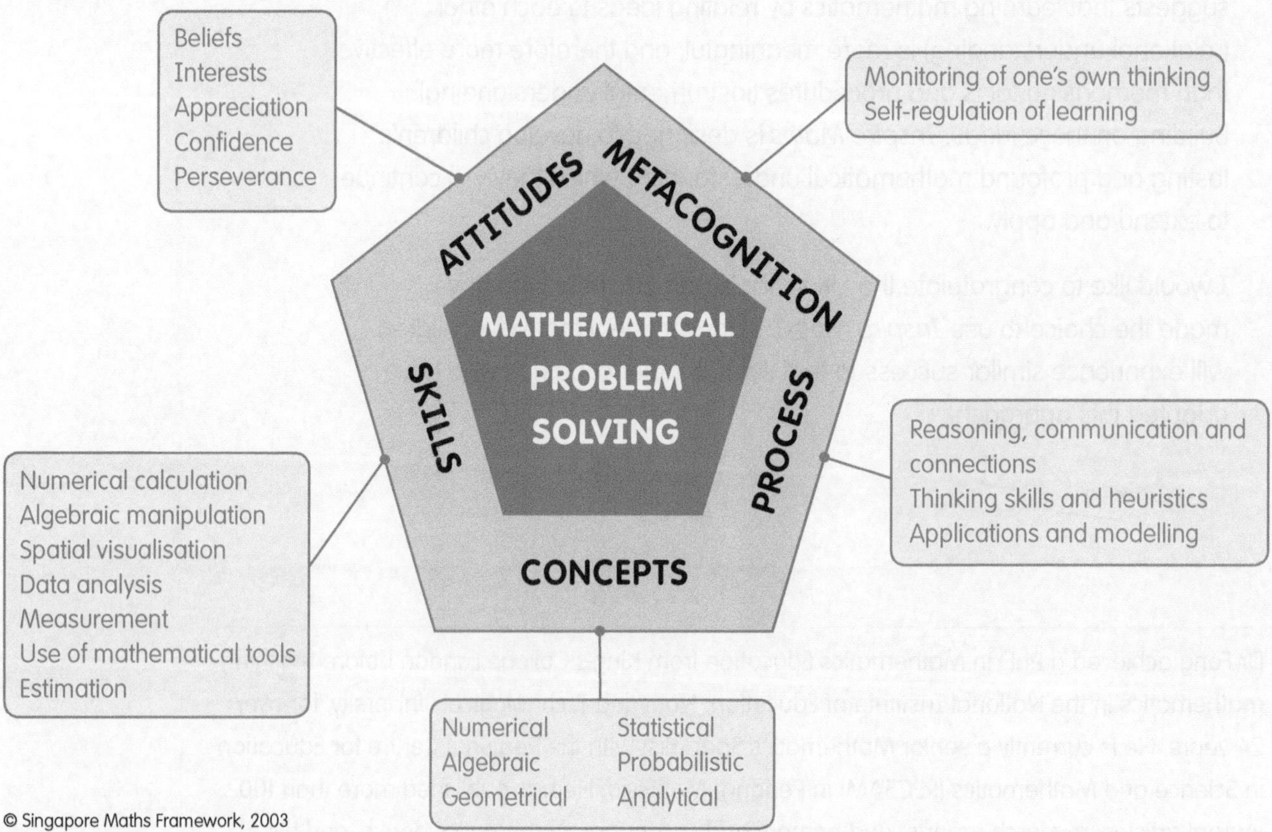

The principles that underpin *Inspire Maths*

1 Mathematics Counts, Dr W.H.Cockroft, 1982

The concrete-pictorial-abstract approach

Inspire Maths emphasises the development of critical thinking and problem solving skills, which help children make connections to develop deeper understanding. The powerful concrete–pictorial–abstract (CPA) approach, including the bar model method, is central to this.

Why is the CPA approach so powerful? From very early on in their school life, we expect children to use and understand numbers, which are abstract concepts. Many children struggle with this and so their first experiences of mathematics can be confusing, leaving them with no solid foundation to build on for later learning. The CPA approach helps children achieve secure number sense – that is, a sense of what numbers really represent and how to use them mathematically. This is done through a series of carefully structured representations – first using physical objects (concrete), then diagrams or pictures (pictorial), and ultimately using representations such as numerals (abstract).

In the example below from *Inspire Maths* Pupil Textbook 6B, children are exploring radius, diameter and circumference. Using the CPA approach, they explore the relationships using circles drawn with a pair of compasses, then pictorial representations of circles, and finally through words, written symbols and calculations.

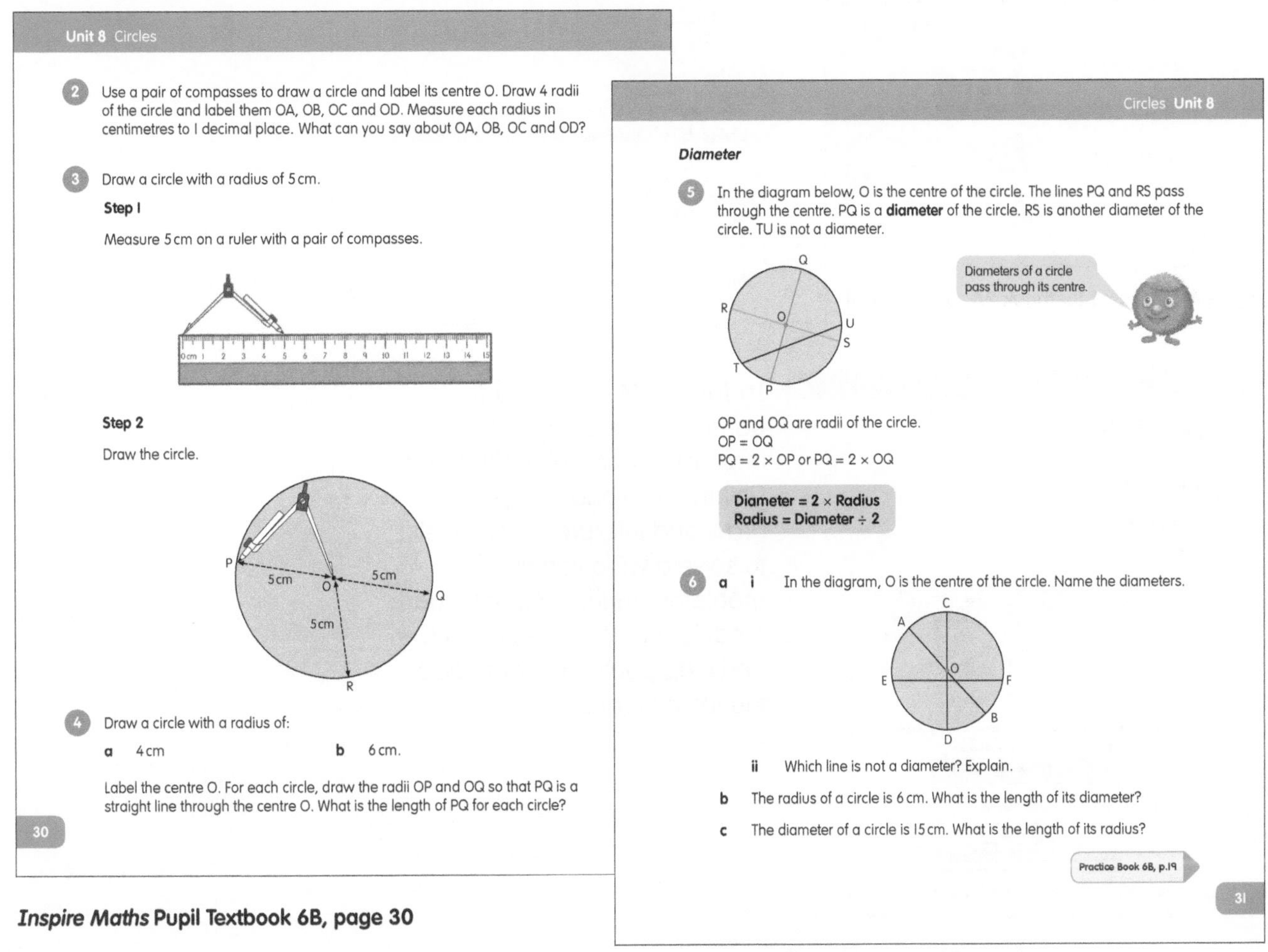

Unit 8 Circles

2 Use a pair of compasses to draw a circle and label its centre O. Draw 4 radii of the circle and label them OA, OB, OC and OD. Measure each radius in centimetres to 1 decimal place. What can you say about OA, OB, OC and OD?

3 Draw a circle with a radius of 5 cm.

Step 1

Measure 5 cm on a ruler with a pair of compasses.

Step 2

Draw the circle.

4 Draw a circle with a radius of:

a 4 cm **b** 6 cm.

Label the centre O. For each circle, draw the radii OP and OQ so that PQ is a straight line through the centre O. What is the length of PQ for each circle?

30

Circles **Unit 8**

Diameter

5 In the diagram below, O is the centre of the circle. The lines PQ and RS pass through the centre. PQ is a **diameter** of the circle. RS is another diameter of the circle. TU is not a diameter.

Diameters of a circle pass through its centre.

OP and OQ are radii of the circle.
OP = OQ
PQ = 2 × OP or PQ = 2 × OQ

Diameter = 2 × Radius
Radius = Diameter ÷ 2

6 **a** i In the diagram, O is the centre of the circle. Name the diameters.

ii Which line is not a diameter? Explain.

b The radius of a circle is 6 cm. What is the length of its diameter?

c The diameter of a circle is 15 cm. What is the length of its radius?

Practice Book 6B, p.19

31

***Inspire Maths* Pupil Textbook 6B, page 30**

***Inspire Maths* Pupil Textbook 6B, page 31**

The bar model

The bar model is a step-by-step method that helps children to understand and extract the information within a calculation or word problem. By drawing a bar model, children translate a calculation or word problem into a picture. The approach helps children process the information given in the problem, visualise the structure, make connections and solve the problem.

The bar model is first introduced in *Inspire Maths* 2. In the following activity, children explore addition and subtraction initially with concrete apparatus before moving on to using a pictorial representation – the bar model.

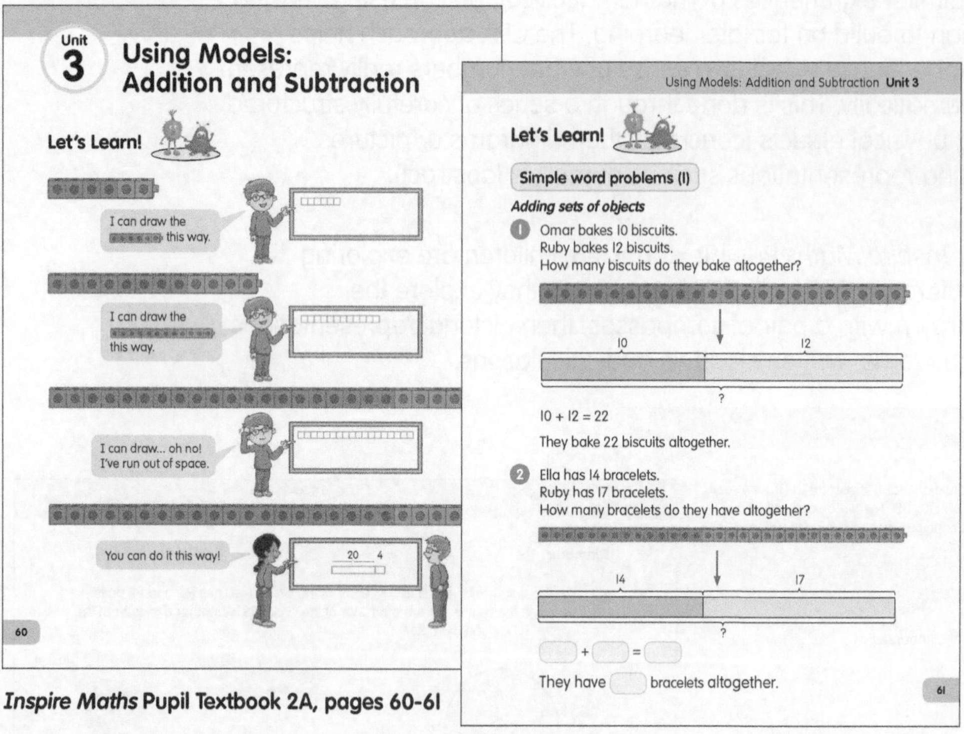

***Inspire Maths* Pupil Textbook 2A, pages 60-61**

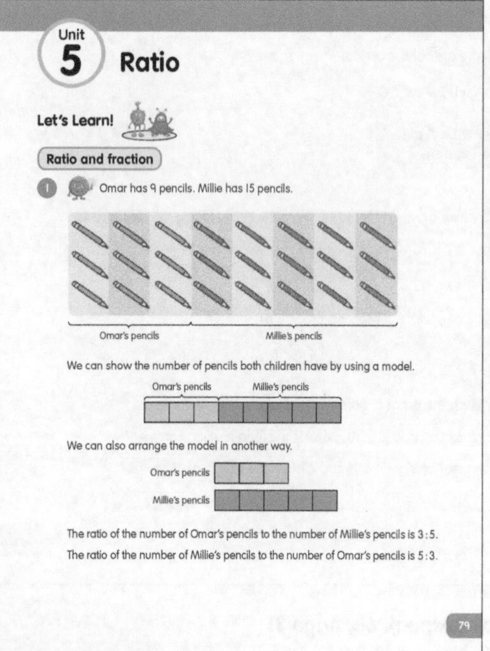

***Inspire Maths* Pupil Textbook 6A, page 79**

In *Inspire Maths* 5 and 6, bar models are applied to increasingly complex situations. Children are encouraged to draw and interpret bar models to solve a wide variety of problems. In this example, bar models are used to introduce and help pupils conceptualise the topic of ratio.

Heuristics for problem solving

Inspire Maths helps children learn to use *heuristics* to solve problems. *Heuristics* refers to the different strategies that children can adopt to solve unfamiliar or non-routine problems. These strategies include drawing the bar model, pattern-spotting, using diagrams and estimating or 'guess and check'.

In this example from *Inspire Maths* Pupil Textbook 6A, children are encouraged to make a list and use 'guess and check' to solve the problem about ratio.

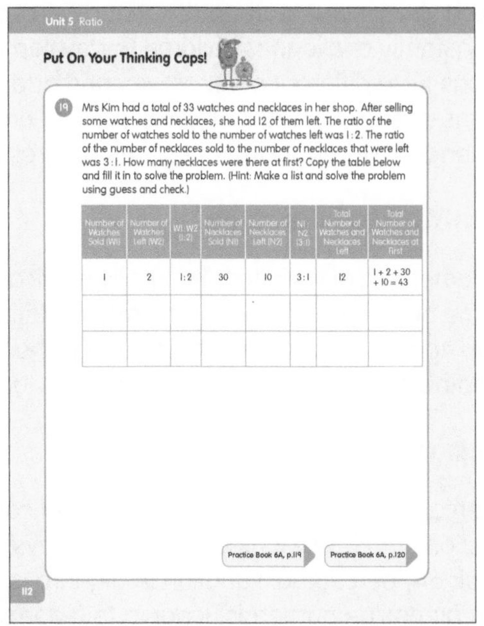

Unit 5 Ratio

Put On Your Thinking Caps!

19 Mrs Kim had a total of 33 watches and necklaces in her shop. After selling some watches and necklaces, she had 12 of them left. The ratio of the number of watches sold to the number of watches left was 1 : 2. The ratio of the number of necklaces sold to the number of necklaces that were left was 3 : 1. How many necklaces were there at first? Copy the table below and fill it in to solve the problem. (Hint: Make a list and solve the problem using guess and check.)

Number of Watches Sold (W1)	Number of Watches Left (W2)	W1 : W2 (1 : 2)	Number of Necklaces Sold (N1)	Number of Necklaces Left (N2)	N1 : N2 (3 : 1)	Total Number of Watches and Necklaces Left	Total Number of Watches and Necklaces at First
1	2	1 : 2	30	10	3 : 1	12	1 + 2 + 30 + 10 = 43

Practice Book 6A, p.119 Practice Book 6A, p.120

112

***Inspire Maths* Pupil Textbook 6A, page 112**

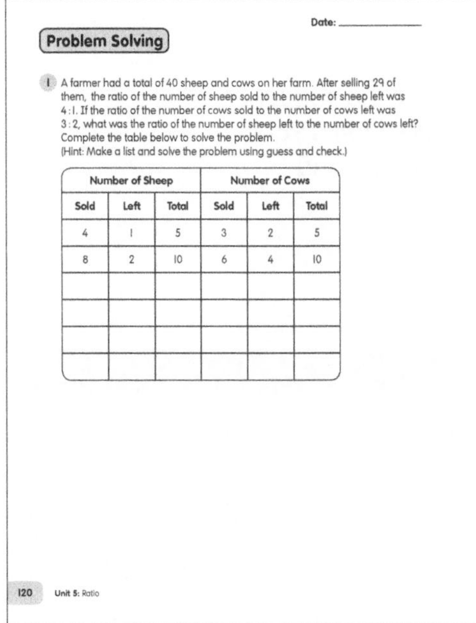

Date: ____________

Problem Solving

1 A farmer had a total of 40 sheep and cows on her farm. After selling 29 of them, the ratio of the number of sheep sold to the number of sheep left was 4 : 1. If the ratio of the number of cows sold to the number of cows left was 3 : 2, what was the ratio of the number of sheep left to the number of cows left? Complete the table below to solve the problem.
(Hint: Make a list and solve the problem using guess and check.)

Number of Sheep			Number of Cows		
Sold	Left	Total	Sold	Left	Total
4	1	5	3	2	5
8	2	10	6	4	10

120 Unit 5: Ratio

***Inspire Maths* Practice Book 6A, page 120**

The *Inspire Maths* Practice Books reinforce concepts introduced in the Pupil Textbooks and provide varied, frequent practice to develop fluency. As they practise, children begin to self-select the appropriate strategy for each problem, helping them to become confident problem solvers.

Higher-order questioning

Inspire Maths is designed to stimulate thinking beyond the activities from the Pupil Textbooks. The activities should kick-start mathematically meaningful conversations through questioning, giving children opportunities to think mathematically, discover connections and be creative.

You can use written problems as a starting point for further questioning by asking open-ended questions. For example, 'Can you see a pattern? Why does it work? Does it always work? What happens if...?'

Modelling higher-order questioning at every opportunity will encourage children to use this strategy to explore and solve problems for themselves.

A heuristics-based question section at the end of this book contains additional questions to supplement your resources for developing pupils' higher-order thinking skills and skills in solving non-routine questions.

Making use of variation

Research shows that mathematical and perceptual variation deepens understanding as it constantly challenges children to develop their existing understanding by looking at questions from different perspectives and adapting to new situations. The numbers and problems in *Inspire Maths* activities have been specifically selected on this basis to challenge children as the questions progress and lead them towards mastery.

Mathematical variation

With mathematical variation, the mathematical concept, for example addition, stays the same but the variation is in the mathematics. For example, addition *without* regrouping and addition *with* regrouping. The variation challenges children to use their mathematical skills flexibly to suit the situation, deepening understanding.

Perceptual variation

With perceptual variation, the mathematical concept is the same throughout the sequence of questions but is presented in different ways. In this example from *Inspire Maths* Pupil Textbook 6A, perceptual variation in algebra is provided by the use of diagrams and models alongside numerals, leading to a deeper understanding.

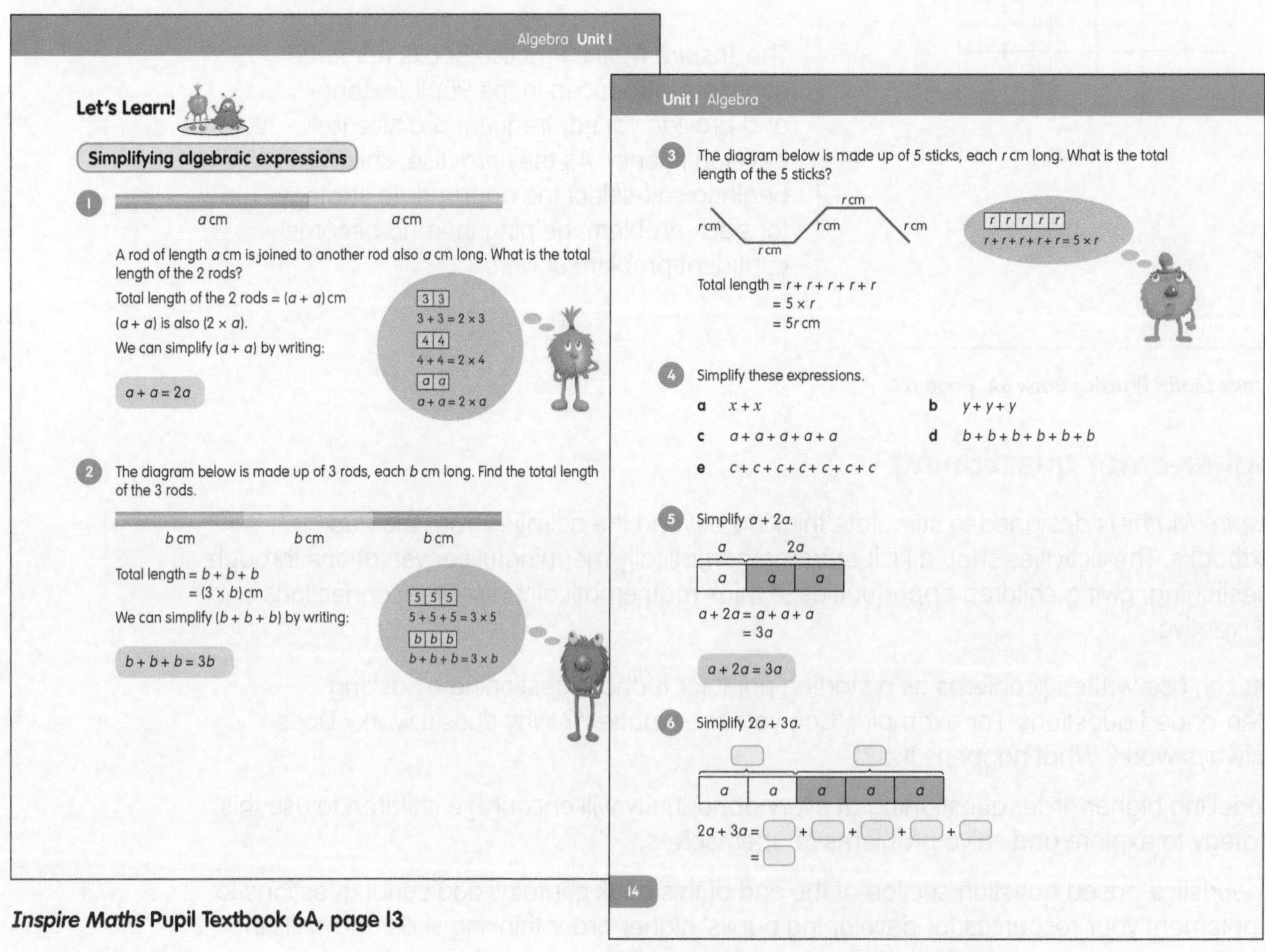

Algebra Unit 1

Let's Learn!

Simplifying algebraic expressions

1 a cm a cm

A rod of length a cm is joined to another rod also a cm long. What is the total length of the 2 rods?

Total length of the 2 rods = $(a + a)$ cm

$(a + a)$ is also $(2 \times a)$.

We can simplify $(a + a)$ by writing:

$a + a = 2a$

2 The diagram below is made up of 3 rods, each b cm long. Find the total length of the 3 rods.

b cm b cm b cm

Total length = $b + b + b$

= $(3 \times b)$ cm

We can simplify $(b + b + b)$ by writing:

$b + b + b = 3b$

Unit 1 Algebra

3 The diagram below is made up of 5 sticks, each r cm long. What is the total length of the 5 sticks?

Total length = $r + r + r + r + r$

= $5 \times r$

= $5r$ cm

4 Simplify these expressions.

a $x + x$

b $y + y + y$

c $a + a + a + a + a$

d $b + b + b + b + b + b$

e $c + c + c + c + c + c + c$

5 Simplify $a + 2a$.

$a + 2a = a + a + a$

$= 3a$

$a + 2a = 3a$

6 Simplify $2a + 3a$.

$2a + 3a = \square + \square + \square + \square + \square$

$= \square$

14

***Inspire Maths* Pupil Textbook 6A, page 13**

***Inspire Maths* Pupil Textbook 6A, page 14**

The *Inspire Maths* teaching pathway

Inspire Maths is a programme that teaches to mastery. It is built on a cumulative spiral curriculum, focusing on core topics to build deep understanding. The *Inspire Maths* teaching pathway scaffolds in-depth learning of key mathematical concepts through the development of problem-solving and critical thinking skills, and extensive opportunities for practice.

Pupil Textbooks to scaffold new learning

Inspire Maths Pupil Textbooks present new learning clearly and consistently, providing a highly scaffolded framework to support all children. Mathematical concepts are presented visually, with specific and structured activities, to build firm foundations. There are two Pupil Textbooks for each level.

Let's Learn! to build firm foundations

Carefully scaffolded learning through *Let's Learn!* activities in the *Inspire Maths* Pupil Textbooks promotes deep mathematical understanding through:

- clearly presented pages to illustrate how the CPA approach can be used to build firm foundations
- careful questioning to support the use of concrete apparatus
- opportunities for higher-order questioning (see page ix) to help children become confident and competent problem solvers
- opportunities to assess each child's understanding and prior knowledge through observing their use of concrete apparatus and how they approach the activity
- use of mathematical talk to explore and develop reasoning skills.

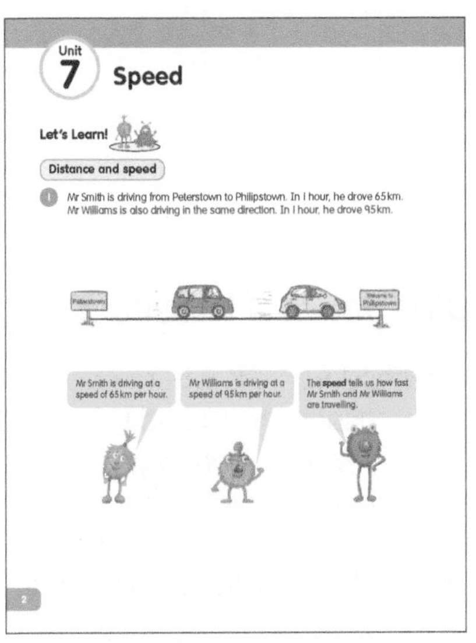
Unit 7 Speed

Let's Learn!

Distance and speed

1 Mr Smith is driving from Peterstown to Philipstown. In 1 hour, he drove 65 km. Mr Williams is also driving in the same direction. In 1 hour, he drove 95 km.

Mr Smith is driving at a speed of 65 km per hour.

Mr Williams is driving at a speed of 95 km per hour.

The **speed** tells us how fast Mr Smith and Mr Williams are travelling.

2

***Inspire Maths* Pupil Textbook 6B, page 2**

Guided practice to develop deep understanding

After a concept has been introduced in *Let's Learn!*, guided practice develops the deep understanding required for mastery. Support and guide children as they work collaboratively in pairs or small groups through the guided practice activities indicated by empty coloured boxes in the Pupil Textbook.

Frequent opportunities for guided practice:

- help children develop deep understanding
- develop mathematical language and reasoning through collaborative work
- provide further opportunities to check children's understanding by observing their use of concrete apparatus and listening to their discussions
- help you to provide appropriate intervention – guiding those who need extra support and challenging those who are ready for the next step.

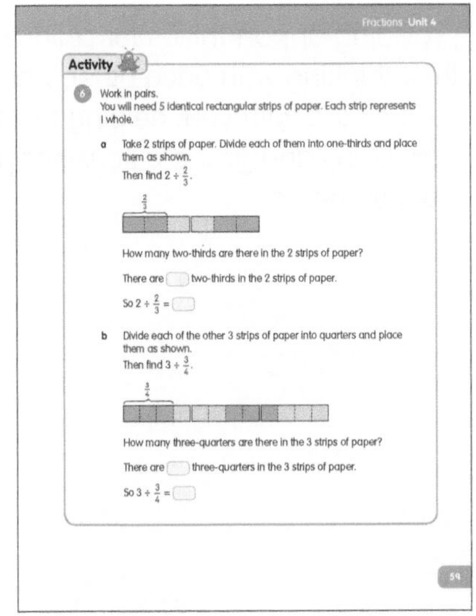
Fractions Unit 4

Activity

6 Work in pairs.
You will need 5 identical rectangular strips of paper. Each strip represents 1 whole.

a Take 2 strips of paper. Divide each of them into one-thirds and place them as shown.
Then find $2 \div \frac{2}{3}$.

How many two-thirds are there in the 2 strips of paper?

There are ☐ two-thirds in the 2 strips of paper.

So $2 \div \frac{2}{3} =$ ☐

b Divide each of the other 3 strips of paper into quarters and place them as shown.
Then find $3 \div \frac{3}{4}$.

How many three-quarters are there in the 3 strips of paper?

There are ☐ three-quarters in the 3 strips of paper.

So $3 \div \frac{3}{4} =$ ☐

59

***Inspire Maths* Pupil Textbook 6A, page 59**

Let's Explore! to investigate and apply learning

Engaging and investigative *Let's Explore!* activities in the *Inspire Maths* Pupil Textbooks encourage children to apply concepts they have been learning and provide an opportunity to assess their reasoning skills by observing how they approach the tasks.

Children work collaboratively in small groups or pairs:

- *Let's Explore!* activities encourage children to investigate connections through mathematical reasoning
- meaningful discussion and conversation develops mathematical language.

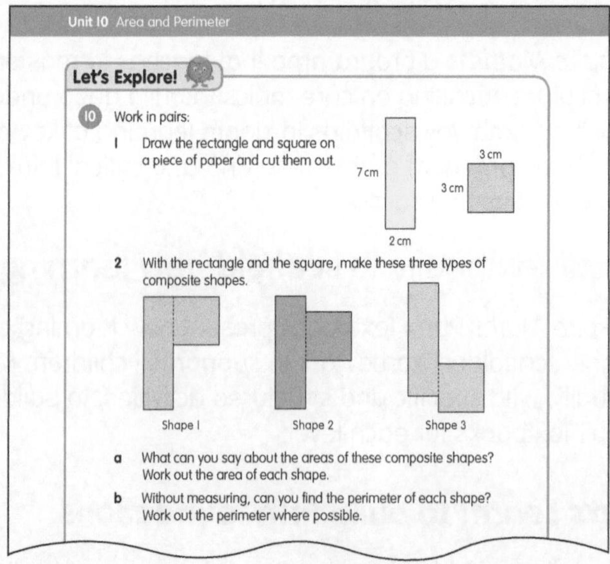

Unit 10 Area and Perimeter

Let's Explore!

10 Work in pairs:

1 Draw the rectangle and square on a piece of paper and cut them out.

2 With the rectangle and the square, make these three types of composite shapes.

a What can you say about the areas of these composite shapes? Work out the area of each shape.

b Without measuring, can you find the perimeter of each shape? Work out the perimeter where possible.

***Inspire Maths* Pupil Textbook 6B, page 68**

Maths Journal to reflect

The *Maths Journal* is where each child records their mathematical thinking and reflects on their learning. The typical *Maths Journal* would be a child's own exercise book or notebook – something that the child 'owns', can share with you, with parents or carers, and that builds up over time.

Children reflect on their learning through their *Maths Journal*:

- giving both the child and you a valuable assessment tool, showing progress over time
- providing opportunities for children to discuss their thinking with each other, parents or carers, and with you, helping to establish next steps and giving a sense of pride in their achievements.

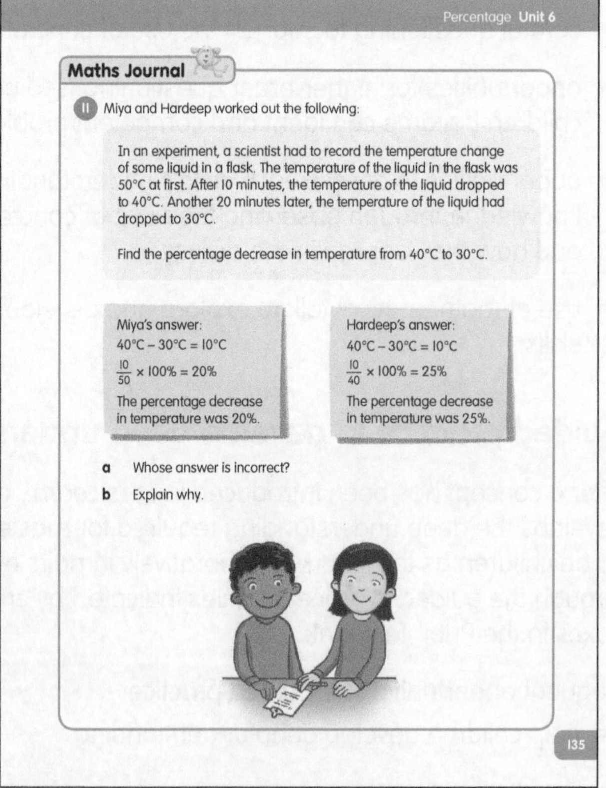

Percentage Unit 6

Maths Journal

11 Miya and Hardeep worked out the following:

In an experiment, a scientist had to record the temperature change of some liquid in a flask. The temperature of the liquid in the flask was 50°C at first. After 10 minutes, the temperature of the liquid dropped to 40°C. Another 20 minutes later, the temperature of the liquid had dropped to 30°C.

Find the percentage decrease in temperature from 40°C to 30°C.

Miya's answer:
40°C – 30°C = 10°C
$\frac{10}{50} \times 100\% = 20\%$
The percentage decrease in temperature was 20%.

Hardeep's answer:
40°C – 30°C = 10°C
$\frac{10}{40} \times 100\% = 25\%$
The percentage decrease in temperature was 25%.

a Whose answer is incorrect?

b Explain why.

135

***Inspire Maths* Pupil Textbook 6A, page 135**

Let's Wrap It Up! and *Let's Revise!* to consolidate learning

The key concepts covered are summarised in *Let's Wrap It Up!* at the end of each unit. Worked examples provided in *Let's Revise!* allow children to explore their own understanding of those key concepts and reinforce strategies learnt.

Learning is consolidated through:

- emphasising key concepts
- discussion and exploration of the strategies used in worked examples
- enabling children to reflect on their own learning.

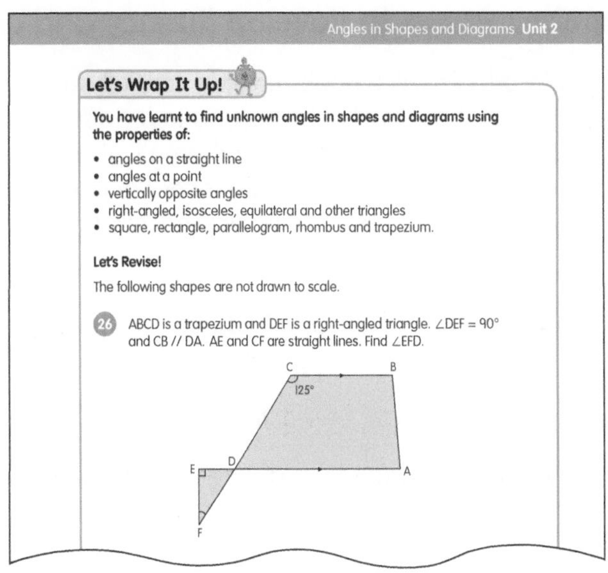

***Inspire Maths* Pupil Textbook 6A, page 35**

Put On Your Thinking Caps! to challenge

Each unit concludes with a *Put On Your Thinking Caps!* activity in the Pupil Textbook which challenges children to solve non-routine problems.

Challenging activities:

- ask children to draw on prior knowledge as well as newly learned concepts
- ask children to use problem solving strategies and critical thinking skills, for example sequencing or comparing
- provide valuable opportunities to assess whether children have developed a deep understanding of a concept by listening to their explanations of their mathematical thinking and looking at how they model the problem, for example using concrete apparatus and pictorial representations.

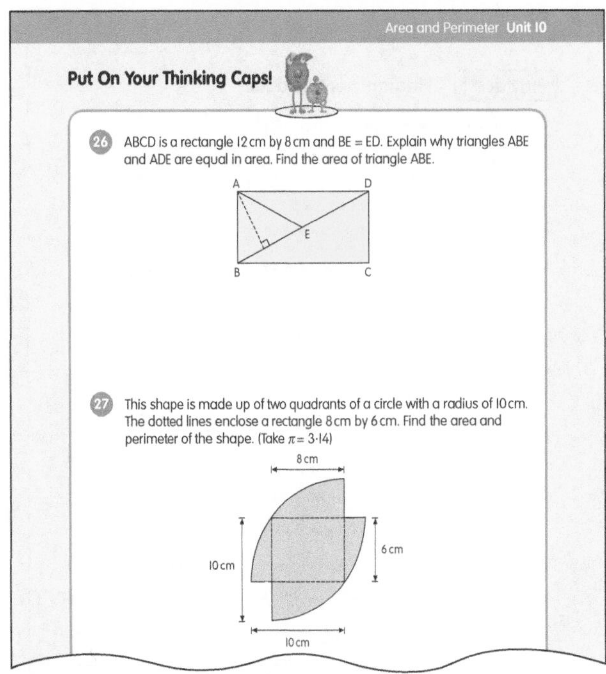

***Inspire Maths* Pupil Textbook 6B, page 73**

Home Maths to encourage mathematical conversations

Home Maths activities in the Pupil Textbooks are engaging, hands-on suggestions that parents and carers can use with children to explore maths further outside the classroom, for example through finding shapes in pictures and around the house.

Engaging home activities:

- help you to involve parents and carers in their child's mathematical learning
- help children to see maths in the world around them.

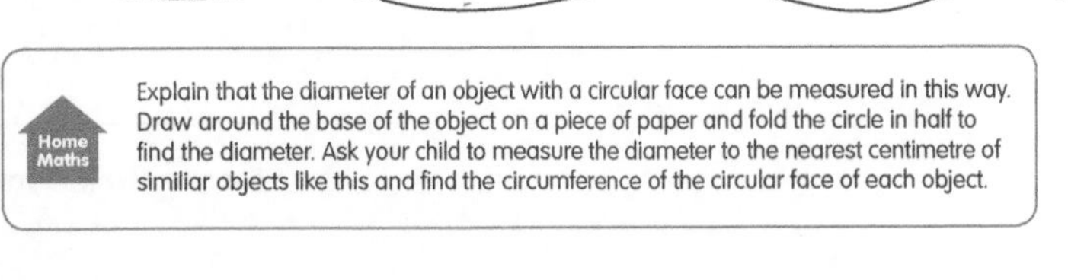

***Inspire Maths* Pupil Textbook 6B, page 33**

Practice Books to develop fluency and consolidate

Inspire Maths Practice Books provide carefully structured questions to reinforce concepts introduced in the Pupil Textbooks and to provide varied, frequent practice. A wealth of activities develop fluency, build mathematical confidence and lead towards mastery. The Practice Books are also a valuable record of individual progress. There are four Practice Books for *Inspire Maths* 1-3 and two Practice Books for *Inspire Maths* 4-6.

Each Practice Book includes:

- **Challenging Practice** and **Problem Solving** activities to develop children's critical thinking skills
- **Reviews** after every two or three units, to reinforce learning
- **Revisions** that draw from a range of preceding topics, concepts and strands, for more complete consolidation.

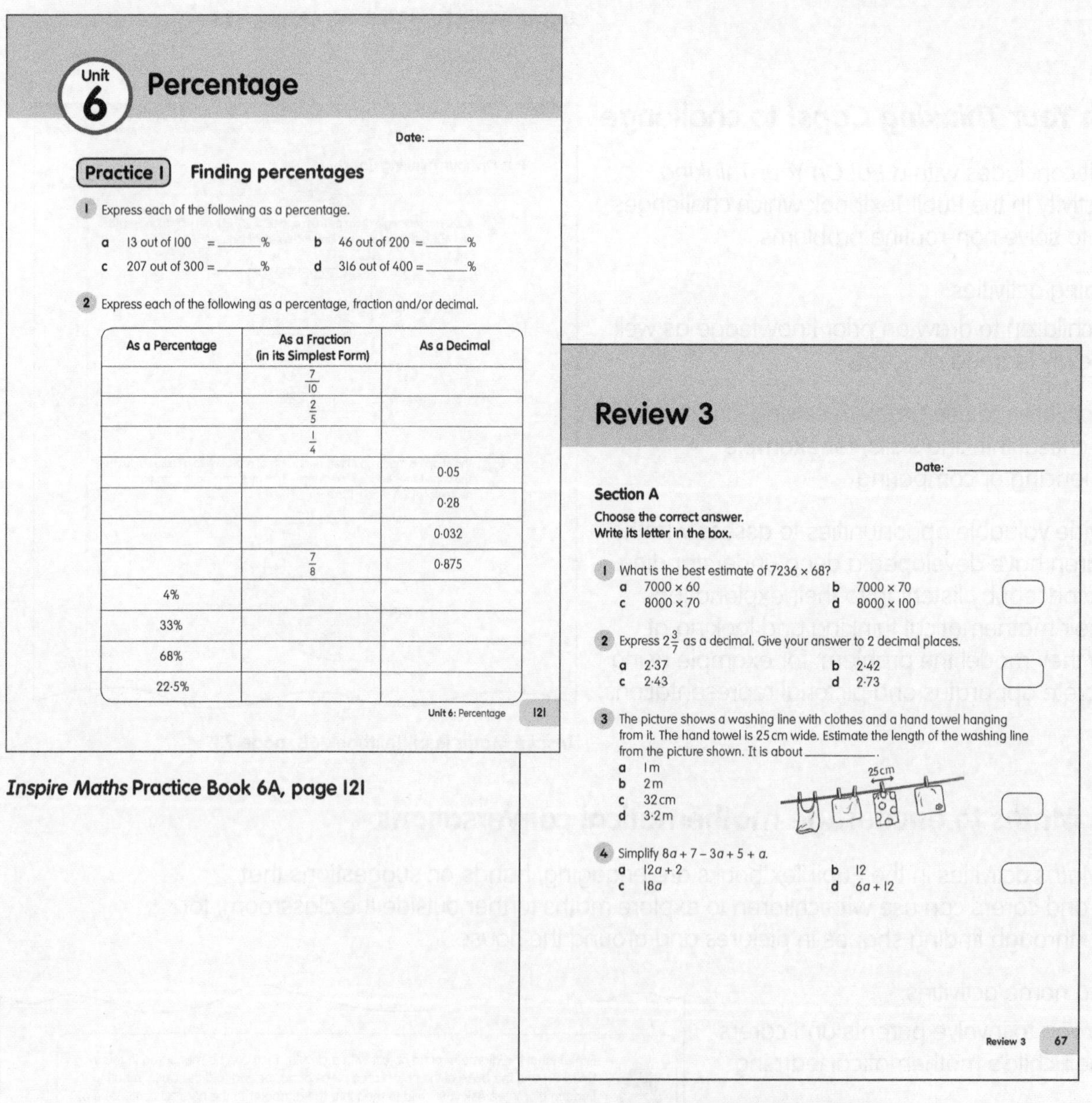

Unit 6 **Percentage**

Date: ____________

Practice 1 **Finding percentages**

1 Express each of the following as a percentage.

a 13 out of 100 = ____ % b 46 out of 200 = ____ %
c 207 out of 300 = ____ % d 316 out of 400 = ____ %

2 Express each of the following as a percentage, fraction and/or decimal.

As a Percentage	As a Fraction (in its Simplest Form)	As a Decimal
	$\frac{7}{10}$	
	$\frac{2}{5}$	
	$\frac{1}{4}$	
		0·05
		0·28
		0·032
	$\frac{7}{8}$	0·875
4%		
33%		
68%		
22·5%		

Unit 6: Percentage 121

Inspire Maths Practice Book 6A, page 121

Review 3

Date: ____________

Section A

Choose the correct answer.
Write its letter in the box.

1 What is the best estimate of 7236 × 68?
a 7000 × 60 b 7000 × 70
c 8000 × 70 d 8000 × 100

2 Express $2\frac{3}{7}$ as a decimal. Give your answer to 2 decimal places.
a 2·37 b 2·42
c 2·43 d 2·73

3 The picture shows a washing line with clothes and a hand towel hanging from it. The hand towel is 25 cm wide. Estimate the length of the washing line from the picture shown. It is about ____.
a 1 m
b 2 m
c 32 cm
d 3·2 m

25 cm

4 Simplify $8a + 7 - 3a + 5 + a$.
a $12a + 2$ b 12
c $18a$ d $6a + 12$

Review 3 67

***Inspire Maths* Practice Book 6B, page 67**

Assessment Books to create a record of progress

Inspire Maths provides comprehensive Assessment Books with regular summative assessments to create a record of progress for each child, as well as giving children opportunities to reflect on their own learning. The wraparound assessment provided through the *Inspire Maths* teaching pathway in combination with the *Inspire Maths* Assessment Books enables rapid, appropriate intervention as soon as a child needs it, before they fall behind and when they are ready to be challenged. Topics and concepts are frequently revisited in the assessments, helping to build mastery.

There is one Assessment Book for each level, providing complete coverage of the key concepts across a year. Each assessment is divided into sections so you can easily break them down into appropriate chunks to suit your class. For the early levels, you may choose to assess in small groups, reading out the questions and scribing answers. Encourage children to use concrete apparatus when they need support to help them work through the questions.

There are three types of assessment within each Assessment Book:

1. **Main assessments:** The main assessments cover the key learning objectives from the preceding two or three units of the Pupil Textbooks. Through the main assessments, children are given opportunities to apply their learning in a variety of different contexts, helping you to quickly identify which children are ready to move on and which need further support. Children may self-mark to reflect on their progress.
2. **Check-ups:** There are two check-ups in Year 6 which revisit the previous units, drawing on prior knowledge to encourage children to make connections and apply their learning to solve problems. These assessments give you valuable opportunities to check children's understanding through observing how they approach questions, use and interpret mathematical language and use heuristics.
3. **Challenging Problems:** These assessments make use of non-routine and unfamiliar questions to see how children use their repertoire of strategies to tackle more challenging problems. Use this as an opportunity to assess children's mathematical thinking, reasoning and problem solving skills by looking at their methods and how they approach the problem. They are particularly suitable for extension and assessing a child's level of mastery.

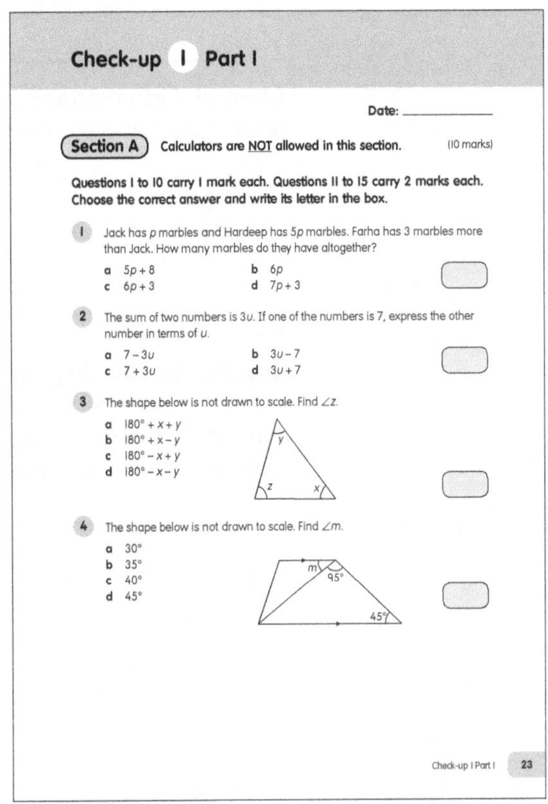

Check-up 1 Part 1

Date: ________

Section A Calculators are NOT allowed in this section. (10 marks)

Questions 1 to 10 carry 1 mark each. Questions 11 to 15 carry 2 marks each. Choose the correct answer and write its letter in the box.

1. Jack has p marbles and Hardeep has $5p$ marbles. Farha has 3 marbles more than Jack. How many marbles do they have altogether?

   a $5p + 8$ b $6p$
   c $6p + 3$ d $7p + 3$

2. The sum of two numbers is $3u$. If one of the numbers is 7, express the other number in terms of u.

   a $7 - 3u$ b $3u - 7$
   c $7 + 3u$ d $3u + 7$

3. The shape below is not drawn to scale. Find $\angle z$.

   a $180° + x + y$
   b $180° + x - y$
   c $180° - x + y$
   d $180° - x - y$

4. The shape below is not drawn to scale. Find $\angle m$.

   a 30°
   b 35°
   c 40°
   d 45°

Inspire Maths **Assessment Book 6, page 23**

Using the Teacher's Guide

There are two *Inspire Maths* Teacher's Guides for each level, one per Pupil Textbook. Each Teacher's Guide contains:

- information on how to get started
- long-term planning support
- medium-term planning support
- suggested teaching sequence for each pupil textbook page
- answers
- photocopiable activities.

Key concepts clearly outline the important ideas children will be introduced to within each unit.

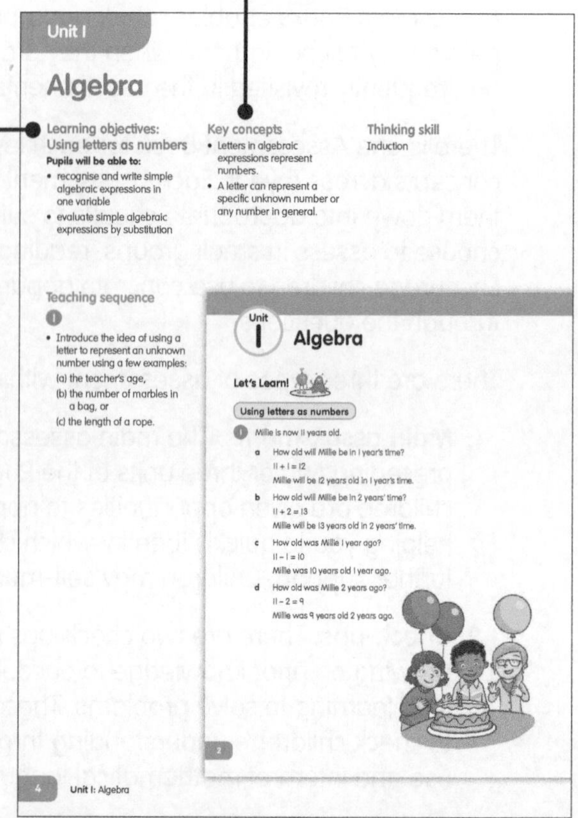

Learning objectives clearly signal the aims of the unit, which are designed to help children develop their understanding of the unit's key concepts. Children are introduced to the learning objectives in the Pupil Textbook. The Practice Book provides opportunities to practise and consolidate for mastery.

Inspire Maths **Teacher's Guide 6A, page 4**

Ideas for **further practice activities** to develop fluency are outlined in every unit.

Opportunities are flagged for children to work independently in their **Maths Journal**, to record and reflect on their learning, leading towards mastery.

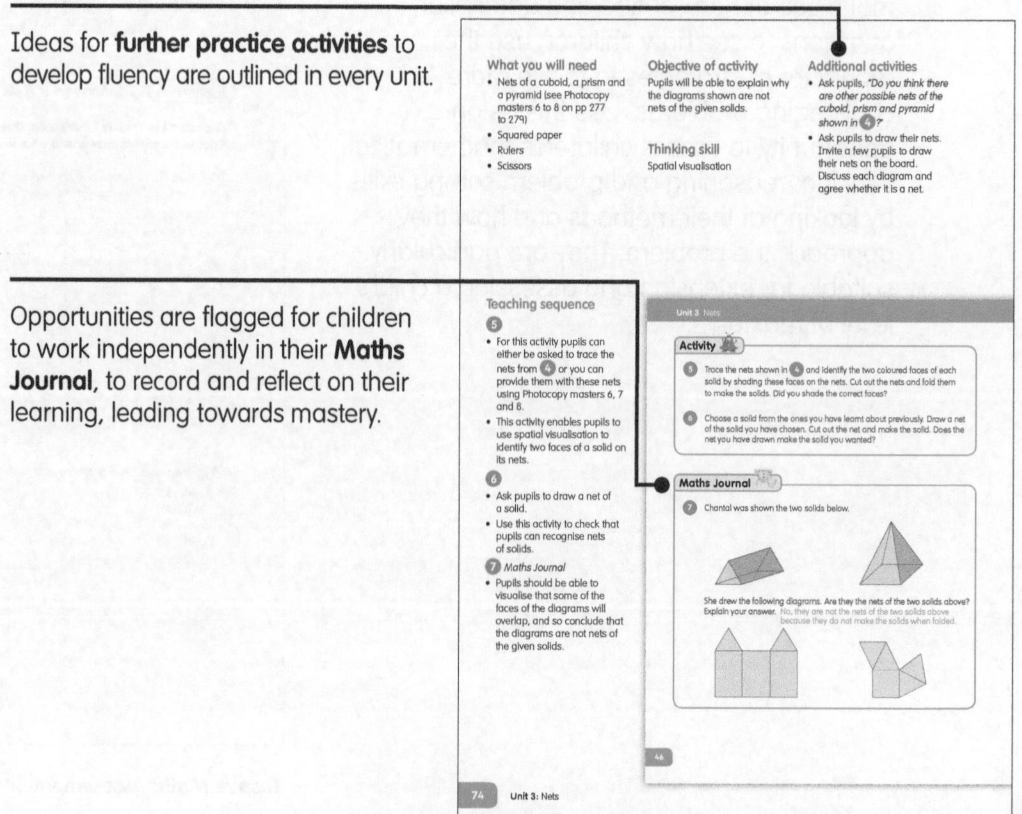

Inspire Maths **Teacher's Guide 6A, page 74**

Equipment needed for each Pupil Textbook page is listed to help you prepare for the activities.

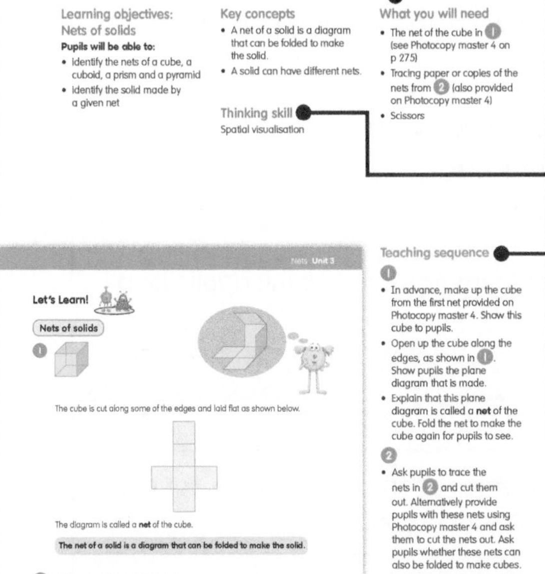

Learning objectives:
Nets of solids

Pupils will be able to:

- identify the nets of a cube, a cuboid, a prism and a pyramid
- identify the solid made by a given net

Key concepts

- A net of a solid is a diagram that can be folded to make the solid.
- A solid can have different nets.

Thinking skill
Spatial visualisation

What you will need

- The net of the cube in 1 (see Photocopy master 4 on p 275)
- Tracing paper or copies of the nets from 2 (also provided on Photocopy master 4)
- Scissors

Nets Unit 3

Let's Learn!

Nets of solids

1

The cube is cut along some of the edges and laid flat as shown below.

The diagram is called a **net** of the cube.

The net of a solid is a diagram that can be folded to make the solid.

2 Here are two other nets of the cube.

Trace them, cut them out and fold each net into a cube.

43

Teaching sequence

1

- In advance, make up the cube from the first net provided on Photocopy master 4. Show this cube to pupils.
- Open up the cube along the edges, as shown in 1. Show pupils the plane diagram that is made.
- Explain that this plane diagram is called a **net** of the cube. Fold the net to make the cube again for pupils to see.

2

- Ask pupils to trace the nets in 2 and cut them out. Alternatively provide pupils with these nets using Photocopy master 4 and ask them to cut the nets out. Ask pupils whether these nets can also be folded to make cubes.
- Guide pupils to conclude that a cube can have different nets.

Unit 3: Nets 71

Key thinking skills and problem solving strategies to look for and encourage are clearly highlighted, helping you to make meaningful assessments of children's understanding.

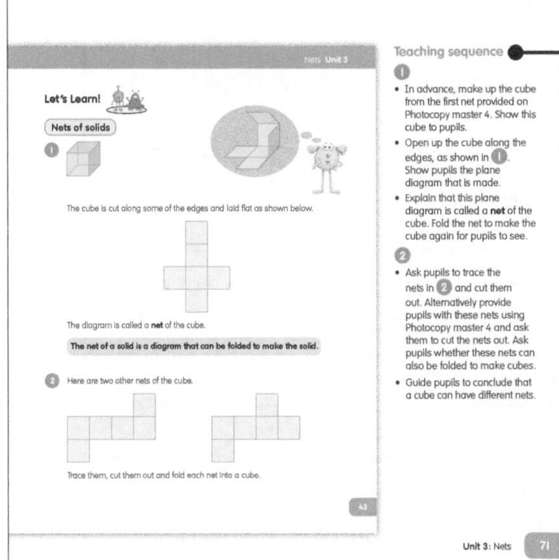

The **teaching sequence** provides clear step-by-step guidance towards meeting the learning objectives. It highlights problem solving strategies to focus on and support for meaningful mathematical conversation and making the best use of concrete apparatus.

Inspire Maths **Teacher's Guide 6A, page 71**

This icon is used to indicate where children recall skills from earlier years and link them to new concepts in the current unit.

This icon indicates that appropriate use of calculators is encouraged for the activities and practices to extend problem-solving skills.

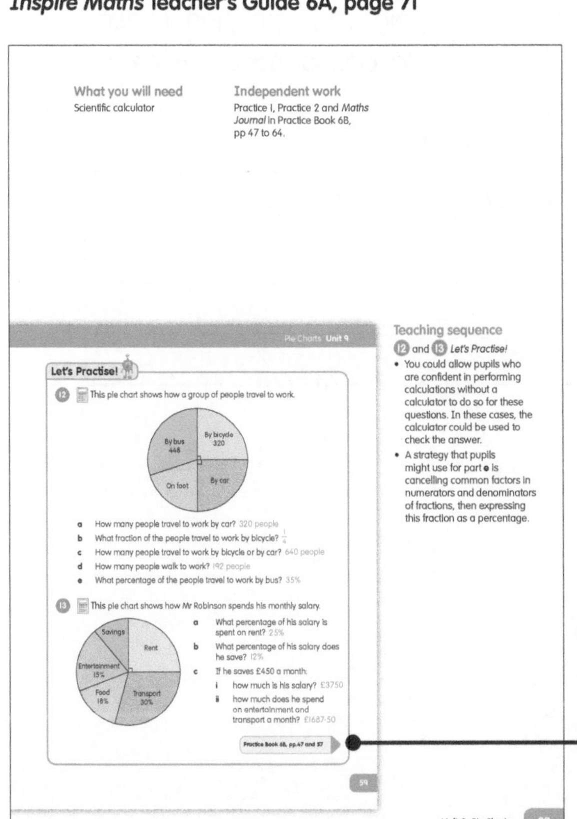

What you will need
Scientific calculator

Independent work
Practice 1, Practice 2 and *Maths Journal* in Practice Book 6B, pp 47 to 64.

Pie Charts Unit 9

Let's Practise!

12 This pie chart shows how a group of people travel to work.

a How many people travel to work by car? 320 people
b What fraction of the people travel to work by bicycle? $\frac{1}{4}$
c How many people travel to work by bicycle or by car? 640 people
d How many people walk to work? 192 people
e What percentage of the people travel to work by bus? 35%

13 This pie chart shows how Mr Robinson spends his monthly salary.

a What percentage of his salary is spent on rent? 25%
b What percentage of his salary does he save? 12%
c If he saves £450 a month:
i how much is his salary? £3750
ii how much does he spend on entertainment and transport a month? £1687·50

Practice Book 6B, pp.47 and 57

59

Teaching sequence

12 and 13 *Let's Practise!*

- You could allow pupils who are confident in performing calculations without a calculator to do so for these questions. In these cases, the calculator could be used to check the answer.
- A strategy that pupils might use for part e is cancelling common factors in numerators and denominators of fractions, then expressing this fraction as a percentage.

Unit 9: Pie Charts 89

Links to the Practice Books provide opportunities for **independent work** when children are ready, to develop fluency and lead towards mastery.

Inspire Maths **Teacher's Guide 6B, page 89**

Long-term planning

Unit title	Key concepts
1 Algebra	
Using letters as numbers	• Letters in algebraic expressions represent numbers • A letter can represent a specific unknown number or any number in general
Simplifying algebraic expressions	• The sum $a + a + a + \ldots + a$ (n terms) $= n \times a = na$ • The sum $ma + na = (m + n) \times a = (m + n)a$ • The difference $ma - na = (m - n) \times a = (m - n)a$
Word problems	• The process of problem solving in mathematics involves the application of concepts and strategies
Assessment Book – Test 1	
2 Angles in Shapes and Diagrams	
Finding unknown angles	• Understanding and applying the properties of angles, triangles, squares, rectangles, parallelograms, rhombuses and trapeziums
Assessment Book – Test 2	
3 Nets	
Solids	• Cubes and cuboids have rectangular faces (including squares) • Prisms have rectangular faces (including squares) and two identical polygonal faces (which could also be rectangles) • Pyramids have triangular faces that meet at a point and a polygonal base • Cylinders have a curved surface and two identical circular bases (at the ends) • Cones have a curved surface and a circular base
Nets of solids	• A net of a solid is a diagram that can be folded to make the solid • A solid can have different nets
Practice Book – Review 1	
Assessment Book – Test 3, Challenging Problems 1, Check-up 1	

Unit title	Key concepts
4 Fractions	
Four operations with fractions	• A fraction is a part of a whole or set, a ratio or a quotient • Addition and subtraction of fractions or mixed numbers can be interpreted in the same way as addition and subtraction of whole numbers • Multiplication of fractions, for example, $\frac{2}{3} \times \frac{3}{4}$ is interpreted as $\frac{2}{3}$ of $\frac{3}{4}$ or $\frac{3}{4}$ of $\frac{2}{3}$ • Division of a fraction by a whole number is interpreted as partition (sharing)
Dividing by a proper fraction	• Division by a proper fraction is interpreted as measurement division; for example, $3 \div \frac{2}{3}$ or $\frac{3}{4} \div \frac{2}{3}$ is interpreted as the number of two-thirds in 3 or $\frac{3}{4}$
Word problems	• The process of problem solving in mathematics involves the application of concepts and strategies
Assessment Book – Test 4	
5 Ratio	
Ratio and fraction	• The ratio of one quantity to another quantity may not represent the actual number of items in each group • A simplified ratio of two quantities shows the relative amount of each quantity with respect to the other
Word problems (1)	• Fractions and ratios can be used to show the relative amounts of two quantities • The multiple concept in multiplication is another comparative tool to show the relative amount of two quantities
Comparing ratios	• The quantities in fixed ratios increase or decrease by the same multiple
Word problems (2)	• When quantities are increased or decreased in relation to each other, the ratios of the quantities are also changed
Assessment Book – Test 5	

Unit title	Key concepts
6 Percentage	
Finding percentages	• Percentages are similar to decimal fractions • A percentage is a special type of decimal fraction, giving the number of parts out of 100 equal parts rather than out of 1
Word problems (1)	• Applying the concepts learnt on percentage to solve word problems using a variety of strategies
Word problems (2)	• Applying the concepts learnt on percentage and a variety of strategies to solve higher-order word problems
Assessment Book – Test 6, Challenging Problems 2, Check-up 2	
7 Speed	
Distance and speed	• Speed is defined as the distance travelled per unit of time • The greater the distance travelled per unit of time, the faster the speed
Average speed	• Average speed is not the mean of two or more speeds • Average speed is the mean distance travelled per unit of time • Average speed is calculated by dividing the total distance travelled by the total time taken
Word problems	• Applying combinations of concepts such as mean (average), speed and rate to solve higher-order word problems
Practice Book – Review 2	
Practice Book – Revision 1	
Assessment Book – Test 7	
8 Circles	
Radius, diameter and circumference	• A radius of a circle is any straight line from the centre to a point on the circumference • A diameter of a circle is any straight line that joins two points on the circumference and passes through the centre • The circumference of a circle is its perimeter • The ratio of the circumference of a circle to its diameter is the constant π
Area of a circle	• The area of a circle is equal to $\pi \times$ Radius $\times$ Radius
Assessment Book – Test 8	

Unit title	Key concepts
9 Pie Charts	
Understanding pie charts	• The circle in a pie chart represents one whole or 100%
Practice Book – Review 3	
Assessment Book – Test 9, Challenging Problems 3	
10 Area and Perimeter	
Area and perimeter of composite shapes	• The properties of squares, rectangles, triangles and circles • Formulae can be used to find the perimeter and area of squares, rectangles and triangles, as well as the circumference and area of circles
Assessment Book – Test 10	
11 Volume of Solids and Liquids	
Volume of solids	• The volume of a cuboid is the product of its length, width and height • The square root of a number n is the number m so that $m \times m = n$ • The cube root of a number n is the number m so that $m \times m \times m = n$
Volume of liquids	• The volume of liquid in a full container is given by the capacity of the container • Liquid in a container takes the shape of the container • Rate is an example of direct proportion, and problems involving rate can be solved using the unitary method
Practice Book – Review 4	
Practice Book – Revision 2	
Assessment Book – Test 11	
Think It Through	

Unit 1: Algebra

Medium-term plan

Week	Learning Objectives	Thinking Skills	Resources
1	**(1) Using letters as numbers** Pupils will be able to: • recognise and write simple algebraic expressions in one variable • evaluate simple algebraic expressions by substitution	• Induction	• Pupil Textbook 6A, pp 2 to 12 • Practice Book 6A, pp 1 to 8 • Teacher's Guide 6A, pp 4 to 14
1	*Let's Explore!* Pupils will be able to conclude that $\frac{y}{2}$ can be interpreted as $\frac{1}{2}$ of y or $\frac{1}{2} \times y$ and $\frac{(y-2)}{3}$ can be interpreted as $(y - 2) \div 3$ or $\frac{1}{3} \times (y - 2)$. *Maths Journal* Pupils will be able to construct one-step word problems with given algebraic expressions as the answers.	• Induction	• Pupil Textbook 6A, pp 10 to 11 • Teacher's Guide 6A, pp 12 to 13
1–2	**(2) Simplifying algebraic expressions** Pupils will be able to simplify algebraic expressions in one variable.	• Comparing • Deduction	• Pupil Textbook 6A, pp 13 to 18 • Practice Book 6A, pp 9 to 10 • Teacher's Guide 6A, pp 15 to 20

Week	Learning Objectives	Thinking Skills	Resources
2	**(3) Word problems** Pupils will be able to solve simple word problems involving algebraic expressions.	• Translating	• Pupil Textbook 6A, pp 19 to 21 • Practice Book 6A, pp 11 to 16 • Teacher's Guide 6A, pp 21 to 23
2	*Maths Journal* Pupils will be able to express their understanding of basic algebraic expressions.	• Identifying relationships	• Pupil Textbook 6A, p 22 • Practice Book 6A, pp 17 to 18 • Teacher's Guide 6A, p 24
2	*Let's Wrap It Up!* Emphasise the key concepts, skills and processes that have been taught in the unit. Discuss the worked example with pupils to assess whether they have mastered these concepts, skills and processes. *Put On Your Thinking Caps!* Pupils will be able to translate verbal statements into symbolic representations to solve the problem.	• Identifying relationships Heuristic for problem solving: • Solve in parts	• Pupil Textbook 6A, pp 22 to 23 • Practice Book 6A, pp 19 to 20 • Teacher's Guide 6A, pp 24 to 25
Summative assessment opportunity			
Assessment Book 6, Test 1, pp 1 to 6			

Algebra

Learning objectives: Using letters as numbers

Pupils will be able to:

- recognise and write simple algebraic expressions in one variable
- evaluate simple algebraic expressions by substitution

Key concepts

- Letters in algebraic expressions represent numbers.
- A letter can represent a specific unknown number or any number in general.

Thinking skill

Induction

Teaching sequence

- Introduce the idea of using a letter to represent an unknown number using a few examples:
  (a) the teacher's age,
  (b) the number of marbles in a bag, or
  (c) the length of a rope.

Algebra

Let's Learn! 

Using letters as numbers

 Millie is now 11 years old.

a How old will Millie be in 1 year's time?
11 + 1 = 12
Millie will be 12 years old in 1 year's time.

b How old will Millie be in 2 years' time?
11 + 2 = 13
Millie will be 13 years old in 2 years' time.

c How old was Millie 1 year ago?
11 − 1 = 10
Millie was 10 years old 1 year ago.

d How old was Millie 2 years ago?
11 − 2 = 9
Millie was 9 years old 2 years ago.

2

2 Mr Green is a class teacher.
Mr Green's class do not know how old he is.

Mr Green is x years old.

a How old will Mr Green be in 1 year's time?

$x + 1$

Mr Green will be $(x + 1)$ years old in 1 year's time.

b How old will Mr Green be in 2 years' time?

$x + 2$

Mr Green will be $(x + 2)$ years old in 2 years' time.

$x + 1$ and $x + 2$ are examples of **algebraic expressions** in terms of x.

3 Refer to the table below. What is Mr Green's age in terms of x?

	Mr Green's Age (Years)
Now	x
In 3 years' time	$x + 3$
In 4 years' time	$x + 4$
In 7 years' time	$x + 7$
In 10 years' time	$x + 10$
In 15 years' time	$x + 15$

Teaching sequence

- Suggest to pupils that when the actual number is not known, we can use a letter to represent this unknown number.
  - (a) Let the **number of marbles** in the bag be ***b***.
  - (b) Let the **length** of the rope be ***y*** cm.
- Emphasise that the letter used represents a number.
- Using the example of the bag of marbles, ask pupils to give expressions to represent the total number of marbles when 2, 5, 10 or more marbles are added to the bag of ***b*** marbles.
- Explain to pupils that ***b* + 2**, ***b* + 5** and ***b* + 10** are called **algebraic expressions**.

- Ask pupils to work on this question as an informal assessment.

Teaching sequence

- Using the example of the bag of marbles again, ask pupils to give expressions to represent the number of marbles remaining when 1, 3, 12 or more marbles are removed from the bag of ***b*** marbles.
- Explain that ***b* – 1**, ***b* – 3** and ***b* – 12** are also algebraic expressions.

- Ask pupils to work on this question as an informal assessment.

- Explain to pupils that the terms *add*, *subtract*, *more than* and *less than* are used in the same way with letters as they are with numbers.

4 Mrs Smith is the headteacher of Greentree Primary School. The pupils do not know her age.

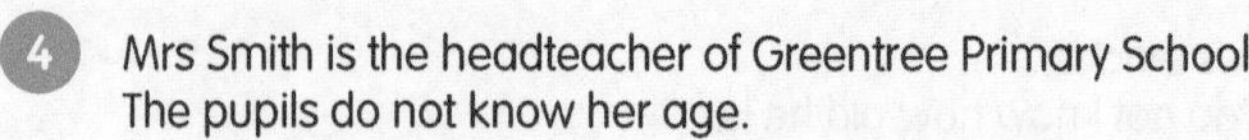

Mrs Smith is y years old.

Any letter can be used to denote an unknown number.

a How old was Mrs Smith 1 year ago?

$y - 1$

Mrs Smith was $(y - 1)$ years old 1 year ago.

b How old was Mrs Smith 2 years ago?

$y - 2$

Mrs Smith was $(y - 2)$ years old 2 years ago.

$y - 1$ and $y - 2$ are examples of algebraic expressions in terms of y.

5 Refer to the table below. What is Mrs Smith's age in terms of y?

	Mrs Smith's Age (Years)
Now	y
3 years ago	$y - 3$
5 years ago	$y - 5$
8 years ago	$y - 8$
12 years ago	$y - 12$
20 years ago	$y - 20$

6 **a** **i** Add 2 to 6.

$6 + 2 = 8$

ii Add x to 6.

$6 + x$

b **i** Subtract 3 from 4.

$4 - 3 = 1$

ii Subtract 3 from y.

$y - 3$

c **i** What is 4 more than 8? **ii** What is x more than 8?

$8 + 4 = 12$ $8 + x$

d **i** What is 5 less than 9? **ii** What is 5 less than y?

$9 - 5 = 4$ $y - 5$

7 State the algebraic expression for each of the following.

a Add 5 to z $z + 5$ **b** Add z to 8 $8 + z$

c Subtract 7 from z $z - 7$ **d** Subtract z from 10 $10 - z$

e 9 more than z $z + 9$ **f** z more than 9 $9 + z$

g 11 less than z $z - 11$ **h** z less than 11 $11 - z$

8 Find the values of the algebraic expressions by using the numbers given below.

a Find the value of $x + 5$ when $x = 9$.

When $x = 9$,
$x + 5 = 9 + 5$
$= 14$

Substitute the letter with the given number.

b Find the value of $5 + x$ when $x = 23$.

When $x = 23$,
$5 + x = 5 + 23$
$= 28$

c Find the value of $y - 7$ when $y = 15$.

When $y = 15$,
$y - 7 = 15 - 7$
$= 8$

d Find the value of $30 - y$ when $y = 7$.

When $y = 7$,
$30 - y = 30 - 7$
$= 23$

Teaching sequence

- Ask pupils to work on these questions as an informal assessment.

- Write the expression $x + 5$ as an example, and ask pupils what they think $x + 5$ is equal to when $x = 9$. Guide pupils to appreciate that, since x has a value of 9, $\boldsymbol{x} + 5 = \mathbf{9} + 5$, which is equal to 14.
- Give other numerical values for x and ask pupils to evaluate the expression $x + 5$ each time.
- Next write the expression $y - 7$, and ask pupils to evaluate it by substituting different numerical values for y.

  Note: To avoid getting negative numbers ensure that numbers greater than or equal to 7 are substituted for y.

Teaching sequence

9

- Ask pupils to work on this question as an informal assessment.

10 and **11**

- Guide pupils to recognise that if the number of pencils in 1 box is n, the number of pencils in 2, 3, 4, ... boxes will be $2 \times n$, $3 \times n$, $4 \times n$, ...
- Explain that $2 \times n$, $3 \times n$ and $4 \times n$ are written as **2*n***, **3*n*** and **4*n*** in algebra and that they are also algebraic expressions. Emphasise that $2n$ means $2 \times n$ and not two instances of the letter n.

9 Refer to the table below. Find the values of the algebraic expressions for the given values of x.

Expression	Value of Expression When:	
	$x = 8$	$x = 30$
$x + 4$	$8 + 4 = 12$	$30 + 4 = 34$
$x + 9$	17	39
$12 + x$	20	42
$x - 3$	5	27
$x - 6$	2	24
$40 - x$	32	10

10 There are 12 pencils in a box.

a How many pencils are there in 2 boxes?

$2 \times 12 = 24$

There are 24 pencils in 2 boxes.

b How many pencils are there in 3 boxes?

$3 \times 12 = 36$

There are 36 pencils in 3 boxes.

11 There are n pencils in a box.

a How many pencils are there in 2 boxes?

$2 \times n = 2n$

There are $2n$ pencils in 2 boxes.

b How many pencils are there in 3 boxes?

$3 \times n = 3n$

There are $3n$ pencils in 3 boxes.

$2n$ and $3n$ are examples of algebraic expressions in terms of n.

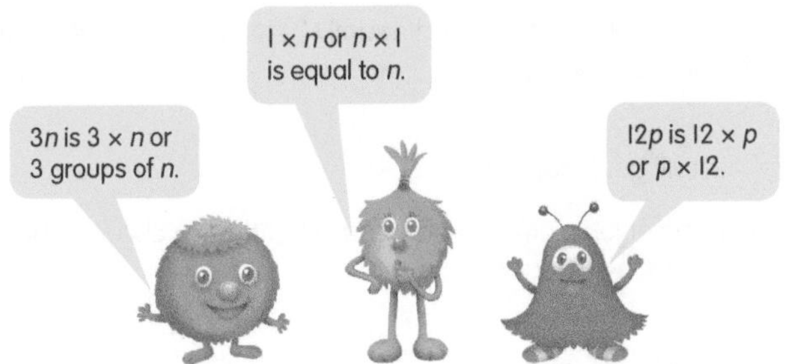

12 Answer these questions.

a $4k =$ [4] × [k] or $k \times 4$

b $7j =$ [7] × [j] or $j \times 7$

c $5p$ means [5] groups of [p].

d 8 groups of x is [8] × [x]. or $x \times 8$

13 Refer to the table below. There are n marbles in a packet. Find the number of marbles in terms of n. Then find the number of marbles for the given values of n.

Number of Packets	Number of Marbles	Number of Marbles When:	
		$n = 15$	$n = 20$
1	n	15	20
4	$4n$	$4 \times 15 = 60$	[80]
7	[$7n$]	[105]	[140]
10	[$10n$]	[150]	[200]
15	[$15n$]	[225]	[300]

Teaching sequence

12 and **13**

- Ask pupils to work on these questions as practice.
  Use them as an informal assessment.
- Emphasise the fact that there is no multiplication sign in the second column between '4' and 'n'.

Teaching sequence

14 and 15

- Introduce expressions involving division in a similar way to expressions involving multiplication (in 10 and 11).
- Explain that just as we miss out the multiplication sign in algebraic expressions where multiplication is involved, we also miss out the division sign in algebraic expressions where division is involved. We use the fraction idea to represent division.

14 There are 6 cartons of juice in a pack.

a If the cartons of juice are shared equally between 2 children, how many cartons will each child get?

$6 \div 2 = 3$

Each child will get 3 cartons.

b If the cartons of juice are shared equally between 3 children, how many cartons will each child get?

$6 \div 3 = 2$

Each child will get 2 cartons.

15 There are m cartons of juice in a pack.

a If the cartons of juice are shared equally between 2 children, how many cartons will each child get?

$m \div 2 = \frac{m}{2}$

Each child will get $\frac{m}{2}$ cartons.

We write $m \div 2$ as $\frac{m}{2}$.

b If the cartons of juice are shared equally among 3 children, how many cartons will each child get?

$m \div 3 = \frac{m}{3}$

Each child will get $\frac{m}{3}$ cartons.

We write $m \div 3$ as $\frac{m}{3}$.

$\frac{m}{2}$ and $\frac{m}{3}$ are also algebraic expressions.

16 Refer to the table below. A packet of m stickers is shared equally among some children. Find the number of stickers each child gets in terms of m. Then find the number of stickers for the given values of m.

Number of Children	Number of Stickers Each Child Gets	Number of Stickers Each Child Gets When:	
		$m = 24$	$m = 48$
1	m	24	48
3	$\frac{m}{3}$	$\frac{24}{3} = 8$	16
6	$\frac{m}{6}$	4	8
8	$\frac{m}{8}$	3	6
12	$\frac{m}{12}$	2	4

17 Refer to the questions below. Find the expressions in terms of p. For the boxes on the right, find the value when $p = 6$. The first one has been done for you.

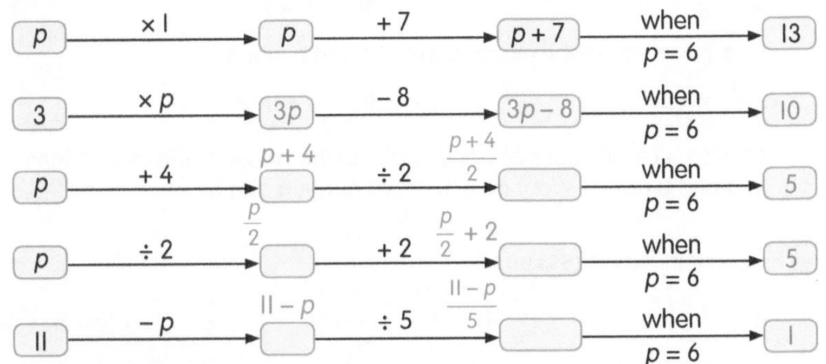

18 Find the value of each expression when $a = 20$.

a $10a - 89$ 111

b $\frac{125 - a}{7}$ 15

c $\frac{11a}{4} + 25$ 80

d $\frac{14a + 80}{30}$ 12

Discuss with your child what the letter x means in these expressions: $x + 6$, $6 - x$, $6x$ and $\frac{x}{6}$. Explain that x stands for an unknown number.

Teaching sequence

16

- Ask pupils to work on this question as an informal assessment.

17 and **18**

- Ask pupils to work on these questions as further practice in writing and evaluating algebraic expressons. We are now combining two operations in a single algebraic expression.

Additional activity

- Extend the activity in 19 by asking pupils to substitute different values of x for $x + 8$ and $8 + x$. Guide pupils to recognise that $x + 8 = 8 + x$.

What you will need

5 letter cards and 5 number cards per pair (see Photocopy master I on p 272)

Thinking skill

Induction

Objective of activity

Let's Explore!

Pupils will be able to conclude that $\frac{y}{2}$ can be interpreted as $\frac{1}{2}$ of y or $\frac{1}{2} \times y$ and $\frac{(y-2)}{3}$ can be interpreted as $(y - 2) \div 3$ or $\frac{1}{3} \times (y - 2)$.

Teaching sequence

- Arrange pupils into pairs and give each pair a set of the cards provided on Photocopy master I. Ask pupils to follow the steps in the textbook to complete the activity.

20 and 21 *Let's Explore!*

- Ask pupils to substitute the given numerical values in the algebraic expressions. Encourage them to reach and express conclusions about the relationship between the algebraic expressions.

- Ask pupils to build on their conclusions from 20 and 21 to give expressions which are equivalent to the given algebraic expression.

Activity

19 Work in pairs.
You will need 5 letter cards and 5 number cards.

1. Pick one letter card and one number card.
2. Write down as many algebraic expressions as you can with the two cards. For example, if you pick the cards x and 8, you can write down '$x + 8$', '$8 + x$', '$x - 8$', '$8 - x$', '$8x$' and '$\frac{x}{8}$'.
3. Repeat steps 1 and 2 until all the cards have been taken.

Let's Explore!

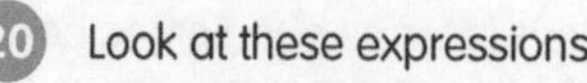

20 Look at these expressions:

a $\frac{y}{2}$ **b** $\frac{1}{2} \times y$

Find the values of the expressions in **a** and **b** when:

i $y = 6$ 3 **ii** $y = 14$ 7

Choose 3 other values of y and work out the values of the expressions in **a** and **b** above. What do you notice about **a** and **b**?
a and **b** are equivalent expressions.

21 Look at these expressions:

a $\frac{y-2}{3}$ **b** $(y - 2) \div 3$ **c** $\frac{1}{3} \times (y - 2)$

Find the values of the expressions in **a**, **b** and **c** when:

i $y = 8$ 2 **ii** $y = 17$ 5

Choose any other 3 values of y and work out **a**, **b** and **c** above. What do you conclude about **a**, **b** and **c**? **a**, **b** and **c** are equivalent expressions.

22 Express $(x + 4) \div 6$ in two other ways. $\frac{x+4}{6}$ or $\frac{1}{6} \times (x + 4)$

Objective of activity

Pupils will be able to construct one-step word problems with given algebraic expressions as the answers.

Independent work

Let's Practise!

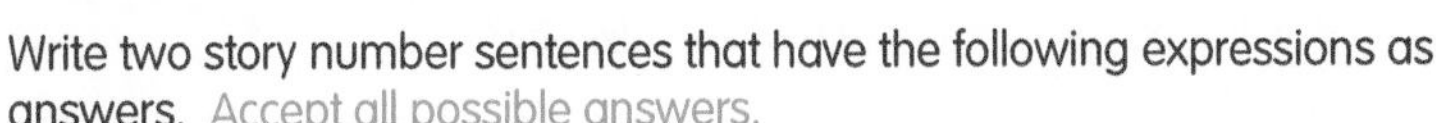

Maths Journal

23 Write two story number sentences that have the following expressions as answers. Accept all possible answers.

a $m - 20$ **b** $5m$

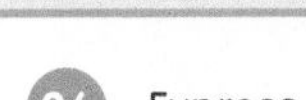

Let's Practise!

24 Express each of the following in one or two other ways.

a $5 \times w$ $5w$

b $v \times 15$ $15v$

c $x \div 3$ $\frac{x}{3}$ or $\frac{1}{3} \times x$

d $\frac{1}{4} \times y$ $y \div 4$ or $\frac{y}{4}$

e $\frac{z+4}{5}$ $(z + 4) \div 5$ or $\frac{1}{5} \times (z + 4)$

f $\frac{1}{2} \times (a - 7)$ $(a - 7) \div 2$ or $\frac{a-7}{2}$

25 John is now x years old. Give an expression in terms of x for each of the following and find the value when $x = 18$.

a The age of his brother, who is 5 years older than him. $x + 5$; 23

b The age of his sister, who is 3 years younger than him. $x - 3$; 15

c The age of his aunt, who is twice as old as him. $2x$; 36

d The age of his cousin, who is half his age. $\frac{x}{2}$; 9

26 There are n pieces of chocolate in a box. Give an expression in terms of n for each of the following and find the value when $n = 24$.

a The number of pieces of chocolate left after 6 pieces have been eaten. $n - 6$; 18

b The number of pieces of chocolate each child gets when the box of chocolate is shared equally among 4 children. $\frac{n}{4}$; 6

c The total number of pieces of chocolate in 10 identical boxes. $10n$; 240

d The number of pieces each child gets when one box and 11 pieces of chocolate are shared equally among 5 children. $\frac{n+11}{5}$; 7

Teaching sequence

23 *Maths Journal*

- Ask pupils to come up with short, one-step word problems reflecting the algebraic expressions.
- Examples:
  - **a** There are 45 balls in a box. If 20 balls are removed, how many balls are left?
  - **b** Liam bought 5 boxes of jam. There were 4 jam jars in each box. How many jam jars were there altogether?

What you will need

Scientific calculator

Independent work

Practice 1 in Practice Book 6A, pp 1 to 8.

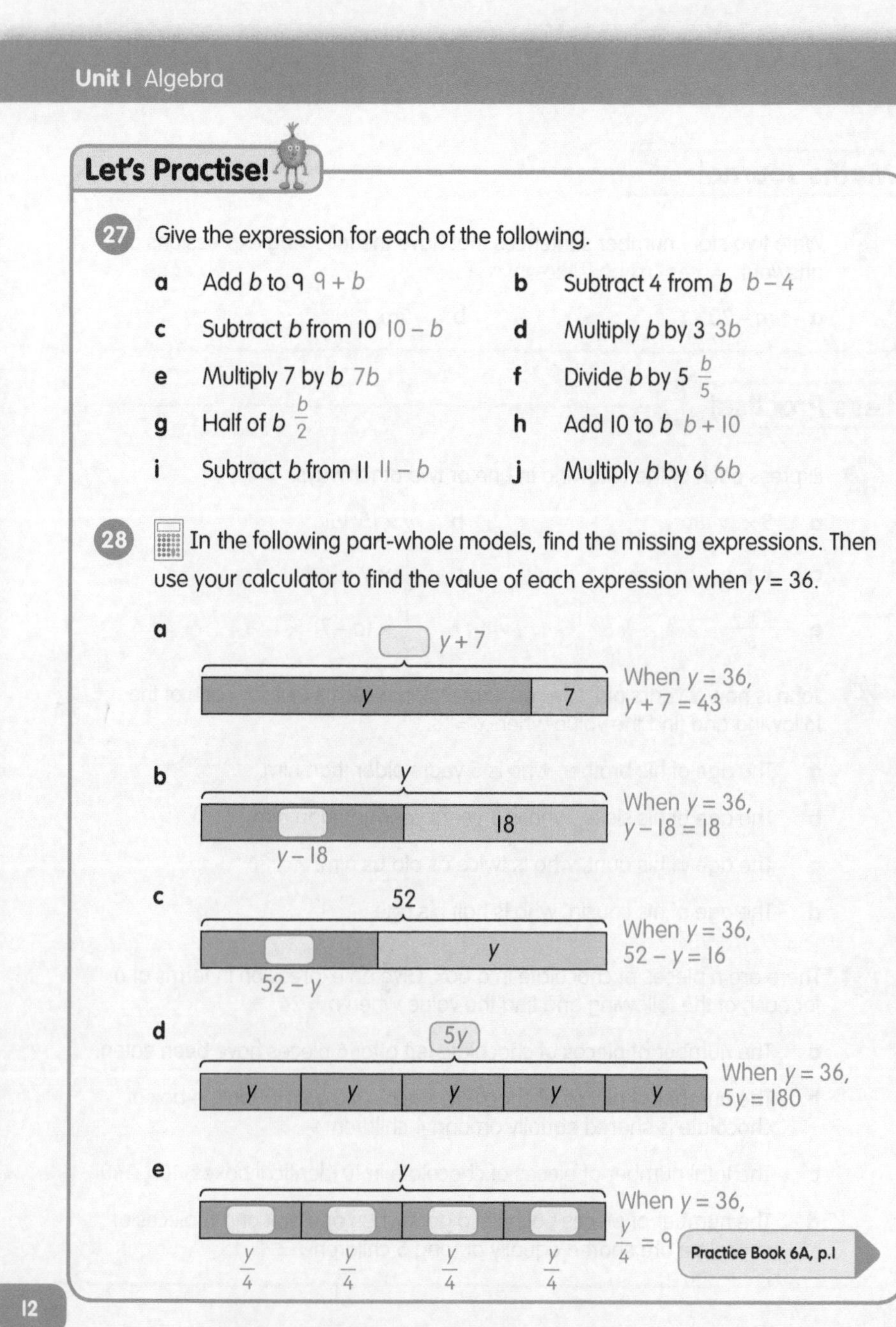

Let's Practise!

27 Give the expression for each of the following.

a Add b to 9 $9 + b$

b Subtract 4 from b $b - 4$

c Subtract b from 10 $10 - b$

d Multiply b by 3 $3b$

e Multiply 7 by b $7b$

f Divide b by 5 $\frac{b}{5}$

g Half of b $\frac{b}{2}$

h Add 10 to b $b + 10$

i Subtract b from 11 $11 - b$

j Multiply b by 6 $6b$

28 In the following part-whole models, find the missing expressions. Then use your calculator to find the value of each expression when $y = 36$.

a $y + 7$ | y | 7 — When $y = 36$, $y + 7 = 43$

b y | $y - 18$ | 18 — When $y = 36$, $y - 18 = 18$

c 52 | $52 - y$ | y — When $y = 36$, $52 - y = 16$

d $5y$ | y | y | y | y | y — When $y = 36$, $5y = 180$

e y | $\frac{y}{4}$ | $\frac{y}{4}$ | $\frac{y}{4}$ | $\frac{y}{4}$ — When $y = 36$, $\frac{y}{4} = 9$

Practice Book 6A, p.1

Learning objective: Simplifying algebraic expressions

Pupils will be able to simplify algebraic expressions in one variable.

Key concepts

- The sum $a + a + a + \ldots + a$ (n terms) $= n \times a = na$
- The sum $ma + na = (m + n) \times a = (m + n)a$
- The difference $ma - na = (m - n) \times a = (m - n)a$

Thinking skills

- Comparing
- Deduction

Let's Learn! 

Simplifying algebraic expressions

a cm a cm

A rod of length a cm is joined to another rod also a cm long. What is the total length of the 2 rods?

Total length of the 2 rods $= (a + a)$ cm

$(a + a)$ is also $(2 \times a)$.

We can simplify $(a + a)$ by writing:

$a + a = 2a$

3 | 3
$3 + 3 = 2 \times 3$
4 | 4
$4 + 4 = 2 \times 4$
a | a
$a + a = 2 \times a$

2 The diagram below is made up of 3 rods, each b cm long. Find the total length of the 3 rods.

b cm b cm b cm

Total length $= b + b + b$
$= (3 \times b)$ cm

We can simplify $(b + b + b)$ by writing:

$b + b + b = 3b$

5 | 5 | 5
$5 + 5 + 5 = 3 \times 5$
b | b | b
$b + b + b = 3 \times b$

Teaching sequence

 and **2**

- Review the concept of multiplication as repeated addition with pupils. Ask pupils how they can write these sums as products:

2 + 2 =	2 + 2 + 2 =
3 + 3 =	3 + 3 + 3 =
4 + 4 =	4 + 4 + 4 =
…	…

Note

Ensure that pupils do not think of $a + 2a$ as being equivalent to (for example) 1 apple plus 2 apples, which can lead to the misconception that letters represent objects.

Teaching sequence

- Introduce the expression $\boldsymbol{a + a}$, emphasising that $\boldsymbol{a}$ represents a number.
- Based on their understanding of multiplication as repeated addition, as reviewed in 1, guide pupils to recognise that any number added to itself is twice that number, that is, $\boldsymbol{a + a = 2 \times a}$, which is written as $\boldsymbol{2a}$. Guide pupils to interpret $a + a + a$ and $a + a + a + a$ in the same way.

- Ask pupils to work on this question as an informal assessment.

- Introduce the expression $a + 2a$. Guide pupils to simplify this expression using the idea that $a + a = 2a$, so $a + 2a = a + a + a = 3a$.
- To shorten the process of simplification, encourage pupils to think of $a + 2a$ as one group of a plus two groups of a, giving a total of three groups of a, or $3a$.

- Ask pupils to work on this question as practice.

3 The diagram below is made up of 5 sticks, each r cm long. What is the total length of the 5 sticks?

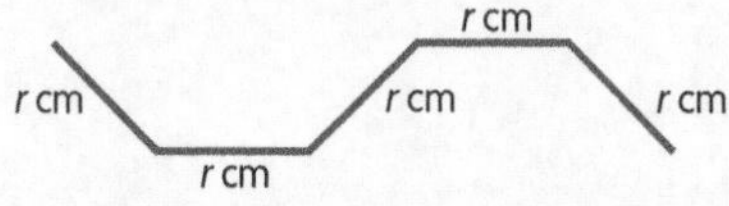

$$\text{Total length} = r + r + r + r + r = 5 \times r = 5r \text{ cm}$$

4 Simplify these expressions.

a $x + x$ $2x$

b $y + y + y$ $3y$

c $a + a + a + a + a$ $5a$

d $b + b + b + b + b + b$ $6b$

e $c + c + c + c + c + c + c$ $7c$

5 Simplify $a + 2a$.

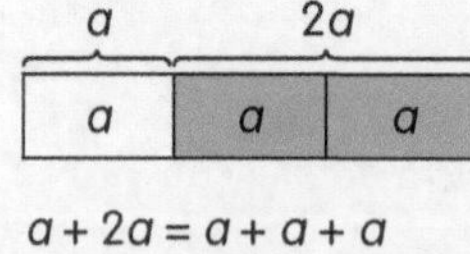

$$a + 2a = a + a + a = 3a$$

$a + 2a = 3a$

6 Simplify $2a + 3a$.

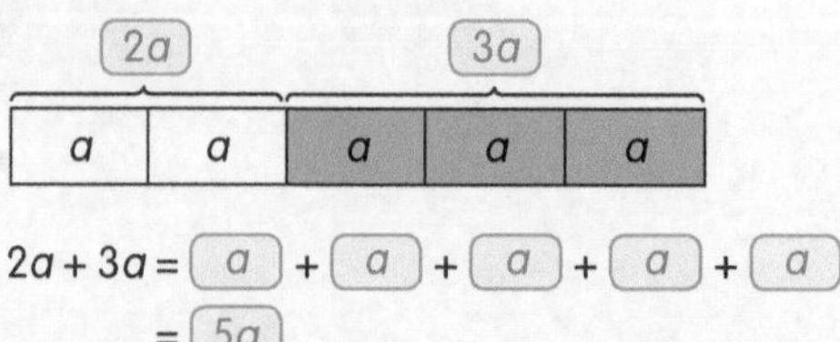

$$2a + 3a = a + a + a + a + a = 5a$$

7 Simplify these expressions.

a $a + 3a$ $4a$ **b** $2z + 5z$ $7z$ **c** $4x + x$ $5x$

d $3y + 6y$ $9y$ **e** $b + 2b + 3b$ $6b$ **f** $4c + 2c + 5c$ $11c$

8 A ribbon is a cm long. Peter uses the whole ribbon to decorate a present. How much ribbon is left?

Length of ribbon left $= a - a$
$= 0$ cm

Compare the following:
$2 - 2 = 0$
$7 - 7 = 0$
$a - a = 0$

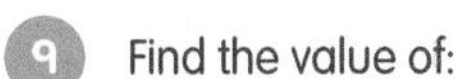

9 Find the value of:

a $x - x$ 0 **b** $2y - 2y$ 0 **c** $10z - 10z$ 0

10 Simplify $3a - a$.

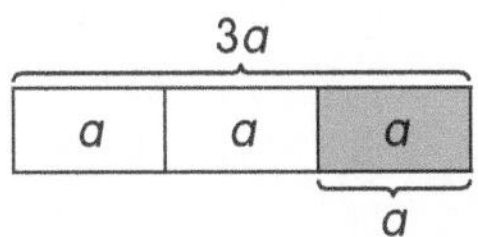

$3a - a = a + a$
$= 2a$

$3a - a = 2a$

11 Simplify $4a - 2a$.

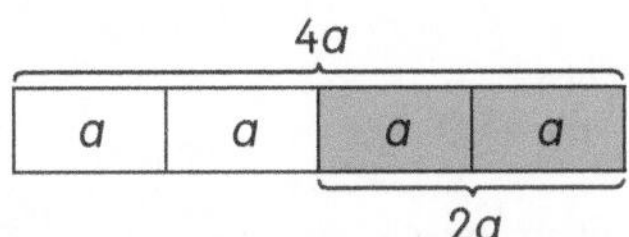

$4a - 2a = a + a$
$= 2a$

$4a - 2a = 2a$

15

Teaching sequence

7

- Ask pupils to work on these questions as an informal assessment.

8

- Guide pupils to conclude that any number minus itself is equal to 0.

9

- Ask pupils to work on these questions as practice.

10 and 11

- Use the subtraction model in a similar way to explain how to simplify $3a - a$, that is: $3a$ is equal to $a + a + a$, so $3a - a = a + a = 2a$
- In the same way, guide pupils to think of $3a - a$ as 3 groups of a minus 1 group of a, leaving 2 groups of a, or $2a$.

Teaching sequence

12 and 13

- Ask pupils to work on these questions as practice. Use them as an informal assessment.

14 and 15

- Show how to simplify algebraic expressions involving both addition and subtraction.
- For expressions such as $6a + 3a - 2a$, encourage pupils to compare $6 + 3 - 2$. Explain that $6a + 3a - 2a$ is worked out in the same way, from left to right.

16 and 17

- Show how to simplify an expression involving numbers and letters. Working from left to right, simplify the numbers and letters separately.
- For expressions such as $5 + 4a + 4 + 3a$, help pupils to understand that we can regroup the expression into the parts that contain numbers only and the parts that contain letters. By separately combining parts of the expression that relate to the letters only and the parts that contain numbers only, we can simplify expressions.
  $5 + 4a + 4 + 3a$
  $= 5 + 4 + 4a + 3a$
  $= 9 + 7a$
- Pupils will build on this in later years when they collect like terms.

12 Simplify $5a - 2a$.

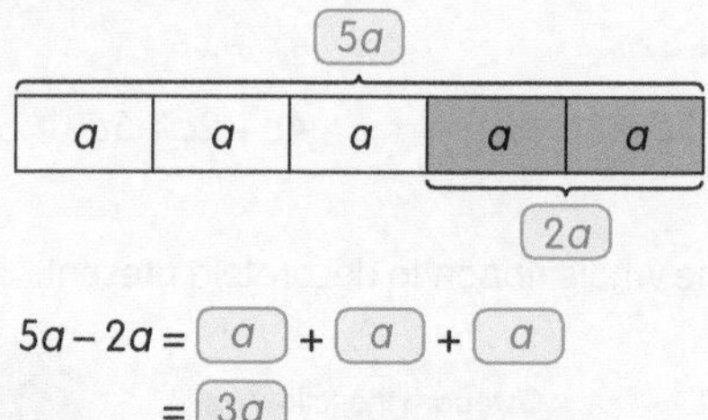

$5a - 2a = a + a + a$
$= 3a$

13 Simplify these expressions.

a $4a - a$ $3a$ **b** $7a - 3a$ $4a$ **c** $5x - 4x$ x

d $10x - 6x$ $4x$ **e** $8y - 3y - 5y$ 0 **f** $12y - 7y - y$ $4y$

14 Simplify $6a + 3a - 2a$.

Working from left to right,
$6a + 3a - 2a = 9a - 2a$
$= 7a$

15 Simplify $6a - 2a + 3a$.

Working from left to right,
$6a - 2a + 3a = 4a + 3a$
$= 7a$

16 Find the distance from Point A to Point B.

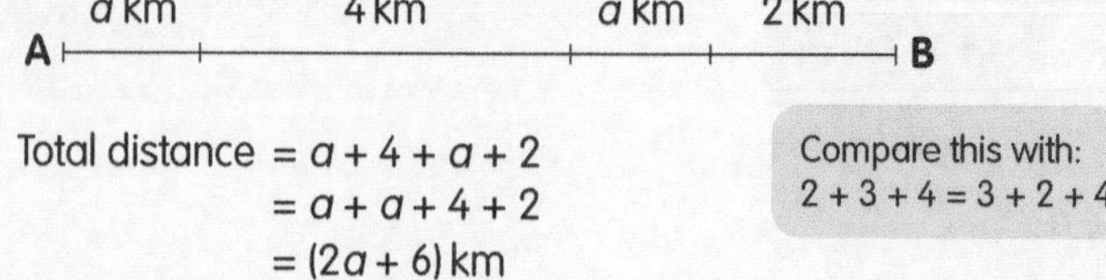

Total distance $= a + 4 + a + 2$
$= a + a + 4 + 2$
$= (2a + 6)$ km

Compare this with:
$2 + 3 + 4 = 3 + 2 + 4$

What you will need

20 lolly sticks per pair of pupils

Thinking skill

Comparing

17 Simplify $4x + 6 - 2x$.

$$4x + 6 - 2x = 4x - 2x + 6$$
$$= 2x + 6$$

18 Simplify these expressions.

a $2x + 3x - 4x$ x

b $x + 5x - 6x$ 0

c $9a - 3a + 4a$ $10a$

d $12a - 7a + 2a$ $7a$

e $b + 5 + b + 5$ $2b + 10$

f $3b + 4b + 2 + 6$ $7b + 8$

g $5s + 9 - 3s$ $2s + 9$

h $8s + 6 - 2s - 1$ $6s + 5$

Activity

19 Work in pairs.
You will need 20 lolly sticks.
Take the length of each lolly stick as p units.

1 Make a closed shape using 3 or more lolly sticks.

Example

2 Write down the total length of the lolly sticks used.

Example

Total length of lolly sticks = $p + p + p = 3p$ units

3 Remove and add lolly sticks to make another shape.

Example

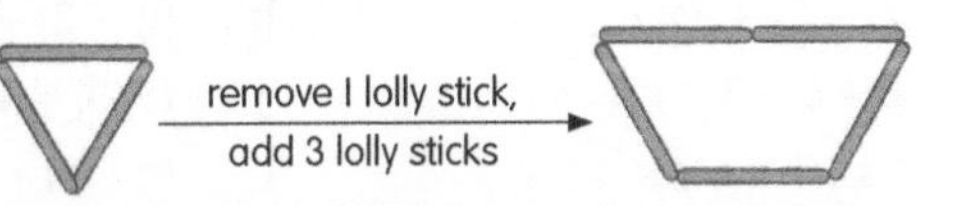

Ask your child to substitute different values of x in the expression $2x + 3x$ and work out the answer in each case. Then help them use these values of x to work out $5x$. Ask them what they can conclude.

Teaching sequence

18

- Ask pupils to work on these questions as an informal assessment.

19

- Ask pupils to work in pairs to use concrete representations to write and simplify algebraic expressions in one variable.
- You could explain to pupils that the name given to a closed shape with straight sides is a **polygon**.

Independent work

- *Let's Practise!*
- Practice 2 in Practice Book 6A, pp 9 to 10.

Teaching sequence

20 *Let's Practise!*

- Stress that the answer for part **f** is 0. We don't write this as $0x$. This is a common mistake.

Activity

4 Write down the total length of the lolly sticks used in the new shape by subtracting the total length of the lolly sticks removed and adding the total length of the lolly sticks added.

Example

When one lolly stick was removed and three lolly sticks were added:
Total length of lolly sticks = $3p - p + 3p$
$= 5p$ units

5 Check your answer in **4** by counting the number of lolly sticks used in the new shape to find the total length.

Example

Total number of lolly sticks used = 5
Total length of lolly sticks = $5 \times p$
$= 5p$ units

6 Make other shapes and repeat the exercise.

Let's Practise!

20 Simplify these expressions.

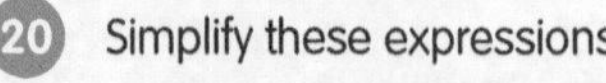

a	$2a + 5a$ $7a$	**b**	$a + 7a$ $8a$
c	$3a + 3a + 6a$ $12a$	**d**	$4x - 2x$ $2x$
e	$6x - 5x$ x	**f**	$10x - 2x - 8x$ 0
g	$7y - 5y + 4y$ $6y$	**h**	$9y + 3y - 5y$ $7y$
i	$a + a + 5$ $2a + 5$	**j**	$b + 4 + 4 + b$ $2b + 8$
k	$2s + 7 - 6 + s$ $3s + 1$	**l**	$9r + 10 + 2 - 3r$ $6r + 12$

Practice Book 6A, p.9

Learning objective: Word problems

Pupils will be able to solve simple word problems involving algebraic expressions.

Key concept

The process of problem solving in mathematics involves the application of concepts and strategies.

Thinking skill

Translating

Let's Learn!

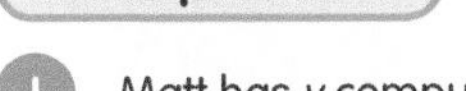

Word problems

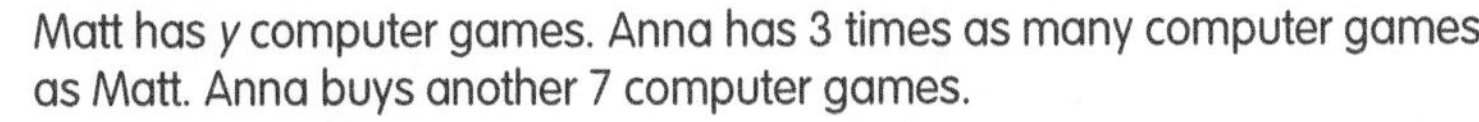

1 Matt has y computer games. Anna has 3 times as many computer games as Matt. Anna buys another 7 computer games.

a How many more computer games does Anna have than Matt after she buys another 7 computer games, in terms of y?

b If Matt has 25 computer games, how many more computer games does Anna have than Matt?

$3y - y = 2y$

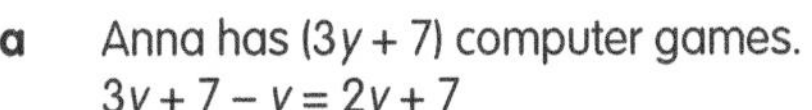

a Anna has $(3y + 7)$ computer games.
$3y + 7 - y = 2y + 7$

Anna has $(2y + 7)$ more computer games than Matt.

b $2y + 7 = (2 \times 25) + 7$
$= 50 + 7$
$= 57$

Anna has 57 more computer games than Matt.

2 Sophie has £m and Ahmed has £15 more.

a Find the amount of money they have altogether in terms of m.

b If Sophie has £75, how much money do they have altogether?

a Ahmed has £( ). $m + 15$
They have £( ) altogether. $m + m + 15 = 2m + 15$

b If $m = 75$, they have £ 165 altogether.

Teaching sequence

1

- Review the procedure for solving word problems with pupils:

  Step 1: *Read and understand*

  Ask pupils to read the problem. Guide them to identify the given and implied information through questioning:

  "How many computer games does Matt have?"

  "How many computer games does Anna have to begin with?"

  "How many more computer games does Anna buy?"

  "What are you required to find?"

  Step 2: *Think of a strategy*

  Ask pupils:

  "What number sentences should you write?"

  Step 3: *Solve the problem*

  Agree that, in this case, since pupils are able to write the relevant number sentences, they are able to solve the problem.

  Step 4: *Check the answer*

  Ask pupils to check the answer by working backwards.

2

- Ask pupils to work on these questions as practice.

Independent work

Let's Practise!

Teaching sequence

- Using the same procedure as in 1, work through this word problem with pupils.

- Ask pupils to work on these questions as practice.

3 Alisha had £x in her purse. She bought a book for £15 and spent the rest of her money on 3 theatre tickets.

a Find the price of 1 theatre ticket in terms of x.

b If Alisha had £39, what was the price of 1 theatre ticket?

a Price of 3 theatre tickets = £$(x - 15)$

£$(x - 15) \div 3 = £\left(\frac{x-15}{3}\right)$

The price of 1 theatre ticket is £$\left(\frac{x-15}{3}\right)$.

b £$\left(\frac{x-15}{3}\right) = £\left(\frac{39-15}{3}\right)$

$= £\left(\frac{24}{3}\right)$

$= £8$

The price of 1 theatre ticket was £8.

4 Mr Elliott had £y in his wallet. He earned £200 and then spent half the total amount of money on sport equipment.

a Find the amount of money he had left in terms of y.

b If $y = 80$, how much money did he have left?

a Total amount of money he had = £($y + 200$)

Mr Elliott had £($\frac{y+200}{2}$) left.

b If $y = 80$, he had £ 140 left.

Let's Practise!

Solve these word problems. Show your workings clearly.

5 Harry is r years old. His brother is 3 times as old as he is. His sister is 4 years younger than his brother.

a Find his brother's age in terms of r. $3r$

b Find his sister's age in terms of r. $3r - 4$

c If $r = 5$, how old is his sister? 11 years old

What you will need

Scientific calculator

Independent work

Practice 3 and *Maths Journal* in Practice Book 6A, pp 11 to 18.

Let's Practise!

6 Mr Davis bought a belt for £x and some shoes that cost twice as much as the belt. He gave the sales assistant £100.

- **a** Find the amount that Mr Davis spent in terms of x. £$3x$
- **b** Find the amount of change Mr Davis received in terms of x. £$(100 - 3x)$
- **c** If $x = 15$, how much change did Mr Davis receive? £55

7 Daniel scored z marks in a maths test. Kerry scored 4 times as many marks. Rajesh scored 5 more marks than Kerry.

- **a** Find the marks that Kerry scored in terms of z. $4z$
- **b** Find the marks that Rajesh scored in terms of z. $4z + 5$
- **c** Find the total marks scored by the three pupils in terms of z. $9z + 5$

8 At a concert, there were t men and twice as many women. During the interval, 5 men and 6 women left the concert.

- **a** How many people left during the interval? 11
- **b** How many people were there at the concert after the interval? $3t - 11$
- **c** If $t = 500$, how many people were there at the concert after the interval? 1489 people

9 Mrs Brook had some blackberries. She packed 14 blackberries into each bag. There were m bags of blackberries altogether. The blackberries were shared equally among her 3 children.

- **a** How many blackberries did each child get? Give your answer in terms of m. $\frac{14m}{3}$ blackberries
- **b** If there were 18 bags of blackberries, how many blackberries did each child get? 84 blackberries

10 A full bucket and a full jug contain $p\,\ell$ of water altogether. The bucket contains 10 times as much water as the jug.

- **a** Find the amount of water in the jug in terms of p. $\frac{p}{11}\,\ell$
- **b** If the full bucket and the full jug contain $25\,\ell$ of water altogether, find the amount of water in the bucket in litres to 1 decimal place. $22{\cdot}7\,\ell$

Practice Book 6A, p.11

Objective of activity

Pupils will be able to express their understanding of basic algebraic expressions.

What you will need

Scientific calculator

Thinking skill

Identifying relationships

Teaching sequence

 *Maths Journal*

- Guide pupils to explain the idea of using a letter to represent an unknown number.
- If necessary, reinforce the point that $3x$ represents 3 groups of x to prevent the misconception that the letters represent objects.

12

- Similarly, make the point that the letter represents a number, not an object.

Let's Wrap It Up!

- Emphasise the key concepts, skills and processes that have been taught in the unit.

- Discuss the worked example with pupils to assess whether they have mastered these concepts, skills and processes. You could allow pupils who are confident in performing the calculations needed for this question without a calculator to do so.

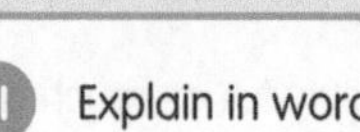

Maths Journal

11 Explain in words what the expression $3x$ means.

Accept all correct answers.

12 Rosa says that $a + a = 2a$ can be thought of as 1 apple + 1 apple = 2 apples. Is her thinking correct? If not, what is the correct way to think of $a + a = 2a$?

No, it is not correct. a does not represent an object. It represents a number. So a can be any number. The correct way to think of $a + a = 2a$ is that any number added to itself is equal to twice that number.

Let's Wrap It Up!

You have learnt:

- that letters in algebra stand for numbers
- to write and evaluate algebraic expressions
- to simplify algebraic expressions.

Let's Revise!

13  At a football match, there were m men and 3 times as many women.

The number of children was 6352 fewer than the number of women.

a Find in terms of m:

i the number of women

Number of women = $3 \times m = 3m$

ii the number of children

Number of children = $3m - 6352$

Objective of activity

Pupils will be able to translate verbal statements into symbolic representations to solve the problem.

Thinking skill

Identifying relationships

Heuristic for problem solving

Solve in parts

Independent work

- *Challenging Practice* and *Problem Solving* in Practice Book 6A, pp 19 and 20.

iii the number of men and women.

Number of men and women = $m + 3m = 4m$

b If $m = 7145$, how many people were there at the football match?

Total number of people $= 4m + 3m - 6352$
$= 7m - 6352$
$= 7 \times 7145 - 6352$
$= 43\,663$

There were 43 663 people at the football match.

Put On Your Thinking Caps!

 Abby thinks of a number. First she multiplies it by 2. She then adds 12 to the result. Finally she takes the result and subtracts twice the original number. What answer will she always get?

Let the number that Abby thinks of be 'x'.

1 $x \times 2 = 2x$
2 $2x + 12$
3 $2x + 12 - 2x = 12$

Abby will always get 12.

Heuristic: Make a systematic list
Thinking skill: Sequencing

Practice Book 6A, p.19 Practice Book 6A, p.20

14 *Put On Your Thinking Caps!*

- Ask pupils to work through the statements provided to arrive at the correct answer.
- If necessary, remind pupils that they should start by representing the unknown number with a letter.

INSPIRE MATHS

PRACTICE BOOK 6A

Consultant and author
Dr Fong Ho Kheong

Authors
Gan Kee Soon and Chelvi Ramakrishnan

UK consultants
Carole Skinner, Simon d'Angelo and Elizabeth Gibbs

Unit 1 Algebra

Date: ____________

Practice 1 Using letters as numbers

1 Write an expression for each of the following.

a Farha has 10 apples and 6 oranges. How many apples and oranges does Farha have altogether?

$10 + 6 = 16$
Farha has 16 apples and oranges altogether.

Millie has x apples and 8 oranges. How many apples and oranges does Millie have altogether? Give your answer in terms of x.

$x + 8$
Millie has $(x + 8)$ apples and oranges altogether.

Ruby has 9 apples and y oranges. How many apples and oranges does Ruby have altogether? Give your answer in terms of y.

$9 + y$
Ruby has $(9 + y)$ apples and oranges altogether.

b Hardeep has £18. He spends £2. How much does Hardeep have left?

£18 – £2 = £16
Hardeep has £16 left.

Jack has £m. He spends £5. How much does Jack have left? Give your answer in terms of m.

£m – £5 = £$(m - 5)$
Jack has £$(m - 5)$ left.

Tai has £20. He spends £n. How much does Tai have left? Give your answer in terms of n.

£20 – £n = £$(20 - n)$
Tai has £$(20 - n)$ left.

2 Write an expression for each of the following:

a Add 9 to y.

$y + 9$

b Subtract p from 15.

$15 - p$

c Divide m by 3.

$m \div 3 = \frac{m}{3}$

d Multiply 4 by g.

$4 \times g = 4g$

e Subtract 12 from $8a$.

$8a - 12$

f Find the sum of 5 and $\frac{t}{2}$.

$5 + \frac{t}{2}$

3 Evaluate each of the following expressions for the given values of y.

Expression	Value of the Expression When:	
	$y = 25$	$y = 16$
$y + 5$	30	21
$y + 43$	68	59
$y - 12$	13	4
$y - 7$	18	9
$18 + y$	43	34
$40 + y$	65	56
$30 - y$	5	14
$35 - y$	10	19

4 Answer these questions.

a $6x$ = 6 × x or $x \times 6$

b $9x$ means 9 groups of x.

c 14 groups of x is $14x$.

d $18m$ = 18 × m or $m \times 18$

e $75y$ means 75 groups of y.

f 12 groups of y is $12y$.

5 Write an expression for each of the following.

a Mrs Williams has 4 boxes of tennis balls. There are 12 tennis balls in each box. How many tennis balls does Mrs Williams have altogether?

$4 \times 12 = 48$
Mrs Williams has 48 tennis balls altogether.

Mrs Patel has k boxes of tennis balls. There are 10 tennis balls in each box. How many tennis balls does Mrs Patel have altogether? Give your answer in terms of k.

$k \times 10 = 10k$
Mrs Patel has $10k$ tennis balls altogether.

Mr Jones has 7 boxes of tennis balls. There are j tennis balls in each box. How many tennis balls does Mr Jones have altogether? Give your answer in terms of j.

$7 \times j = 7j$
Mr Jones has $7j$ tennis balls altogether.

b 20 kg of pasta was distributed equally among 4 restaurants. How much pasta did each restaurant get?

$20 \div 4 = 5$
Each restaurant got 5 kg of pasta.

m kg of pasta was distributed equally among 3 restaurants. How much pasta did each restaurant get? Give your answer in terms of m.

$m \div 3 = \frac{m}{3}$
Each restaurant got $\frac{m}{3}$ kg of pasta.

$15r$ kg of pasta was distributed equally among 5 restaurants. How much pasta did each restaurant get? Give your answer in terms of r.

$15r \div 5 = \frac{15r}{5} = 3r$
Each restaurant got $3r$ kg of pasta.

6 Find the value of the expressions when $x = 5$.

a $13x - 4 = 13 \times 5 - 4$
$= 65 - 4$
$= 61$

b $20 - 2x = 20 - 2 \times 5$
$= 20 - 10$
$= 10$

c $\frac{x}{10} + 2 = \frac{5}{10} + 2$
$= \frac{1}{2} + 2$
$= 2\frac{1}{2}$

d $\frac{6x}{5} + 12 = \frac{6 \times 5}{5} + 12$
$= 6 + 12$
$= 18$

7 Find the value of each of the following expressions when $t = 12$.

a $2t = 2 \times t$
$= 2 \times 12$
$= 24$

b $\frac{t}{6} = \frac{12}{6}$
$= 2$

c $5t = 5 \times t$
$= 5 \times 12$
$= 60$

d $\frac{t}{4} = \frac{12}{4}$
$= 3$

e $20t = 20 \times t$
$= 20 \times 12$
$= 240$

f $\frac{t}{2} = \frac{12}{2}$
$= 6$

8 Fill in the boxes with the correct expression. In the last box on the right, evaluate each expression when $m = 6$.

	Start	Operation	Expression	Operation	Expression		Value
a	m	$\times 2$ →	$2m$	-3 →	$2m - 3$	→	9
b	3	$\times m$ →	$3m$	$+5$ →	$3m + 5$	→	23
c	76	$-m$ →	$76 - m$	$\div 2$ →	$\frac{76 - m}{2}$	→	35
d	m	$+5$ →	$m + 5$	$\div 11$ →	$\frac{m + 5}{11}$	→	1
e	m	$\div 3$ →	$\frac{m}{3}$	$+1$ →	$\frac{m}{3} + 1$	→	3
f	m	$\times 4$ →	$4m$	$\div 6$ →	$\frac{4m}{6}$	→	4

9 Write down as many algebraic expressions as you can using the two cards below:

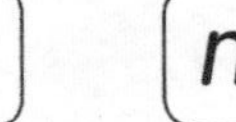

Answers vary
Example:
$7 + m$, $7 - m$, $7m$ and $\frac{m}{7}$.

10 Write an algebraic expression for the following.

a Miya has £12. She received £x from her mum. How much money does she have now?

£12 + £x = £$(12 + x)$
Miya has £$(12 + x)$.

b A bucket of sand weighs 4 kg. The bucket weighs y kg. What is the mass of the sand?

$4 - y = (4 - y)$
The mass of the sand is $(4 - y)$ kg.

c A tank has $x\,\ell$ of water. Mr Clark added $3\,\ell$ of water into the tank. Then he poured the water equally into 4 smaller containers. How much water is in each container?

$x + 3 = (x + 3)$
The tank contains $(x + 3)\,\ell$ of water.
$(x + 3) \div 4 = \left(\frac{x + 3}{4}\right)$

There is $\left(\frac{x + 3}{4}\right)\ell$ of water in each container.

11 Write an algebraic expression for the following.

a Mrs Miller had £y. She bought 2 jumpers that cost £45 each. How much had she left?

£45 × 2 = £90
£y – £90 = £(y – 90)

She had £(y – 90) left.

b Mike runs x km in 6 h. How far does he run in 1 hour?

$x \div 6 = \frac{x}{6}$ km

He runs $\frac{x}{6}$ km in 1 hour.

c A school collected 400 bags of clothing. It used g bags of clothing for a jumble sale. The rest of the bags were shared equally among 4 charities. How many bags of clothing did each charity get?

The 4 charities share (400 – g) bags of clothing.

$(400 - g) \div 4 = \frac{400 - g}{4}$

Each charity got $\left(\frac{400 - g}{4}\right)$ bags of clothing.

d Peter needs x eggs for every 200 g of flour to bake a cake. If he uses 1000 g of flour, how many eggs does he use?

200 g → x eggs

$1000\text{ g} \rightarrow \frac{1000}{200} \times x$
$= 5 \times x$
$= 5x$

Peter uses $5x$ eggs.

Date: ____________

Practice 2 Simplifying algebraic expressions

1 Simplify the following expressions.

a $c + c + c + c = 4c$

b $5 \times k = 5k$

c $6p + 3p = 9p$

d $b + 3b + 5b = 9b$

e $10k - 3k = 7k$

f $12p - 12p = 0$

g $6p - 2p - 3p = p$

h $10a - a + 2a = 11a$

i $4c + c - 5c = 0$

j $10f - 4f + f = 7f$

2 Simplify the following expressions.

a $5x + 2x + 4 = 7x + 4$

b $6y - 8 + y = 7y - 8$

c $2m + 4 + 6m = 8m + 4$

d $x - 9 + 5x = 6x - 9$

e $10p - 4p - 5 = 6p - 5$

f $4 + 5k - 4k = 4 + k$

g $2 + 6b - 1 + 4b = 1 + 10b$

h $5c + 3 - 2c + 5 = 3c + 8$

i $9e - 2e - 3 + 5e = 12e - 3$

j $6h + 12 + 2h - 6 = 8h + 6$

Date: ____________

Practice 3 Word problems

1 The length of a piece of material is $8y$ m. Mr Douglas cut 7 m from it to make a pair of curtains. Then he cut $3y$ m to make another pair of curtains. The remaining material was cut into 4 equal pieces. How long was each piece in terms of y?

Length of remaining piece $= 8y - 3y - 7$
$= (5y - 7)$ m

Length of each piece $= (5y - 7) \div 4$
$= \left(\frac{5y-7}{4}\right)$ m

The length of each piece was $\left(\frac{5y-7}{4}\right)$ m.

2 Miss Brook has $4m$ kg of pasta. She bought 2 more bags of pasta, each with a mass of m kg. How much pasta does she have now in terms of m?

$2 \times m = 2m$
The mass of the 2 packets of pasta is $2m$ kg.

$4m + 2m = 6m$
Miss Brook has $6m$ kg of pasta now.

3 On Monday, Jack made $5k$ paper aeroplanes and gave $2k$ paper aeroplanes to his friends. On Tuesday, he made another $4k$ paper aeroplanes. His friend gave him 5 paper aeroplanes. How many paper aeroplanes does he have now in terms of k?

$5k - 2k = 3k$
Jack had $3k$ paper aeroplanes left on Monday.

$3k + 4k + 5 = 7k + 5$
Jack has $(7k + 5)$ paper aeroplanes now.

4 At a market, a pear cost b pence and an apple cost 7 pence less than a pear. Ella bought 4 pears and an apple. Find the total amount Ella paid in terms of b.

An apple costs $(b - 7)$ pence.
Cost of 4 pears = $4b$ pence

Total amount paid $= 4b + b - 7$
$= (5b - 7)$ pence

The total amount Ella paid was $(5b - 7)$ pence.

5 Tai has 5 sheets of stickers. Each sheet contains y stickers. His teacher gives him another 8 stickers.

a Find the total number of stickers Tai has in terms of y.
b If $y = 4$, how many stickers does Tai have altogether?

a $5 \times y = 5y$
$5y + 8$

The total number of stickers Tai has is $(5y + 8)$.

b If $y = 4$, $5y + 8 = 5 \times 4 + 8$
$= 20 + 8$
$= 28$

Tai has 28 stickers altogether.

6 Mrs Sheridan bought z bags of rice at £9 each. She gave the sales assistant £50.

a Find the change Mrs Sheridan received in terms of z.
b If $z = 3$, how much change did Mrs Sheridan receive?

a $z \times £9 = £9z$
$£50 - £9z = £(50 - 9z)$

The change Mrs Sheridan received was $£(50 - 9z)$.

b If $z = 3$, $50 - 9z = 50 - 9(3)$
$= 50 - 27$
$= 23$

Mrs Sheridan received £23 as change.

7 Alex is w years old. His mum is 4 times his age. His dad is 3 years older than his mum.

a How old is Alex's dad in terms of w?
b If $w = 9$, how old is Alex's dad?

a $w \times 4 = 4w$
$4w + 3$
Alex's dad is $(4w + 3)$ years old.

b If $w = 9$, $4w + 3 = 4 \times 9 + 3$
$= 36 + 3$
$= 39$

Alex's dad is 39 years old.

8 A shop owner bought 16 boxes of cards. Each box contained m cards. 10 cards were sold on the first day.

a How many cards were left after the first day? Give your answer in terms of m.
b If $m = 5$, how many cards were left after the first day?

a $16 \times m = 16m$
$16m - 10$
$(16m - 10)$ cards were left after the first day.

b If $m = 5$, $16m - 10 = 16 \times 5 - 10$
$= 80 - 10$
$= 70$

70 cards were left after the first day.

9 Emma has y m of material. She used 2 m to sew a cushion cover. She used the remaining material to make 5 identical jackets.

a Find the amount of material that was used to make each jacket in terms of y.
b If she has 17 m of material, how much material was used for each jacket?

a $y - 2 = (y - 2)$
Emma used $(y - 2)$ m of material to make 5 jackets.
$(y - 2) \div 5 = \left(\frac{y-2}{5}\right)$
$\left(\frac{y-2}{5}\right)$ m of material was used to make each jacket.

b If $y = 17$, $\frac{y-2}{5} = \frac{17-2}{5}$
$= \frac{15}{5}$
$= 3$

3 m of material was used to make each jacket.

10 A magazine costs half as much as a book. The book costs £x. A pen costs £2 more than the magazine.

a How much is the pen in terms of x?
b If the book costs £5, how much is the pen?

a £$x \div 2 =$ £$\frac{x}{2}$
The magazine costs £$\frac{x}{2}$.

£$\frac{x}{2}$ + £2 = £$\left(\frac{x}{2} + 2\right)$
The pen costs £$\left(\frac{x}{2} + 2\right)$.

b If $x = 5$, £$\left(\frac{x}{2} + 2\right)$ = £$\left(\frac{5}{2} + 2\right)$
= £4·50
The pen costs £4·50.

11 A recycling company collected d kg of waste paper in February and 2400 kg of waste paper in March. The amount of waste paper collected in both February and March was 3 times that of the amount collected in January.

a Find the amount of waste paper collected in January in terms of d.
b If the recycling company collected 4500 kg of paper in February, what was the amount of waste paper collected in January?

a Amount of waste paper collected in January = $\left(\frac{d + 2400}{3}\right)$ kg

The amount of waste paper collected in January was $\left(\frac{d + 2400}{3}\right)$ kg.

b If $d = 4500$, $\left(\frac{d + 2400}{3}\right) = \left(\frac{4500 + 2400}{3}\right)$
$= 2300$

The amount of waste paper collected in January was 2300 kg.

12 In 2013, there were g white storks migrating from Europe to Africa in winter. The next year, only half of the white storks made the journey to Africa. In 2015, the number of migrating white storks decreased by another 45.

a Find the number of white storks that migrated in 2015 in terms of g.
b If the number of white storks that migrated in 2013 was 1800, how many white storks migrated in 2015?

a Number of white storks that migrated in 2014 = $\frac{g}{2}$

Number of white storks that migrated in 2015 = $\frac{g}{2} - 45$

The number of white storks that migrated in 2015 is $\left(\frac{g}{2} - 45\right)$.

b If $g = 1800$, $\left(\frac{g}{2} - 45\right) = \frac{1800}{2} - 45$
$= 855$

855 white storks migrated in 2015.

Date: __________

Maths Journal

Identify and explain the mistakes Peter has made in the calculations below. Then write the correct answer.

1 **a** Peter's answer:
$4w + 12w - 10 = 16w - 10 = 6w$

He should not have subtracted 10 from the numerical value in $16w$.

Correct answer:
$4w + 12w - 10 = 16w - 10$

b Peter's answer:
$20p - 2p + 4p = 20p - 6p = 14p$

He did not follow the order of operations. He added first before subtracting. He should have followed the left to right rule, and subtracted before adding.

Correct answer:
$20p - 2p + 4p = 18p + 4p = 22p$

c Peter's answer:
$3 + p = 3p$

He multiplied 3 by p, instead of adding 3 to p.

Correct answer:
$3 + p = p + 3$

2 Mrs Adams bought 3 tins of beans for y pence each. She gave the sales assistant £10. How much change did she receive?

Peter's answer:
Cost of 3 tins = $3 \times y = 3y$

Change received = £$(10 - 3y)$

He calculated the cost of the 3 tins in pence but gave his answer for the change received in pence. He should convert £10 to pence first.

Correct answer:
Cost of 3 tins = $3 \times y = 3y$

£10 = 1000 pence
Change received = $(1000 - 3y)$ pence

Date: ____________

Challenging Practice

1 Millie thinks of a number x and adds 5. Then she adds 3 times the number to the answer. Finally she divides the answer by 8. What is the final answer in terms of x?

$x + 5$
$x + 5 + 3x = 4x + 5$
$(4x + 5) \div 8 = \frac{4x + 5}{8}$

The final answer is $\frac{4x + 5}{8}$.

Date: ____________

Problem Solving

1 There are 40 pupils in a school play. There are x more girls than boys.

a How many boys are there in terms of x?
b If $x = 4$, how many boys are there?

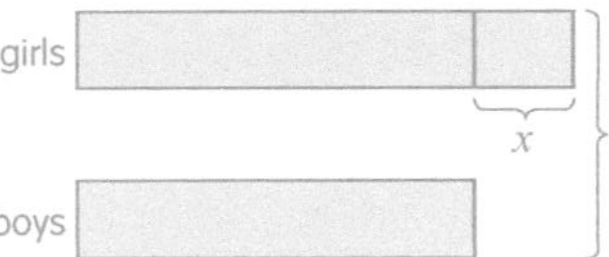

a $(40 - x) \div 2 = \frac{40 - x}{2}$

There are $\left(\frac{40 - x}{2}\right)$ boys.

b If $x = 4$, $\frac{40 - x}{2} = \frac{40 - 4}{2}$

$= \frac{36}{2}$

$= 18$

There are 18 boys.

Heuristic: Draw a model
Thinking Skill: Analysing parts and whole

Unit 2: Angles in Shapes and Diagrams

Medium-term plan

Week	Learning Objectives	Thinking Skills	Resources
3	**(I) Finding unknown angles** Pupils will be able to: • find unknown angles in geometric shapes using the properties of: (a) angles on a straight line (b) angles at a point (c) vertically opposite angles (d) triangles (e) four-sided shapes (square, rectangle, parallelogram, rhombus and trapezium) *Let's Explore!* Pupils will be able to name three- and four-sided geometric shapes based on the descriptions provided. *Maths Journal* Pupils will be able to: • explain why a parallelogram with two equal adjacent sides and a right angle between them is a square • apply the angle properties they have learnt to state the relationship between the given angles	• Spatial visualisation • Identifying relationships • Deduction	• Pupil Textbook 6A, pp 24 to 34 • Practice Book 6A, pp 21 to 35 • Teacher's Guide 6A, pp 40 to 50

Unit 2: Angles in Shapes and Diagrams

Medium-term plan

Week	Learning Objectives	Thinking Skills	Resources
3	*Let's Wrap It Up!* Emphasise the key concepts, skills and processes that have been taught in the unit. Discuss the worked examples with pupils to assess whether they have mastered these concepts, skills and processes. *Put On Your Thinking Caps!* Pupils will be able to use the properties of an equilateral triangle, an isosceles triangle and a square to deduce the size of the unknown angle.	• Deduction Heuristic for problem solving: • Simplify the problem	• Pupil Textbook 6A, pp 35 to 37 • Practice Book 6A, pp 36 to 38 • Teacher's Guide 6A, pp 51 to 53
Summative assessment opportunity			
Assessment Book 6, Test 2, pp 7 to 14			

Angles in Shapes and Diagrams

Learning objectives: Finding unknown angles

Pupils will be able to:

- find unknown angles in geometric shapes using the properties of:
  (a) angles on a straight line
  (b) angles at a point
  (c) vertically opposite angles
  (d) triangles
  (e) four-sided shapes (square, rectangle, parallelogram, rhombus and trapezium)

Key concept

Understanding and applying the properties of angles, triangles, squares, rectangles, parallelograms, rhombuses and trapeziums.

Thinking skills

- Spatial visualisation
- Identifying relationships
- Deduction

Teaching sequence

1 and 2

- Using the examples in the textbook, review the following properties with pupils:
  (a) The sum of angles on a straight line is equal to 180°.
  (b) The sum of angles at a point is equal to 360°.

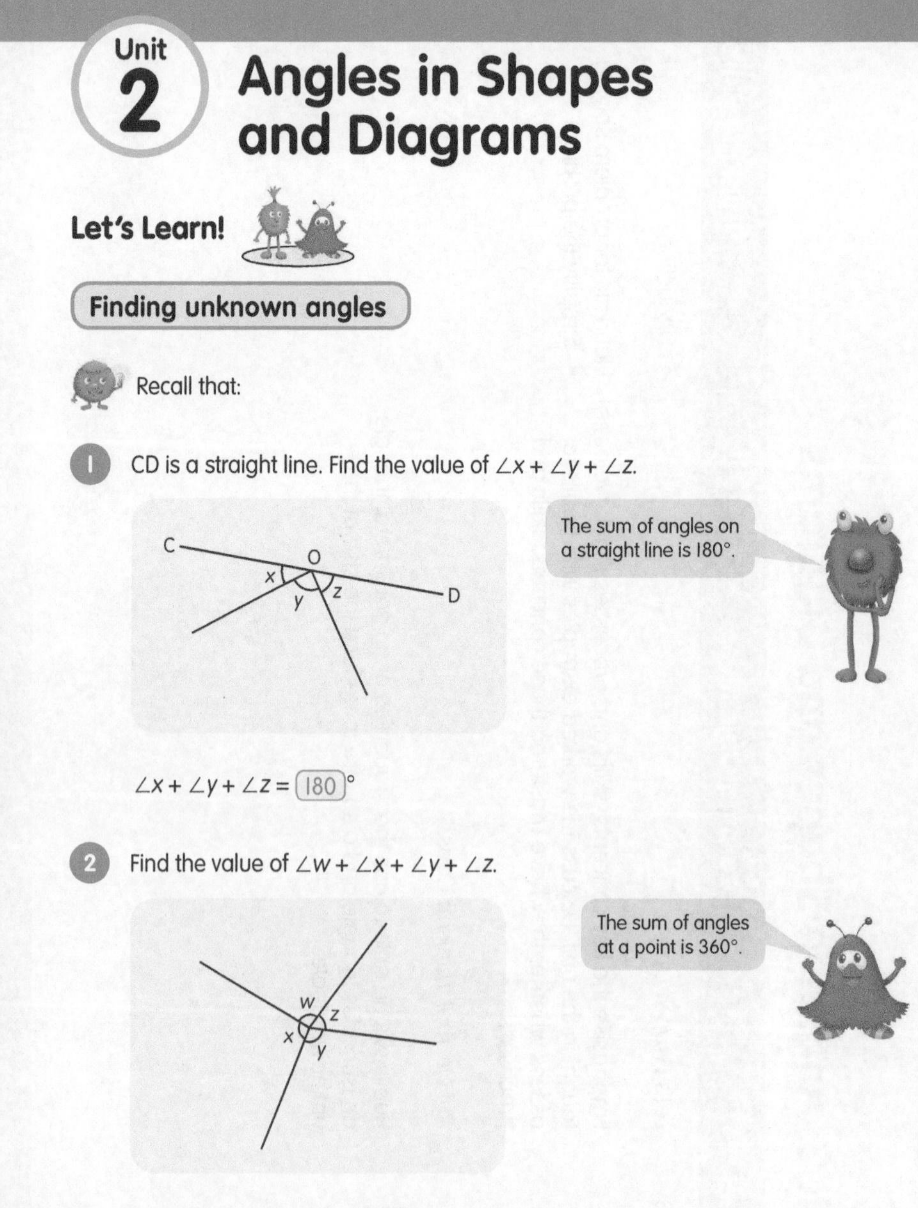

Independent work

Practice 1 in Practice Book 6A, pp 21 to 22.

3 AB and CD are straight lines.

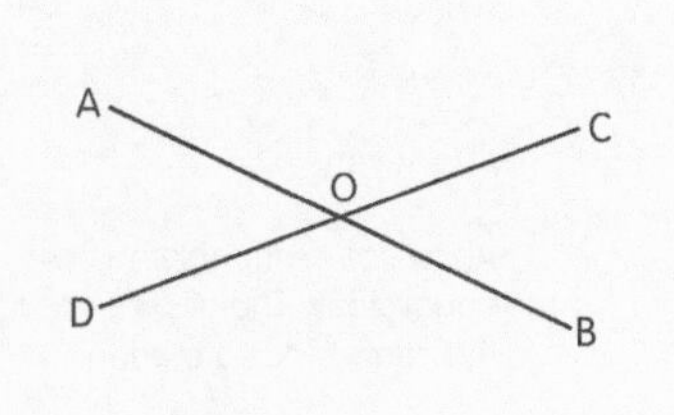

∠AOC = ∠ DOB

∠BOC = ∠ DOA

Vertically opposite angles are equal.

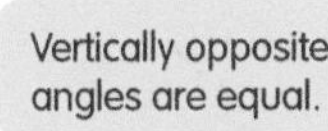

4 ABC is a triangle.

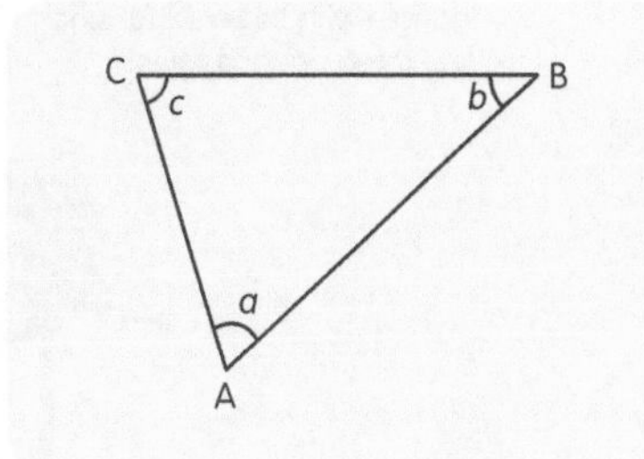

$\angle a + \angle b + \angle c = 180°$

The sum of the angles in a triangle is 180°.

Teaching sequence

3 and 4

- Using the examples in the textbook, review the following properties with pupils:
  - (a) Vertically opposite angles are equal.
  - (b) The sum of the angles in a triangle is 180°.

Teaching sequence

5 and 6

- Using the examples in the textbook, review the following properties with pupils:
  (a) An isosceles triangle has two equal sides. The angles opposite the equal sides are equal.
  (b) An equilateral triangle is a triangle with three equal sides and three equal angles. Each angle of an equilateral triangle is equal to 60°.

5 ABC is an isosceles triangle with AB = AC.

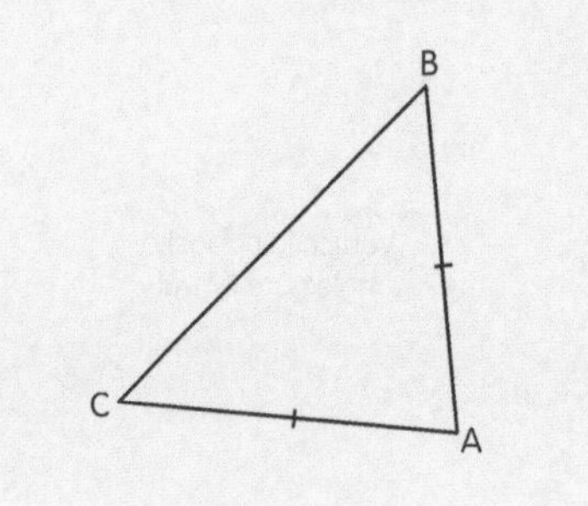

An isosceles triangle has two equal sides. The angles opposite the equal sides are equal.

∠ ACB = ∠ ABC

6 ABC is an equilateral triangle.

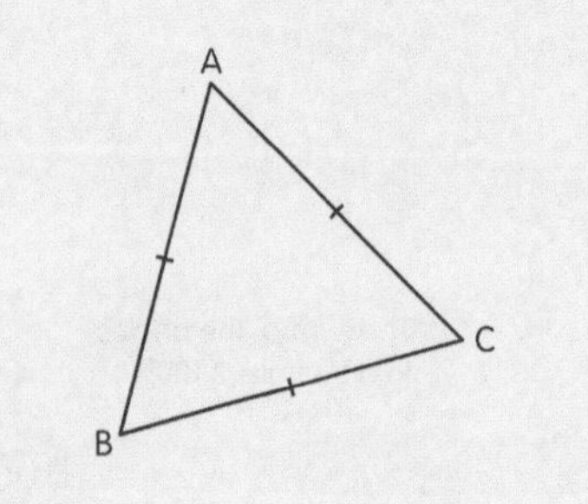

An equilateral triangle is a triangle with three equal sides and three equal angles.

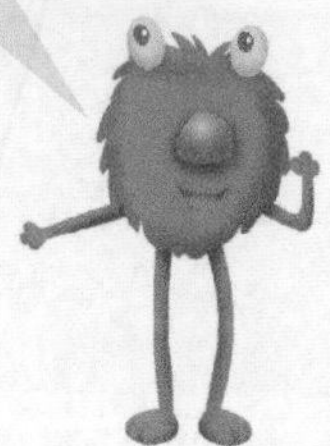

∠ABC = ∠ BCA = ∠ CAB = 60 °

7 EFGH is a rhombus and WXYZ is a parallelogram.

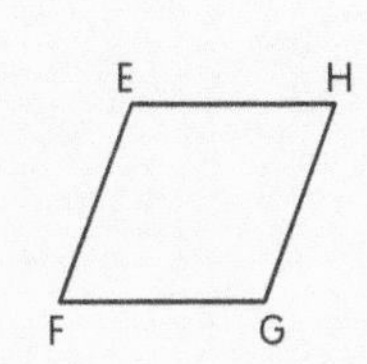

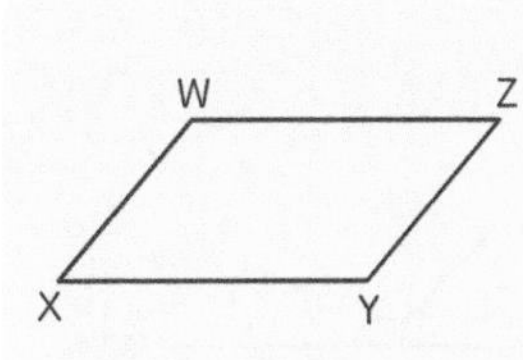

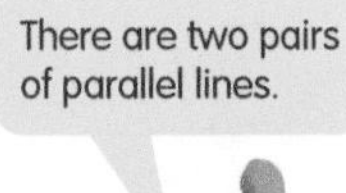

EF = FG = GH = HE

∠EFG = ∠GHE

∠HEF = ∠FGH

∠HEF + ∠EFG = 180°

∠EFG + ∠FGH = 180°

WZ = XY and WX = ZY

∠WXY = ∠WZY

∠XYZ = ∠ZWX

∠WXY + ∠XYZ = 180°

∠ZWX + ∠WXY = 180°

8 STUV is a trapezium where SV // TU.

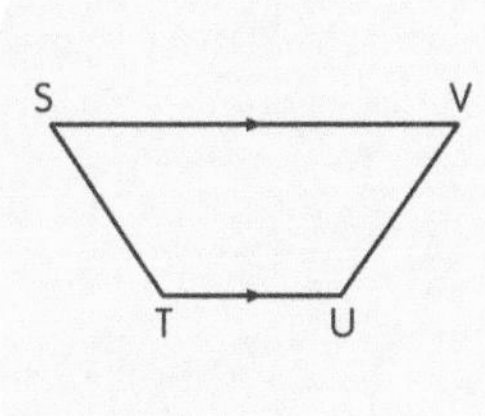

∠TUV and ∠UVS are a pair of angles between two parallel sides.

∠TUV + ∠UVS = 180°

∠VST + ∠STU = 180°

Teaching sequence

7 and 8

- Using the examples in the textbook, review the following properties with pupils:
  - (a) The four sides of a rhombus are equal.
  - (b) The opposite sides of a parallelogram are equal.
  - (c) The opposite angles of a rhombus and a parallelogram are equal.
  - (d) The sum of each pair of angles between two parallel sides (allied interior angles) of a rhombus and a parallelogram is equal to 180°.
  - (e) The sum of each pair of angles between the parallel sides (allied interior angles) of a trapezium is equal to 180°.

  Note: a rhombus has all the properties of a parallelogram with the extra property that all its sides are equal.

Independent work

Practice 2 in Practice Book 6A, pp 23 to 26.

Teaching sequence

- Guide pupils to use reasoning to find unknown angles in geometric shapes and diagrams.
- Ask pupils:
  "Since triangle ABC is an isosceles triangle, what can you say about ∠ABC and ∠ACB?" (They are equal.)
  "What can you say about ∠ACB and ∠ACD?" (∠ACB and ∠ACD are angles on a straight line.)
  ∠ACB + ∠ACD = 180°
  ∠ACB + 135° = 180°,
  so ∠ACB = 180° – 135°.
  This conclusion is based on the previous statement and the inverse relationship between addition and subtraction, e.g.
  3 + 4 = 7 → 3 = 7 – 4
  Now ∠ABC = ∠ACB.
  As ∠ACB = 45°,
  so ∠ABC = 45°.
- Some pupils may also notice that the exterior angle of the triangle equals the sum of the two interior opposite angles.

10

- Ask pupils to work on this question as practice.

Unit 2 Angles in Shapes and Diagrams

9 The diagram below is not drawn to scale. ABC is an isosceles triangle in which AB = AC. BD is a straight line. Find ∠ACB and ∠ABC.

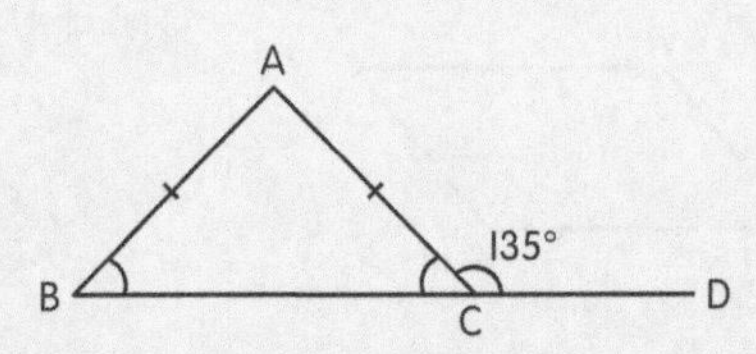

∠ACB = 180° – 135°
= 45°

∠ABC = ∠ACB = 45°

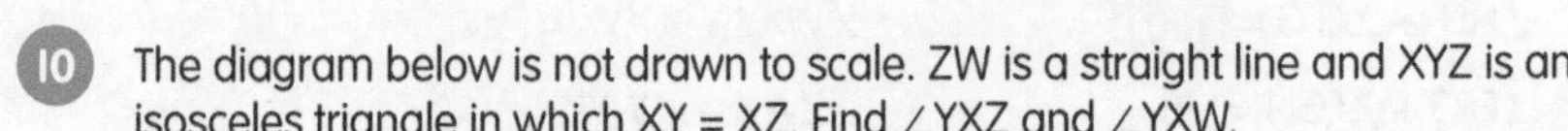

10 The diagram below is not drawn to scale. ZW is a straight line and XYZ is an isosceles triangle in which XY = XZ. Find ∠YXZ and ∠YXW.

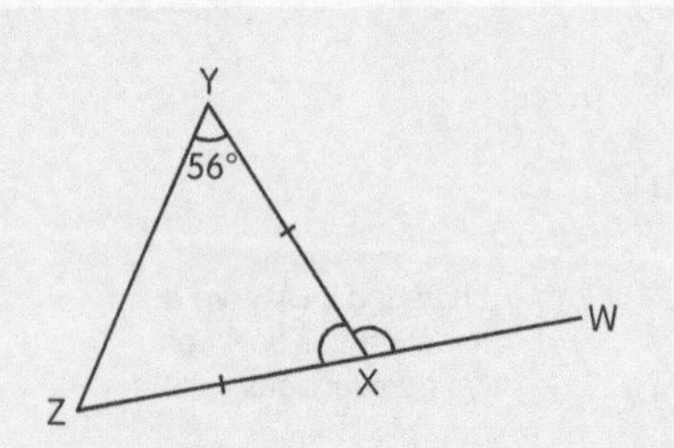

∠XZY = ∠ XYZ = 56 °

∠YXZ = 180 ° – 56 ° – 56 °
= 68 °

∠YXW = 180 ° – 68 °
= 112 °

Practice Book 6A, p.23

11 The diagram below is not drawn to scale. ABC is a triangle. AD and AE are straight lines. Find ∠ABC and ∠CBD.

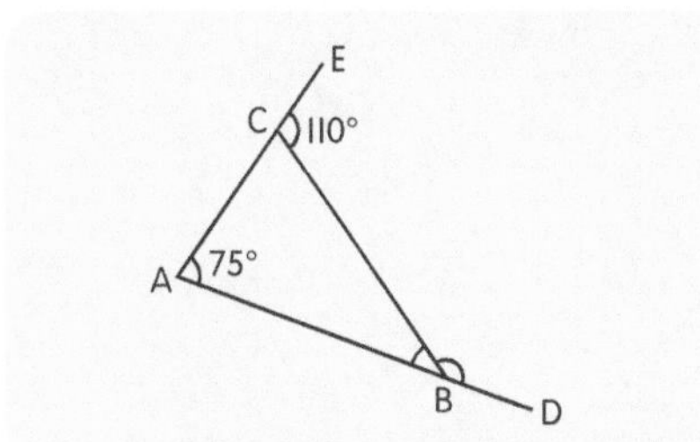

∠ACB = 180° – 110°
= 70°

∠ABC = 180° – 75° – 70°
= 35°

∠CBD = 180° – 35°
= 145°

Angles on a straight line...

Sum of angles in a triangle...

Angles on a straight line...

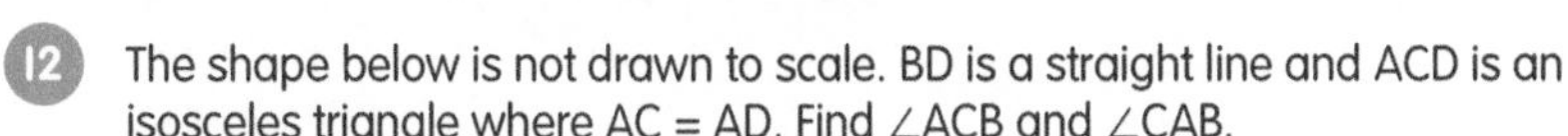

12 The shape below is not drawn to scale. BD is a straight line and ACD is an isosceles triangle where AC = AD. Find ∠ACB and ∠CAB.

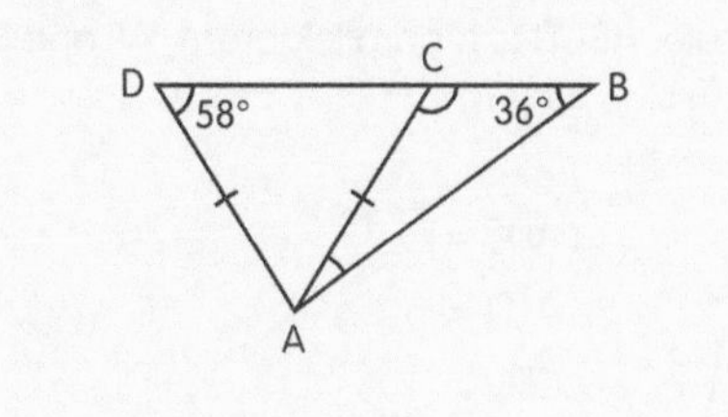

∠ACD = 58°

∠ACB = 180° – 58° = 122°

∠CAB = 180° – 122° – 36°
= 22°

Teaching sequence

11

- Using the example in **11**, guide pupils to use reasoning to find unknown angles in geometric shapes and diagrams.
- Explain that they may have to find other angles in the shapes and diagrams in order to find the size of the angle they are asked to find.

12

- Ask pupils to work on this question as practice.

Teaching sequence

- Using the example in 13, guide pupils to use reasoning to find unknown angles in geometric shapes.

- Ask pupils to work on this question as practice.

13 The shape below is not drawn to scale. ABCD is a parallelogram. BE and CE are straight lines. Find ∠EDF and ∠BEC.

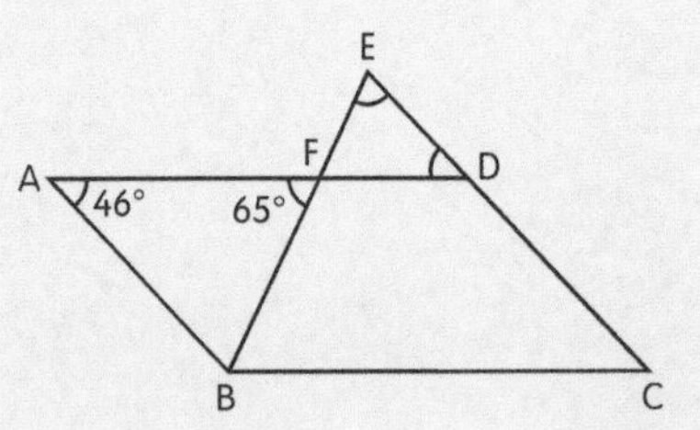

∠ADC = 180° – 46°
= 134°

∠EDF = 180° – 134°
= 46°

∠EFD = 65°

∠BEC = 180° – 46° – 65°
= 69°

Angles between two parallel sides AB and DC...

Angles on a straight line...

Vertically opposite angles...

Sum of angles in a triangle...

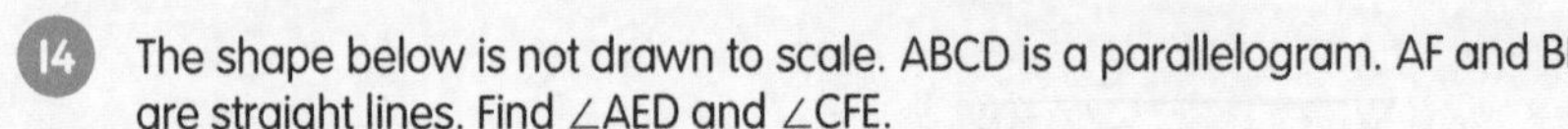

14 The shape below is not drawn to scale. ABCD is a parallelogram. AF and BF are straight lines. Find ∠AED and ∠CFE.

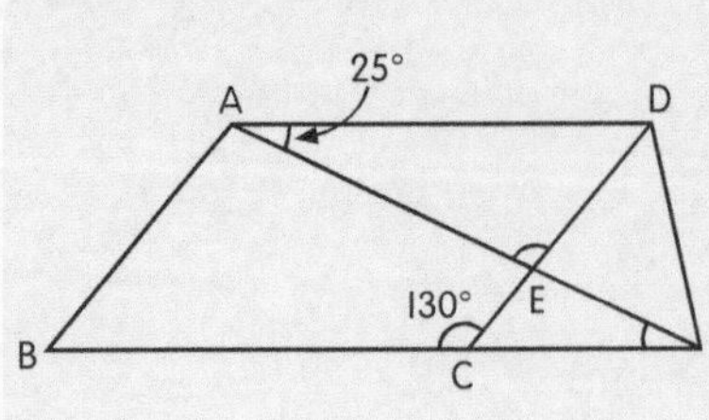

∠ADC = 50 ° 180° – 130° = 50°

∠AED = 105 ° 180° – 50° – 25° = 105°

∠CEF = 105 °

∠ECF = 50 ° 180° – 130° = 50°

∠CFE = 25 ° 180° – 105° – 50° = 25°

30

Objective of activity

Pupils will be able to name three- and four-sided geometric shapes based on the descriptions provided.

Thinking skill

Spatial visualisation

Activity 

15 Work in pairs.
Look at the 7 statements in the box below.

1. Read the first statement. Then draw a shape that fits the description.
2. Read the second statement and redraw your shape accordingly.
3. Continue redrawing your shape, if necessary, after each of the remaining statements.
4. After the last statement, compare the shape you have drawn with the shape your partner has drawn.

- **i** The shape has 4 sides.
- **ii** One pair of the opposite sides is parallel.
- **iii** The other pair of opposite sides is equal.
- **iv** The equal sides are also parallel.
- **v** The opposite angles are equal.
- **vi** All the four sides are equal.
- **vii** There are no right angles in the shape.

What is the shape? A rhombus

Let's Explore! 

16 A shape ABC has 3 sides. What is the shape? A triangle.
If AC = BC, describe the shape. An isosceles triangle.
Give another condition to make the shape ABC a right-angled isosceles triangle. $\angle ABC$ or $\angle CAB = 45°$

17 A shape ABCD has 4 sides. AB // CD and AD // BC. What is the shape? A parallelogram.
If AB = BC, describe the shape. A rhombus.
Give another condition to make the shape ABCD a square.
$\angle ABC$ or $\angle BCD$ or $\angle CDA$ or $\angle DAB = 90°$

Teaching sequence

15 

- Ask pupils to work in pairs.
- This activity enables pupils to interpret statements to draw geometric shapes.
- Emphasise to pupils that the shape they draw (or redraw) should have only the properties described in the statements, e.g. if they are redrawing the shape to have a pair of equal sides, those sides should not also be parallel.

16 and **17** *Let's Explore!*

- These questions enable pupils to identify a geometric shape given some properties of the shape, and to make changes to the shape by giving an additional condition.

What you will need

A copy of the shape in 19 (see Photocopy master 2 on p 273)

Additional activity

Ask pupils to give the reason for each relationship they have identified in 19.

For example, in **a**, they should identify that the reason ∠ABC = ∠ADC is that these are opposite angles of a parallelogram.

Teaching sequence

18 *Maths Journal*

- Guide pupils to explain why a parallelogram with two equal adjacent sides and a right angle between them is a square.

- Provide pupils with a copy of the diagram provided on Photocopy master 2. Pupils may find it easier to answer the question if they are able to draw and write on the photocopied shape.
- Pupils should be able to apply the angle properties they have learnt to state the relationship between the given angles.

Unit 2 Angles in Shapes and Diagrams

Maths Journal

 JKLM is a parallelogram. JK = KL and ∠JKL = 90°. Explain why JKLM is a square.

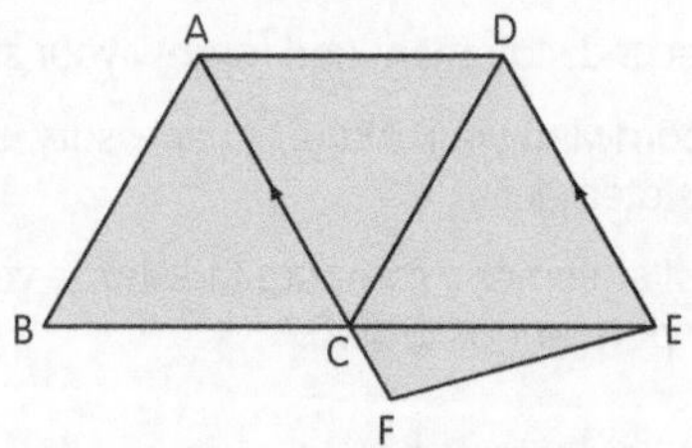

The shape above is not drawn to scale. ABCD is a rhombus and CFED is a trapezium in which DE // AF. BE and AF are straight lines.
Using '+', '=', '180°' or '360°', state the relationship between the angles in each set.

For example, in **a**, ∠ABC = ∠ADC.

a ∠ABC and ∠ADC ∠ABC = ∠ADC Opposite angles of a parallelogram are equal.

b ∠ACB and ∠ECF ∠ACB = ∠ECF Vertically opposite angles are equal.

c ∠AFE and ∠DEF ∠AFE + ∠DEF = 180° Sum of internal angles of two parallel lines.

d ∠ACB and ∠BCF ∠ACB + ∠BCF = 180° Angles on a straight line = 180°

e ∠CAD and ∠ACD ∠CAD = ∠ACD Diagonal bisects angle in a rhombus.

f ∠ACB, ∠ACD and ∠DCE ∠ACB + ∠ACD + ∠DCE = 180° Angles of a straight line.

g ∠BCD, ∠DCF and ∠BCF ∠BCD + ∠DCF + ∠BCF = 360° Angles at a point.

18

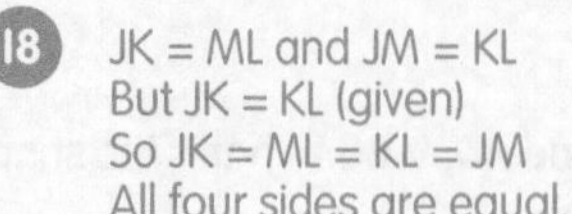

JK = ML and JM = KL
But JK = KL (given)
So JK = ML = KL = JM
All four sides are equal.

∠JKL = ∠JML = 90°
∠KJM = 180° − 90° = 90°
∠KLM = ∠KJM = 90°
There are four right angles.

Therefore JKLM is a square.

32

What you will need

A copy of the diagrams in 20, 21 and 22 (see Photocopy master 3 on p 274)

Independent work

Let's Practise!

The diagrams shown are not drawn to scale.

20 BCD is a triangle. AC, BE and CF are straight lines. ∠ABD = 134° and ∠FDE = 85°. Find ∠DBC and ∠BCD. ∠DBC = 46°

∠BCD° = 180° – 46° – 85° = 49°

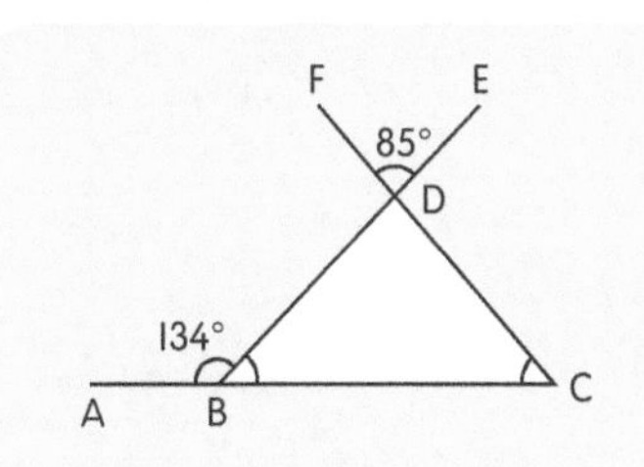

21 ABC is an isosceles triangle where AC = BC. ∠BEA = 78° and ∠CBE = 36°. Find ∠ABE. ∠ABE = 33°

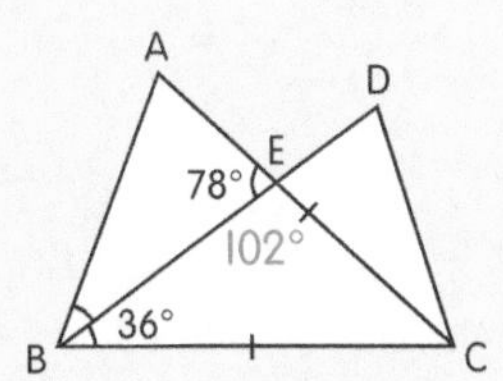

∠BEC = 102° (180° – 78°)
∠BCE = 42° (180° – 102° – 36°)
$\angle ABC = \frac{180° - 42°}{2} = 69°$
∠ABE = 69° – 36° = 33°

22 XYZ is an isosceles triangle where XY = XZ. ∠WXZ = 142° and ∠YXW = 106°. Find ∠YZX. ∠YZX = 34°

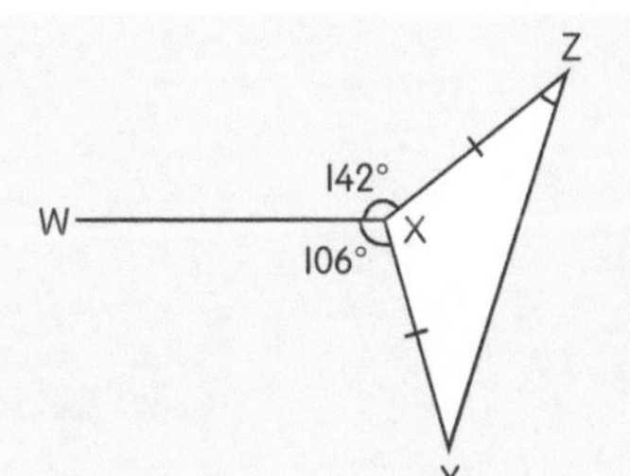

∠ZXY = 360° – 142° – 106°
= 112°
$\angle YZX = \frac{180° - 112°}{2} = 34°$

33

Teaching sequence

20 to 25 *Let's Practise!*

- Provide pupils with a copy of Photocopy master 3. Pupils may find it easier to answer the questions if they are able to record angles and their workings on this photocopy master of 20 to 25.

Independent work

Practice 3 and *Maths Journal* in Practice Book 6A, pp 27 to 35.

Let's Practise!

23 KLMN is a parallelogram. LK and JM are straight lines. ∠OLM = 68° and ∠KOM = 120°. Find ∠NJM. ∠NJM = 180° − 60° − 68° = 52°

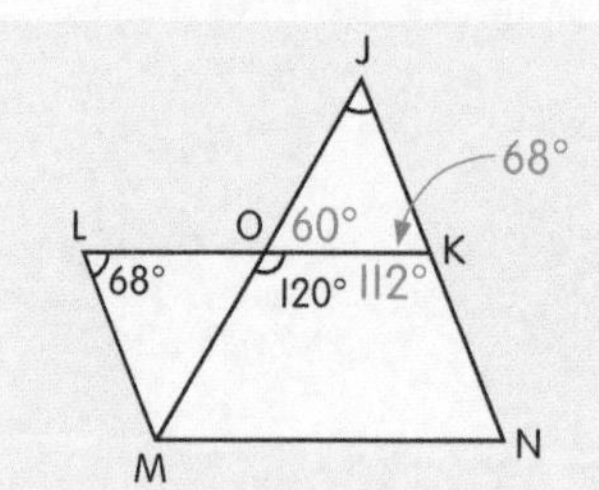

24 PQRS is a trapezium in which PS // QR. PQR is an equilateral triangle and ∠RSP = 35°. Find ∠PRS. ∠PRS = 180° − 35° − 60° = 85°

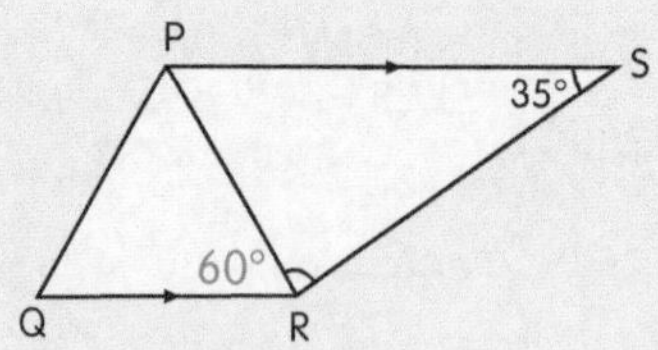

25 WXYZ is a rhombus and WSTZ is a parallelogram. ∠YZW = 54°. Find ∠ZYS and ∠TZY. ∠ZYS = 117°, ∠TZY = 63°

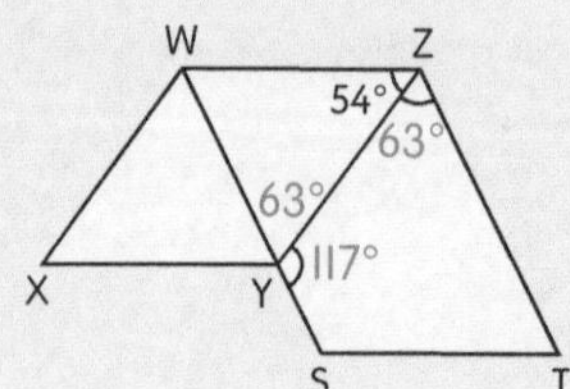

Practice Book 6A, p.27

Let's Wrap It Up! 

You have learnt to find unknown angles in shapes and diagrams using the properties of:

- angles on a straight line
- angles at a point
- vertically opposite angles
- right-angled, isosceles, equilateral and other triangles
- square, rectangle, parallelogram, rhombus and trapezium.

Let's Revise!

The following shapes are not drawn to scale.

 ABCD is a trapezium and DEF is a right-angled triangle. ∠DEF = 90° and CB // DA. AE and CF are straight lines. Find ∠EFD.

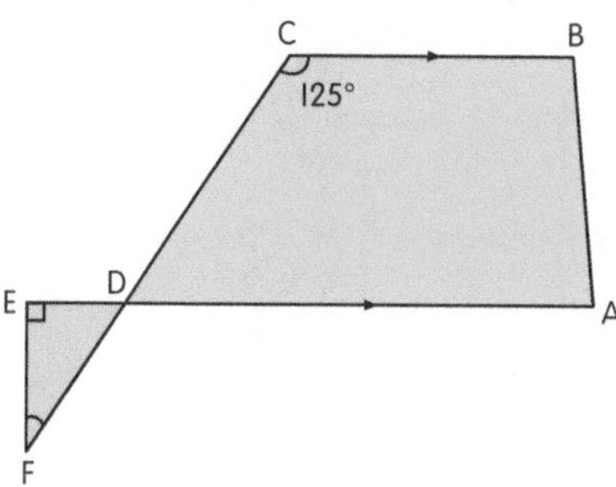

Since AD // BC, ∠ADC = 180° – 125° = 55°

∠EDF = ∠ADC = 55°

∠EFD = 180° – 90° – 55° = 35°

Teaching sequence

Let's Wrap It Up!

- Emphasise the key concepts, skills and processes that have been taught in the unit.

- Discuss the worked example with pupils to assess whether they have mastered these concepts, skills and processes.

Teaching sequence

Let's Wrap It Up!

- Discuss the worked example with pupils to assess whether they have mastered these concepts, skills and processes.

Let's Wrap It Up!

ABCD is a parallelogram and BECD is a rhombus. AE is a straight line.
Find ∠CBE and ∠CDA.

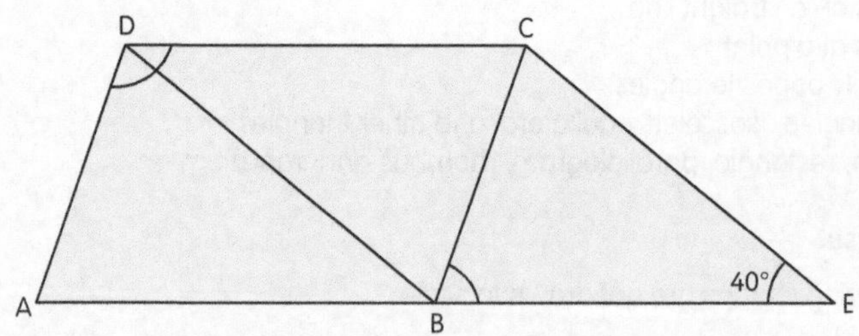

Since BECD is a rhombus, BE = CE.

∠CBE = (180° – 40°) ÷ 2
= 70°

Since AE is a straight line, ∠ABC = 180° – 70°
= 110°

Since ABCD is a parallelogram, ∠CDA = ∠ABC
= 110°

Objective of activity

Pupils will be able to use the properties of an equilateral triangle, an isosceles triangle and a square to deduce the size of the unknown angle.

Thinking skill

Deduction

Heuristic for problem solving

Simplify the problem

Independent work

- *Challenging Practice* in Practice Book 6A, pp 36 to 38.

Put On Your Thinking Caps!

28 ABCD is a square and ABE is an equilateral triangle. Find ∠CDE.

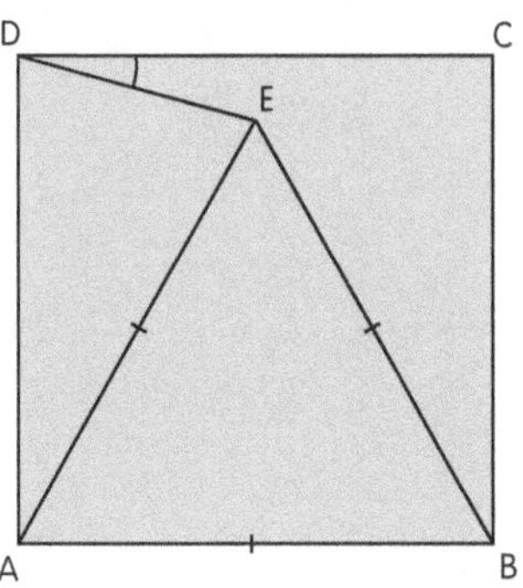

Since ABCD is a square and ABE is an equilateral triangle, AD = AB = AE.
Therefore Triangle AED is an isosceles triangle.

∠DAE = 90° – 60°
= 30°

∠ADE = (180° – 30°) ÷ 2
= 75°

∠CDE = 90° – 75°
= 15°

Practice Book 6A, p.36

Teaching sequence

28 *Put On Your Thinking Caps!*

- Ask pupils to point out which sides of the diagram are equal, based on the properties of the square and equilateral triangle.

Unit 2 Angles in Shapes and Diagrams

Date: ____________

Practice 1 Finding unknown angles

1 The following diagrams are not drawn to scale.

a AC is a straight line. Find $\angle a$.

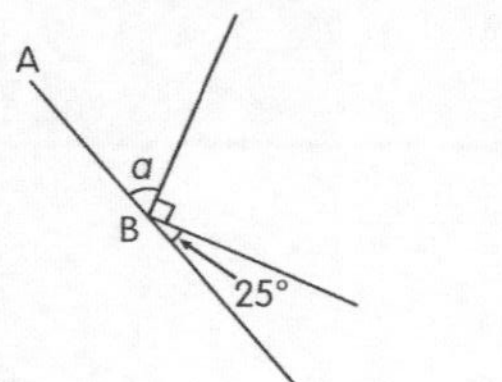

$\angle a = 180° - 90° - 25°$
$= 90° - 25°$
$= 65°$

b Find $\angle b$.

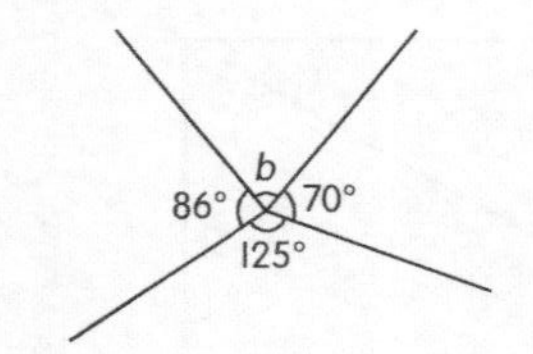

$\angle b = 360° - 70° - 125° - 86°$
$= 290° - 125° - 86°$
$= 165° - 86°$
$= 79°$

c AB and CD are straight lines. Find $\angle AOD$ and $\angle BOD$.

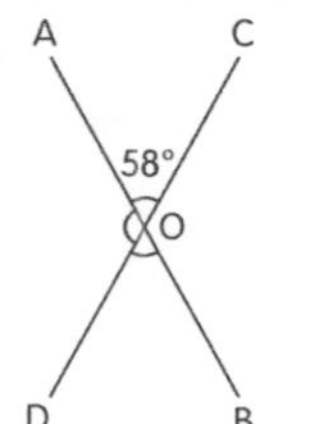

$\angle AOD = 180° - 58°$
$= 122°$

Method 1

$\angle BOD = \angle AOC$
$= 58°$

Method 2

$\angle BOD = 180° - 122°$
$= 58°$

d EF and GH are straight lines. Find $\angle e$.

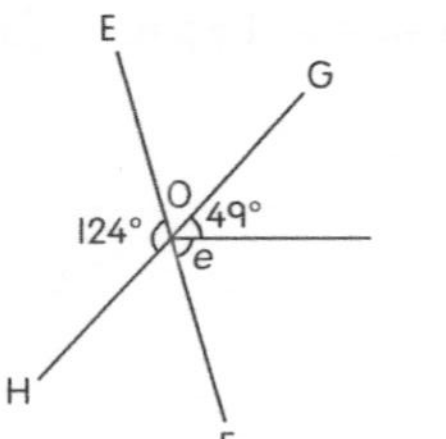

Method 1

$\angle e = 124° - 49°$
$= 75°$

Method 2

$\angle FOH = 180° - 124°$
$= 56°$

$\angle e = 180° - 49° - 56°$
$= 75°$

Date: ____________

Practice 2 Finding unknown angles

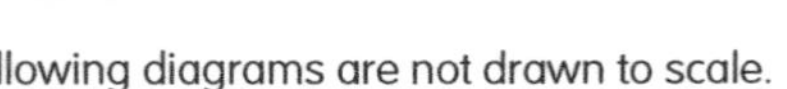

1 The following diagrams are not drawn to scale.

a Find $\angle p$.

$\angle p = 180° - 50° - 67°$
$= 130° - 67°$
$= 63°$

b MNO is an isosceles triangle. Find $\angle MNO$.

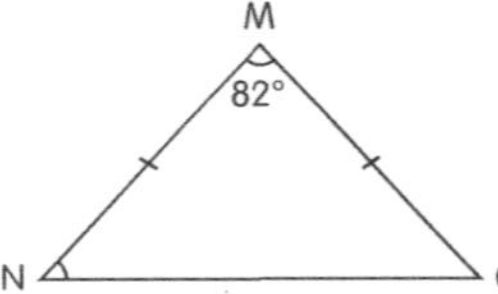

$\angle MNO = (180° - 82°) \div 2$
$= 98° \div 2$
$= 49°$

c SV is a straight line. STU is an isosceles triangle.
Find ∠TUS and ∠TUV.

∠STU = ∠UST = 70°

∠TUS = 180° – 70° – 70°
= 40°

∠TUV = 180° – 40°
= 140°

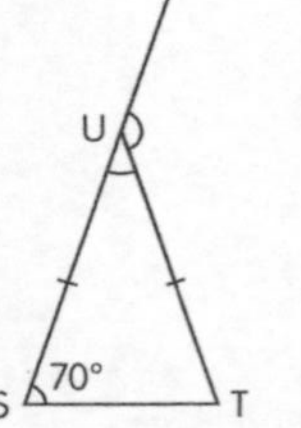

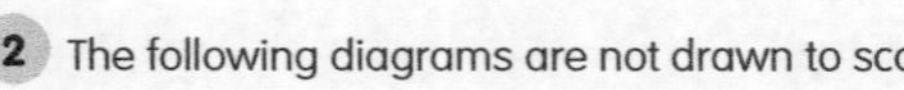

2 The following diagrams are not drawn to scale.

a JKLM is a parallelogram.
Find ∠KLM and ∠LMJ.

∠KLM = 180° – 116°
= 64°

Method 1

∠LMJ = ∠JKL
= 116°

Method 2

∠LMJ = 180° – 64°
= 116°

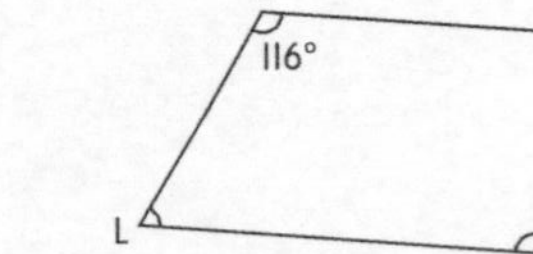
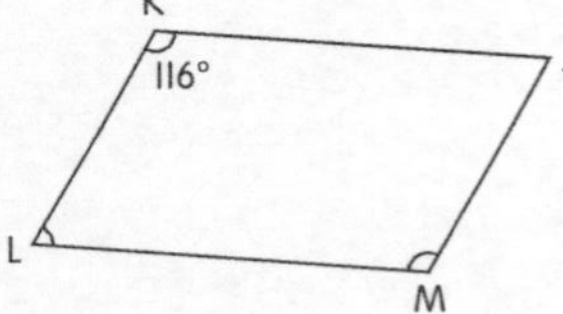

b MNOP is a rhombus. Find ∠MNO and ∠PMN.

∠MNO = ∠OPM = 54°

∠PMN = 180° – 54°
= 126°

c QRST is a trapezium. Find ∠f.

∠f = 180° – 107°
= 73°

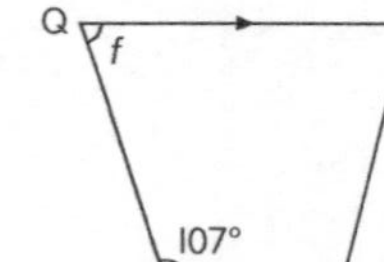

d ABC is an equilateral triangle and BD is a straight line.
Find ∠ABC and ∠ACE.

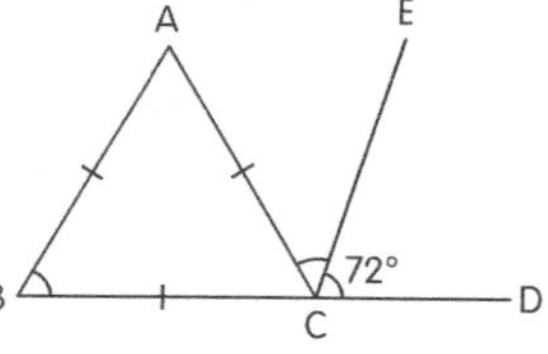

∠ABC = 180° ÷ 3
= 60°

∠ACB = ∠ABC
= 60°

∠ACE = 180° – 60° – 72°
= 48°

e PQR and STU are triangles. Find the value of ∠*a* + ∠*b* + ∠*c* + ∠*d*.

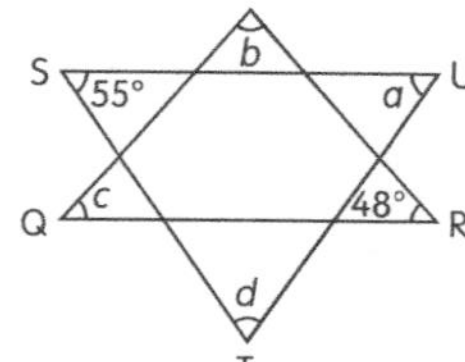

∠*a* + ∠*d* = 180° – 55°
= 125°

∠*b* + ∠*c* = 180° – 48°
= 132°

∠*a* + ∠*b* + ∠*c* + ∠*d* = 125° + 132°
= 257°

Date: ____________

Practice 3 Finding unknown angles

1 The following diagrams are not drawn to scale.

a AD, BG and CF are straight lines. Find ∠*a* and ∠*b*.

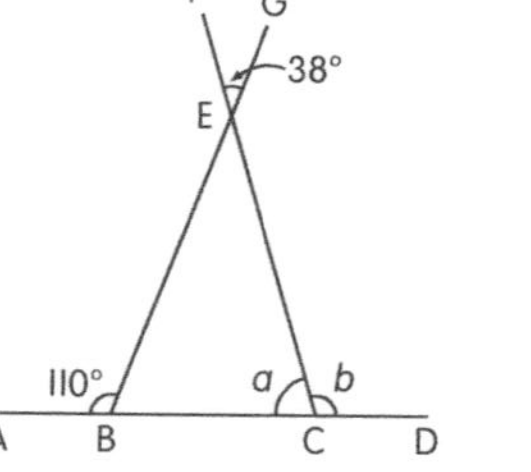

∠BEC = ∠FEG
= 38°

∠CBE = 180° – 110°
= 70°

∠*a* = 180° – 70° – 38°
= 72°

∠*b* = 180° – 72°
= 108°

b PQR is an isosceles triangle where PQ = QR. PS is a straight line.
Find ∠SRQ and ∠RQS.

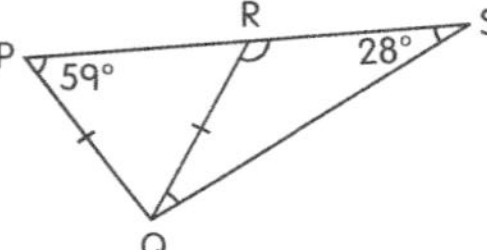

∠PRQ = 59°

∠SRQ = 180° – 59°
= 121°

∠RQS = 180° – 121° – 28°
= 31°

c MP and NQ are straight lines. Find ∠MNO.

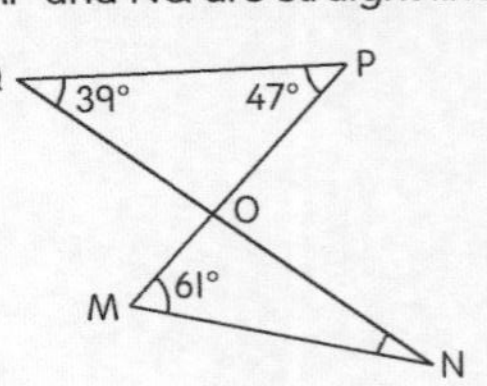

∠POQ = 180° − 39° − 47°
= 94°

∠MON = ∠POQ
= 94°

∠MNO = 180° − 94° − 61°
= 25°

d ABC and CDE are triangles. Find ∠*g*.

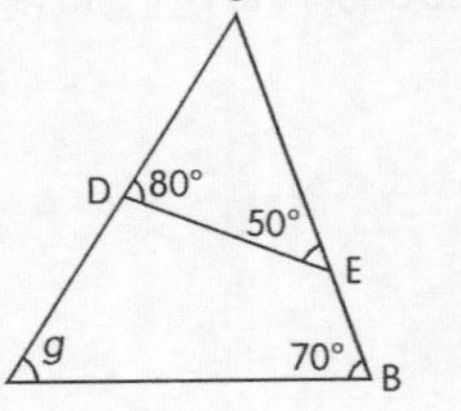

∠DCE = 180° − 80° − 50°
= 50°

∠*g* = 180° − 50° − 70°
= 60°

e ABD is an isosceles triangle and BCD is an equilateral triangle. Find ∠ADC.

∠CDB = 60°

∠ADB = (180° − 32°) ÷ 2
= 148° ÷ 2
= 74°

∠ADC = 60° + 74°
= 134°

f EFG is a right-angled triangle. EH is a straight line and FHJ is an isosceles triangle. Find ∠GFJ.

∠EFG = 180° − 90° − 78°
= 12°

∠JFH = (180° − 52°) ÷ 2
= 128° ÷ 2
= 64°

∠GFJ = 180° − 12° − 64°
= 104°

g ABCD is a parallelogram. AF and BF are straight lines. Find ∠AED, ∠DEF and ∠CFE.

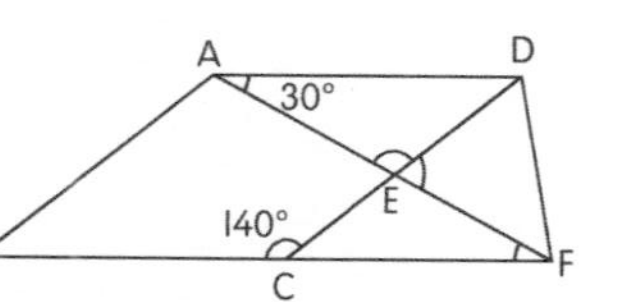

∠ADE = 180° – 140°
= 40°

∠AED = 180° – 30° – 40°
= 110°

∠DEF = 180° – 110°
= 70°

∠DCF = 180° – 140°
= 40°

∠CFE = 70° – 40°
= 30°

h JKNO is a parallelogram and KM and JM are straight lines. Find ∠*g* and ∠*h*.

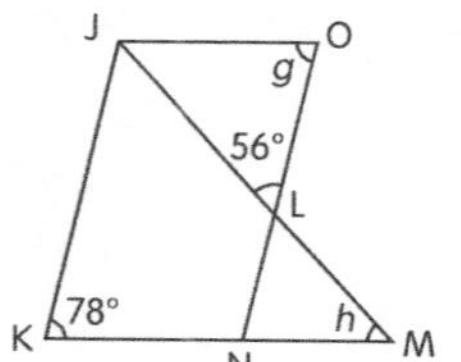

∠*g* = ∠JKN
= 78°

∠MLN = ∠JLO
= 56°

∠KNO = 180° – 78°
= 102°

∠ONM = 180° – 102°
= 78°

∠*h* = 180° – 78° – 56°
= 46°

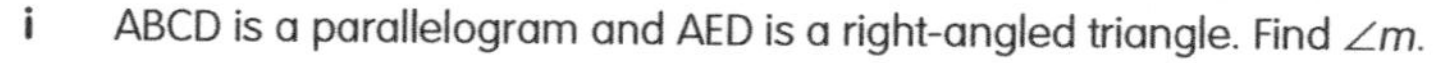

i ABCD is a parallelogram and AED is a right-angled triangle. Find ∠*m*.

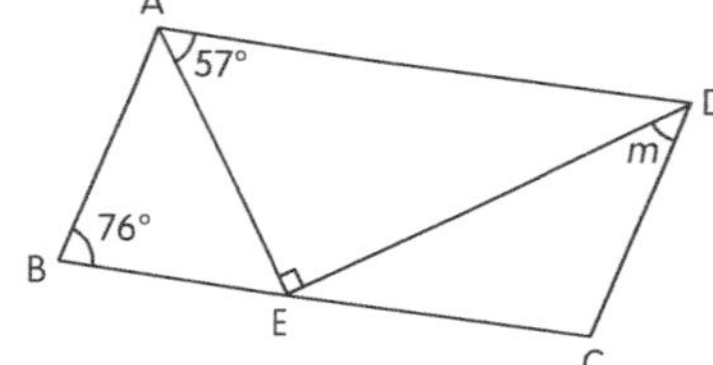

∠ADE = 180° – 90° – 57°
= 33°

∠ADC = ∠ABC
= 76°

∠*m* = 76° – 33°
= 43°

j PQR is an isosceles triangle and PRST is a rhombus. TQ is a straight line. Find ∠QRP.

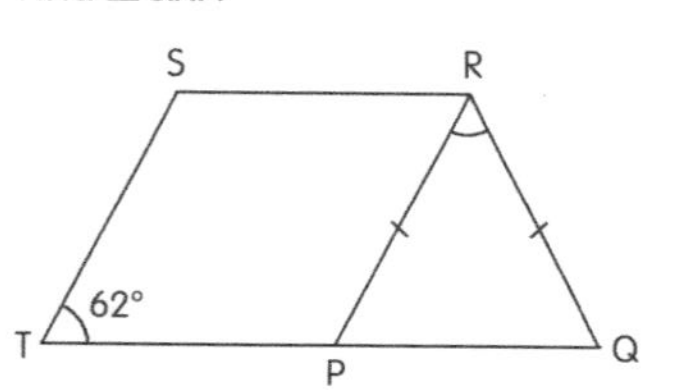

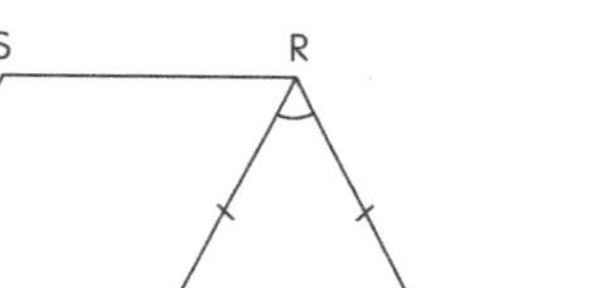

∠TPR = 180° – 62°
= 118°

∠RPQ = 180° – 118°
= 62°

∠QRP = 180° – 62° – 62°
= 56°

k EFGK is a parallelogram and EJL is a triangle. FG // JL. Find $\angle m$.

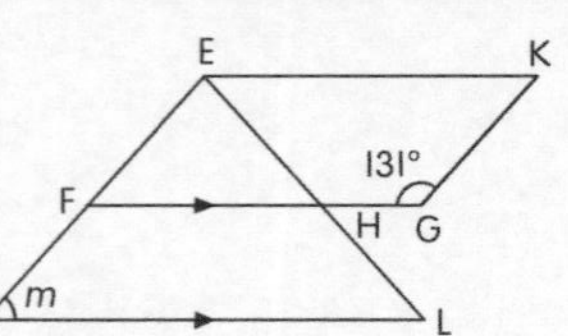

$\angle EFG = 180° - 131°$
$= 49°$

$\angle JFG = 180° - 49°$
$= 131°$

FJLH is a trapezium with FH // JL.

$\angle m = 180° - 131°$
$= 49°$

l ABC is an isosceles triangle. ACDE is a parallelogram. Find $\angle BCD$.

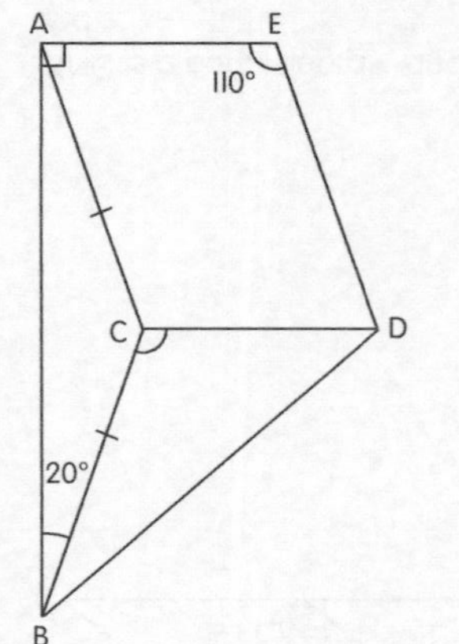

$\angle BCA = 180° - 20° - 20°$
$= 140°$

$\angle ACD = 110°$

$\angle BCD = 360° - 140° - 110°$
$= 110°$

m ABCD is a rhombus and AEFD is a parallelogram. Find $\angle DCE$, $\angle CDF$ and $\angle ECB$.

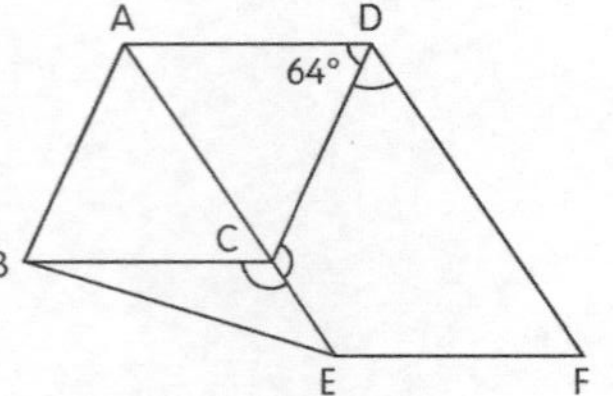

Since AD = CD, ACD is an isosceles triangle.

$\angle ACD = (180° - 64°) \div 2$
$= 116° \div 2$
$= 58°$

$\angle DCE = 180° - 58°$
$= 122°$

$\angle DAC = \angle ACD$
$= 58°$

$\angle CDF = (180° - 58°) - 64°$
$= 122° - 64°$
$= 58°$

or CDFE is a trapezium so CE // DF.

$\angle CDF = 180° - 122°$
$= 58°$

$\angle BCA = \angle ACD$
$= 58°$

$\angle ECB = 360° - 122° - 58° - 58°$
$= 122°$

Date: ____________

Maths Journal

The following diagrams are not drawn to scale.

1 ABCD is a rhombus and DCEF is a trapezium. AF, BE and DG are straight lines.

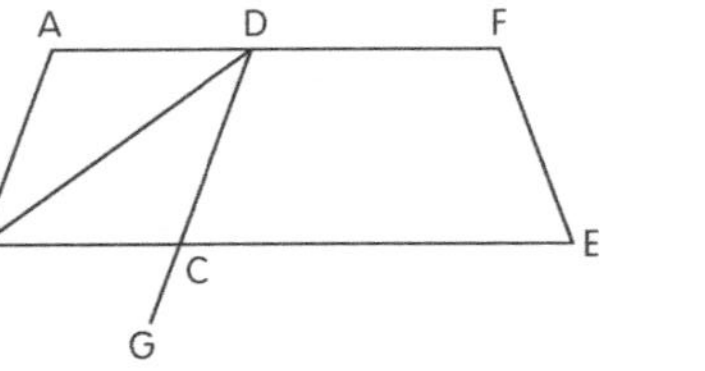

Write one or two statements about the following:

a the angles at point B

Answers vary

Example:
$\angle ABD$ and $\angle DBC$ are equal.

b the angles at point C

Answers vary

Example:
$\angle BCD + \angle DCE = 180°$

c the triangles in the diagram

Answers vary

Example:
The triangles in the diagram are identical.

d the angles in the trapezium DCEF.

Answers vary

Example:
$\angle DCE + \angle FDC = 180°$

2 In the diagram below, CF is a straight line. Jill found some shapes in the diagram and made these statements.

ABEF is a square.
BCDE is a rhombus.
CDEF is a trapezium.
ABEF is a rhombus.

Are her statements correct? Explain your answer.

Answers vary

Example:

'ABEF is a square' is correct because it has four equal sides and four right angles.

'BCDE is a rhombus' is incorrect because it does not have four equal sides. BCDE is a parallelogram.

'CDEF is a trapezium' is correct because it is a 4-sided quadrilateral in which only one pair of opposite sides is parallel.

'ABEF is a rhombus' is correct because it is a 4-sided quadrilateral in which the opposite sides are parallel and all four sides are equal.

Challenging Practice

Date: ____________

The following shapes are not drawn to scale.

1 ABC is an equilateral triangle and ABD is an isosceles triangle. Find $\angle a$.

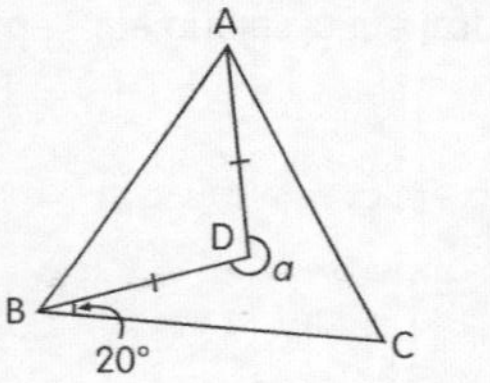

$\angle ABC = 60°$

$\angle ABD = 60° - 20°$
$= 40°$

$\angle BDA = 180° - 40° - 40°$
$= 100°$

$\angle a = 360° - 100°$
$= 260°$

2 CDE is an equilateral triangle and ABCE is a square. BC = CD. Find $\angle s$.

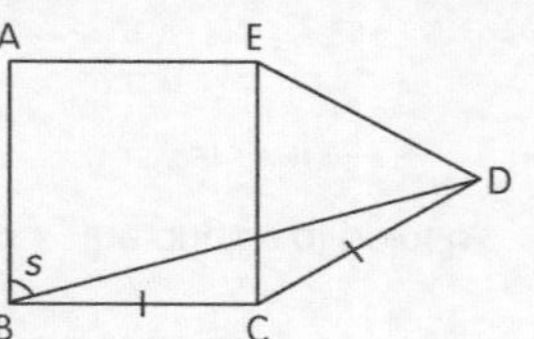

$\angle ECD = 60°$

$\angle BCE = 90°$

$\angle BCD = 60° + 90°$
$= 150°$

Since BC = CD, BCD is an isosceles triangle.

$\angle DBC = (180° - 150°) \div 2$
$= 30° \div 2$
$= 15°$

$\angle s = 90° - 15°$
$= 75°$

3 WXYZ and UYVZ are rhombuses. Find $\angle a$.

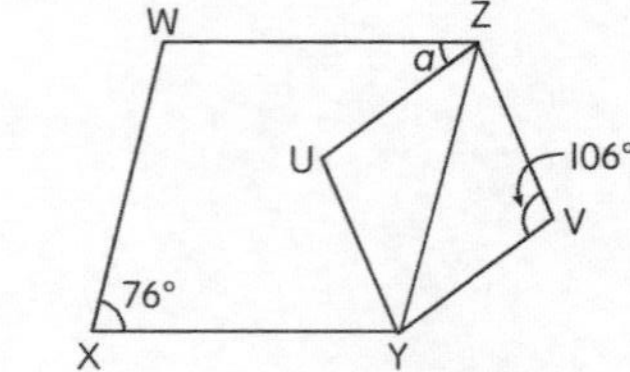

$\angle ZUY = \angle ZVY = 106°$

Since UZ = UY, UZY is an isosceles triangle.

$\angle UZY = (180° - 106°) \div 2$
$= 74° \div 2$
$= 37°$

$\angle WZY = \angle WXY$
$= 76°$

$\angle a = 76° - 37°$
$= 39°$

4 ACF is an equilateral triangle and BDEG is a trapezium. Find $\angle p$ and $\angle q$.

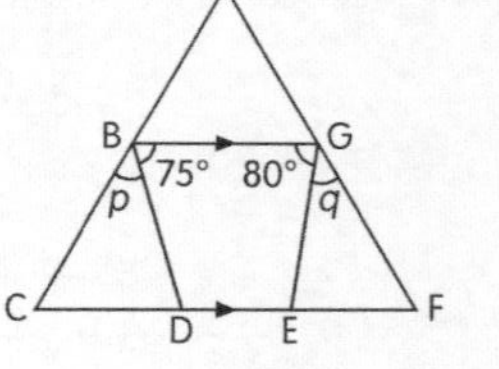

$\angle ACF = 60°$

$\angle BDE = 180° - 75°$
$= 105°$

$\angle CDB = 180° - 105°$
$= 75°$

$\angle p = 180° - 60° - 75°$
$= 45°$

$\angle CFA = 60°$

$\angle DEG = 180° - 80°$
$= 100°$

$\angle GEF = 180° - 100°$
$= 80°$

$\angle q = 180° - 80° - 60°$
$= 40°$

5 MNO and MPO are isosceles triangles. Find $\angle t$.

$\angle OMN = (180° - 70°) \div 2$
$= 110° \div 2$
$= 55°$

$\angle OMP = (180° - 110°) \div 2$
$= 70° \div 2$
$= 35°$

$\angle t = 55° - 35°$
$= 20°$

6 FC and AG are straight lines. ABCD is a parallelogram and AEC is an isosceles triangle. Find $\angle n$.

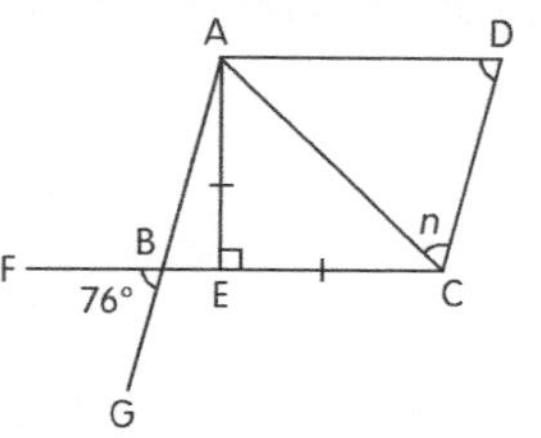

$\angle ABC = \angle GBF$
$= 76°$

$\angle DCE = 180° - 76°$
$= 104°$

$\angle BCA = (180° - 90°) \div 2$
$= 90° \div 2$
$= 45°$

$\angle n = 104° - 45°$
$= 59°$

Unit 3: Nets

Medium-term plan

Week	Learning Objectives	Thinking Skills	Resources
4	**(1) Solids** Pupils will be able to: • identify and name cubes, cuboids, prisms, pyramids, cylinders and cones • identify the faces of a solid, state the number of faces and name their shapes. This excludes the cylinder and cone, which have surfaces but do not have faces.	• Comparing • Identifying relationships • Spatial visualisation	• Pupil Textbook 6A, pp 38 to 42 • Practice Book 6A, pp 39 to 44 • Teacher's Guide 6A, pp 66 to 70
4	**(2) Nets of Solids** Pupils will be able to: • identify the nets of a cube, a cuboid, a prism and a pyramid • identify the solid made by a given net	• Spatial visualisation	• Pupil Textbook 6A, pp 43 to 49 • Practice Book 6A, pp 45 to 52 • Teacher's Guide 6A, pp 71 to 77
4	*Maths Journal* Pupils will be able to explain why the diagrams shown are not nets of the given solids.	• Spatial visualisation	• Pupil Textbook 6A, p 46 • Practice Book 6A, pp 53 to 54 • Teacher's Guide 6A, p 74

Unit 3: Nets

Medium-term plan

Week	Learning Objectives	Thinking Skills	Resources
4	*Let's Wrap It Up!* Emphasise the key concepts, skills and processes that have been taught in the unit. Discuss the worked example with pupils to assess their understanding of these concepts, skills and processes. *Put On Your Thinking Caps!* Pupils will be able to identify different nets of a cube in a given set of diagrams.	• Spatial visualisation Heuristic for problem solving: • Act it out	• Pupil Textbook 6A, pp 50 to 53 • Practice Book 6A, pp 55 to 56 • Teacher's Guide 6A, pp 78 to 81
	Review 1		• Practice Book 6A, pp 57 to 74 • Teacher's Guide 6A, pp 92 to 101

Summative assessment opportunities
Assessment Book 6, Test 3, pp 15 to 20 For extension, Assessment Book 6, Challenging Problems 1, pp 21 to 22 Assessment Book 6, Check-up 1, pp 23 to 38

Nets

Learning objectives: Solids

Pupils will be able to:

- identify and name cubes, cuboids, prisms, pyramids, cylinders and cones
- identify the faces of a solid, state the number of faces and name their shapes. This excludes the cylinder and cone, which have surfaces but do not have faces

Key concepts

- Cubes and cuboids have rectangular faces (including squares).
- Prisms have rectangular faces (including squares) and two identical polygonal faces (which could also be rectangles).
- Pyramids have triangular faces that meet at a point and a polygonal base.
- Cylinders have a curved surface and two identical circular bases (at the ends).
- Cones have a curved surface and a circular base.

Thinking skills

- Comparing
- Identifying relationships
- Spatial visualisation

Teaching sequence

1 and 2

- Show pupils an example of a cube, such as a dice. Ask pupils to identify the faces and name the shape of each face. Ask them to count the faces. State that this solid is an example of a cube. Emphasise that a cube is a solid with six square faces. Ask pupils to give examples of cubes. (*E.g. ice cubes.*)
- Show pupils an example of a cuboid, such as a shoe box. Ask pupils to identify the faces and name the shape of each face. (*Each face is a rectangle.*) Ask them to count the faces. (*six faces.*)
- Explain that some cuboids have two faces that are squares. Show pupils an example of such a cuboid (alternatively, if an example is not available, show an illustration). Guide pupils to recognise that **a cuboid is a solid with six faces**. Agree that a cuboid can have six rectangular faces, or four rectangular faces and two square faces.

3

- This activity enables pupils to identify the faces of a cube as squares and those of a cuboid as rectangles (including squares), and identify how many faces each of these solids has.

Unit 3

Nets

Let's Learn!

Solids

1  The solid shown is a **cube**.

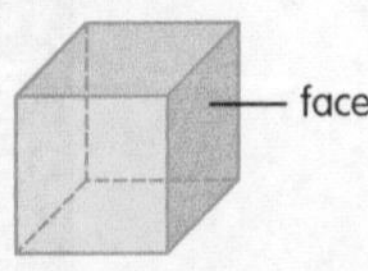

A cube has six faces.
The six faces are squares.

2 The solids shown are **cuboids**.

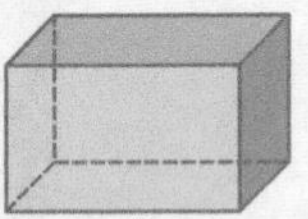

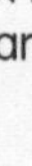

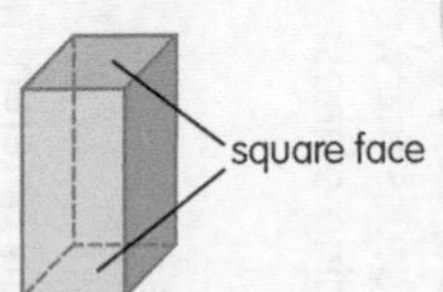

A cuboid has six faces.
The six faces are rectangles.

3 Work in pairs.
You will need a cube and a cuboid.

- **a** Count the number of faces on the cube. Then place the cube on a piece of paper and draw the outline of each face in turn.
- **b** Write the names of the shapes of the faces you have drawn.
- **c** Repeat **a** and **b** for the cuboid.

What you will need

- Dice
- Shoe box
- Drink carton
- Some examples of prisms, pyramids and cylinders

Note

- The definition of the term 'prism' when going through the examples below is not required. Cubes and cuboids are also prisms. However, there is no need to emphasise this.
- Help pupils realise that a cube is a special type of cuboid, with six square faces.

Activity

Then record your answers in a table as shown.

	Cube	Cuboid
Number of faces	6	6
Shape(s) of faces	Square	Square, Rectangle

The solids shown are **prisms**.

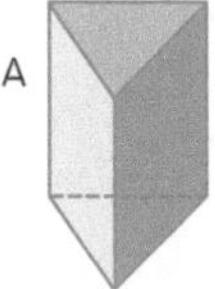

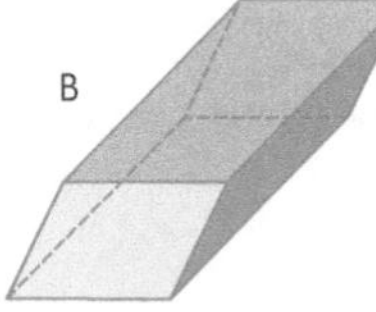

Prism A has five faces. Three faces are rectangles and two faces are triangles.

Prism B has six faces. Four faces are rectangles and two faces are parallelograms.

The solids shown are **pyramids**.

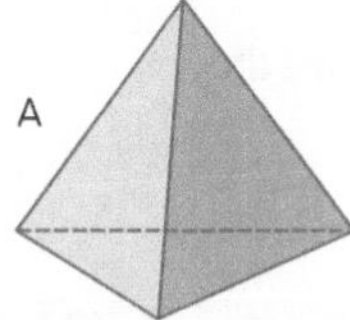

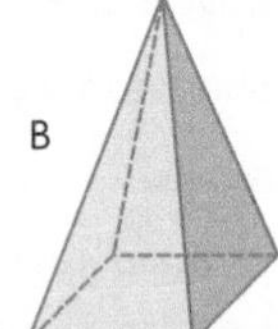

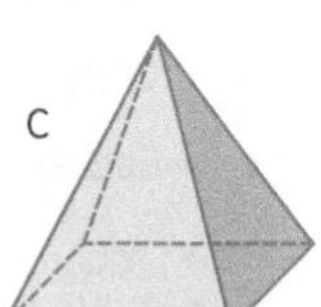

Pyramid A has four faces. The four faces are triangles.

Pyramid B has five faces. Four faces are triangles and one face is a square.

Pyramid C has five faces. Four faces are triangles and one face is a rectangle.

The solids shown are **cylinders**.

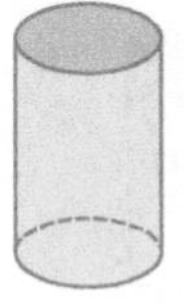

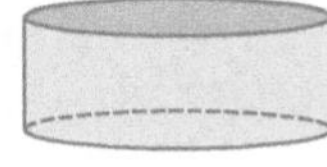

Teaching sequence

- Show pupils a prism with three rectangular faces and two triangular faces. Ask pupils to identify, name and count the number of faces. Then show further types of prisms. Again, ask pupils to identify, name and count the faces. Explain that **a prism is a solid with two end faces that are the same shape and size**. These two faces must be polygons. They can be triangles, 4-sided shapes, 5-sided shapes, etc. The **other faces** of the prism are **rectangles** (including squares).
- Guide pupils to recognise that a prism with triangular end faces has five faces and a prism with 4-sided end faces has six faces.

5

- Show pupils examples of pyramids with different bases. Ask pupils to identify the faces of the pyramids, and to name and count them. Explain that **a pyramid is a solid with a base and triangular faces that meet at a point**. The base can be a triangle, square, rectangle, etc. or any polygon.
- Guide pupils to recognise that a pyramid with a triangular base has four faces and a pyramid with a 4-sided base has five faces.

- Show pupils examples of cylinders. Ask pupils to identify the curved surface of a cylinder and the two bases. A cylinder has no faces because a circle is not a polygon. Ask pupils to name some examples of cylinders.

What you will need

- Some examples of cones, e.g. an ice-cream cone, a conical hat
- A prism with triangular end faces, a pyramid with a triangular base and a pyramid with a rectangular base per group

Teaching sequence

- Show pupils examples of cones. Ask them to identify the circular base and the curved surface of a cone.

- This activity enables pupils to identify the faces of prisms and pyramids, state the number of faces each has and name their shapes.

- Ask pupils to work on these questions as an informal assessment.

Unit 3 Nets

7 The solids shown are **cones**.

Activity

8 Work in pairs.
You will need the solids shown.

Solid A Solid B Solid C

a Count the number of faces on Solid A. Then place Solid A on a piece of paper and draw the outline of each face in turn.

b Write the names of the shapes of the faces you have drawn.

c Repeat **a** and **b** for every solid.

Then record your answers in a table as shown.

	Solid A	Solid B	Solid C
Number of faces	5	4	5
Shape(s) of faces	Triangle, Rectangle	Triangle	Triangle, Rectangle

9 Name the shapes of these objects.

a 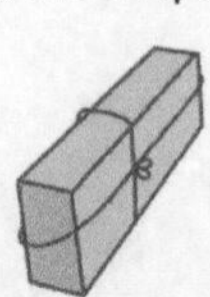 cuboid

b cylinder

40

What you will need

A cube, cuboid, prism and pyramid

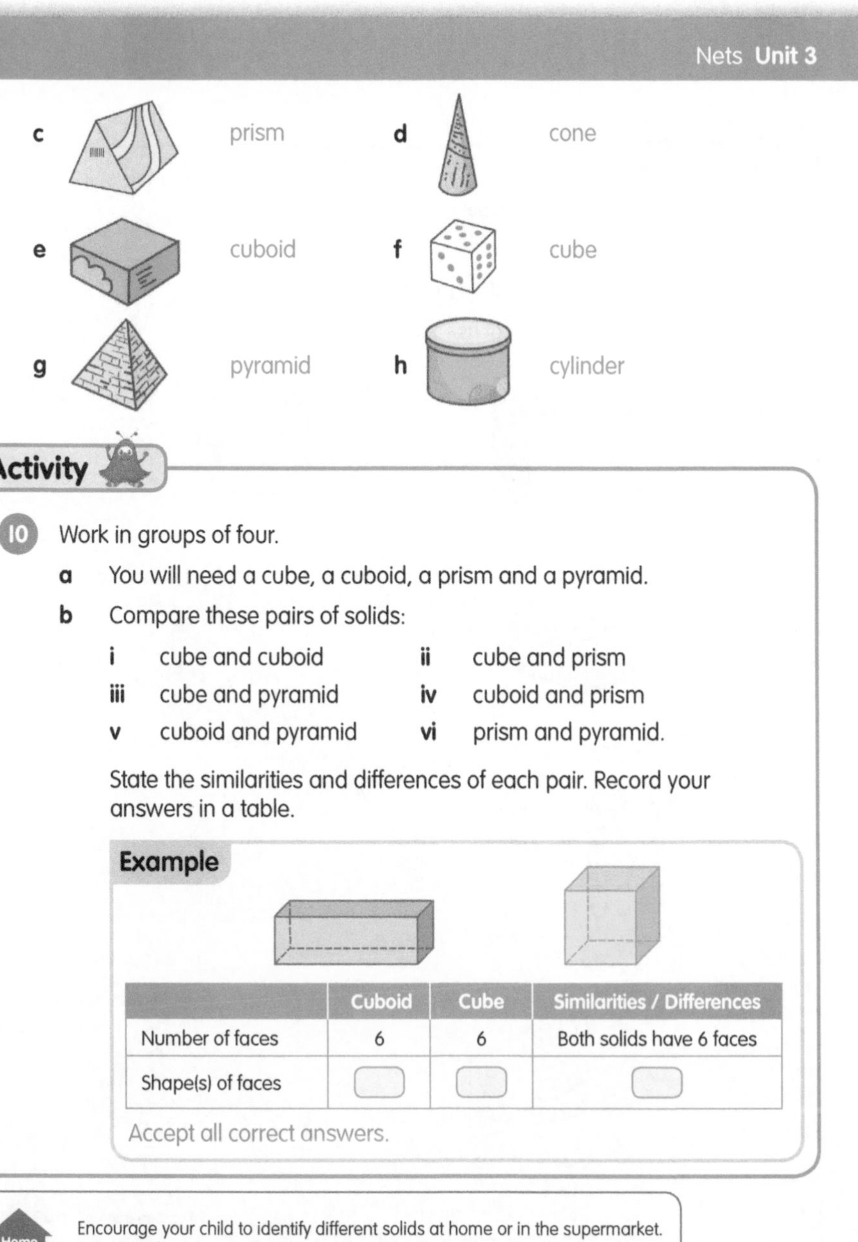

c prism

d cone

e cuboid

f cube

g pyramid

h cylinder

Activity

10 Work in groups of four.

a You will need a cube, a cuboid, a prism and a pyramid.

b Compare these pairs of solids:

i	cube and cuboid	**ii**	cube and prism
iii	cube and pyramid	**iv**	cuboid and prism
v	cuboid and pyramid	**vi**	prism and pyramid.

State the similarities and differences of each pair. Record your answers in a table.

Example

	Cuboid	Cube	Similarities / Differences
Number of faces	6	6	Both solids have 6 faces
Shape(s) of faces			

Accept all correct answers.

Home Maths Encourage your child to identify different solids at home or in the supermarket. For example, ask your child to identify a cuboid object used as food packaging.

Teaching sequence

- Ask pupils to work in groups of four.
- Provide each group with a cube, a cuboid, a prism and a pyramid. In this activity, pupils compare and contrast different pairs of solids. It is an open-ended activity; encourage pupils to think of as many similarities and differences as they can.

Independent work

- *Let's Practise!*
- Practice 1 in Practice Book 6A, pp 39 to 44.

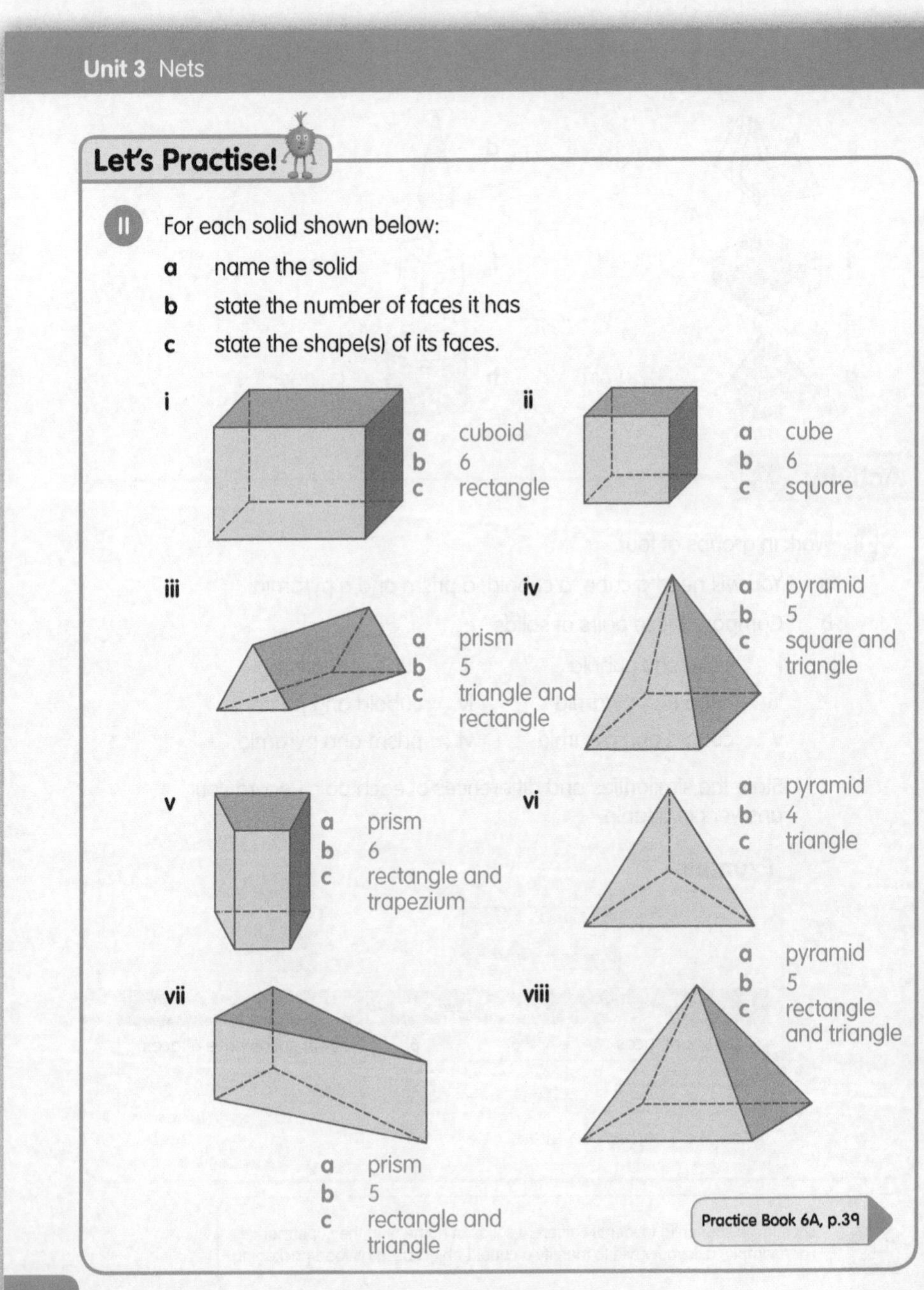

Learning objectives: Nets of solids

Pupils will be able to:

- identify the nets of a cube, a cuboid, a prism and a pyramid
- identify the solid made by a given net

Key concepts

- A net of a solid is a diagram that can be folded to make the solid.
- A solid can have different nets.

Thinking skill

Spatial visualisation

What you will need

- The net of the cube in 1 (see Photocopy master 4 on p 275)
- Tracing paper or copies of the nets from 2 (also provided on Photocopy master 4)
- Scissors

Let's Learn! 

Nets of solids

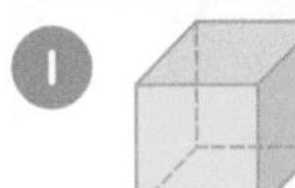

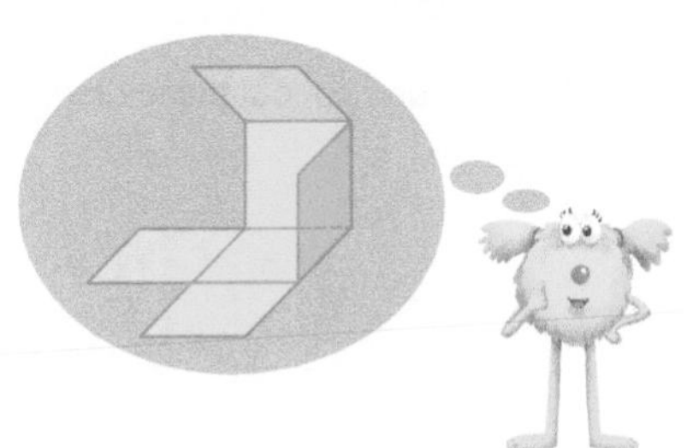

The cube is cut along some of the edges and laid flat as shown below.

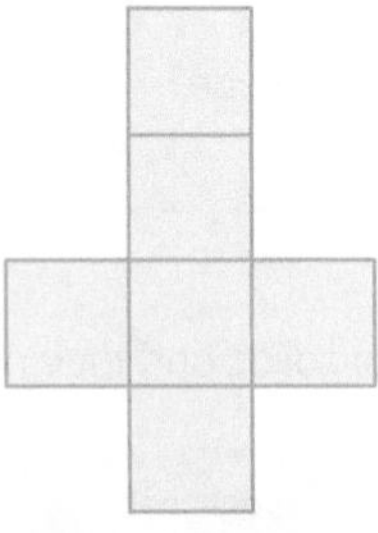

The diagram is called a **net** of the cube.

The net of a solid is a diagram that can be folded to make the solid.

2 Here are two other nets of the cube.

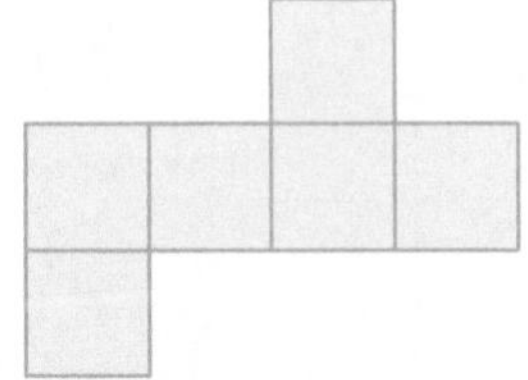

Trace them, cut them out and fold each net into a cube.

Teaching sequence

- In advance, make up the cube from the first net provided on Photocopy master 4. Show this cube to pupils.
- Open up the cube along the edges, as shown in 1. Show pupils the plane diagram that is made.
- Explain that this plane diagram is called a **net** of the cube. Fold the net to make the cube again for pupils to see.

- Ask pupils to trace the nets in 2 and cut them out. Alternatively provide pupils with these nets using Photocopy master 4 and ask them to cut the nets out. Ask pupils whether these nets can also be folded to make cubes.
- Guide pupils to conclude that a cube can have different nets.

What you will need

- Diagrams to fold into a cube (see Photocopy master 5 on p 276) or tracing paper
- Cuboids made by folding the nets (see Photocopy master 6 on p 277)
- Scissors

Teaching sequence

- Pupils can be asked to trace the nets shown in this activity, or you can provide them with these nets using Photocopy master 5.
- This activity enables pupils to conclude that not all plane diagrams made up of six squares are nets of a cube.

- Show pupils some cuboids made by folding the nets provided on Photocopy master 6. Open up the cuboids along the edges to obtain the nets for pupils to see.

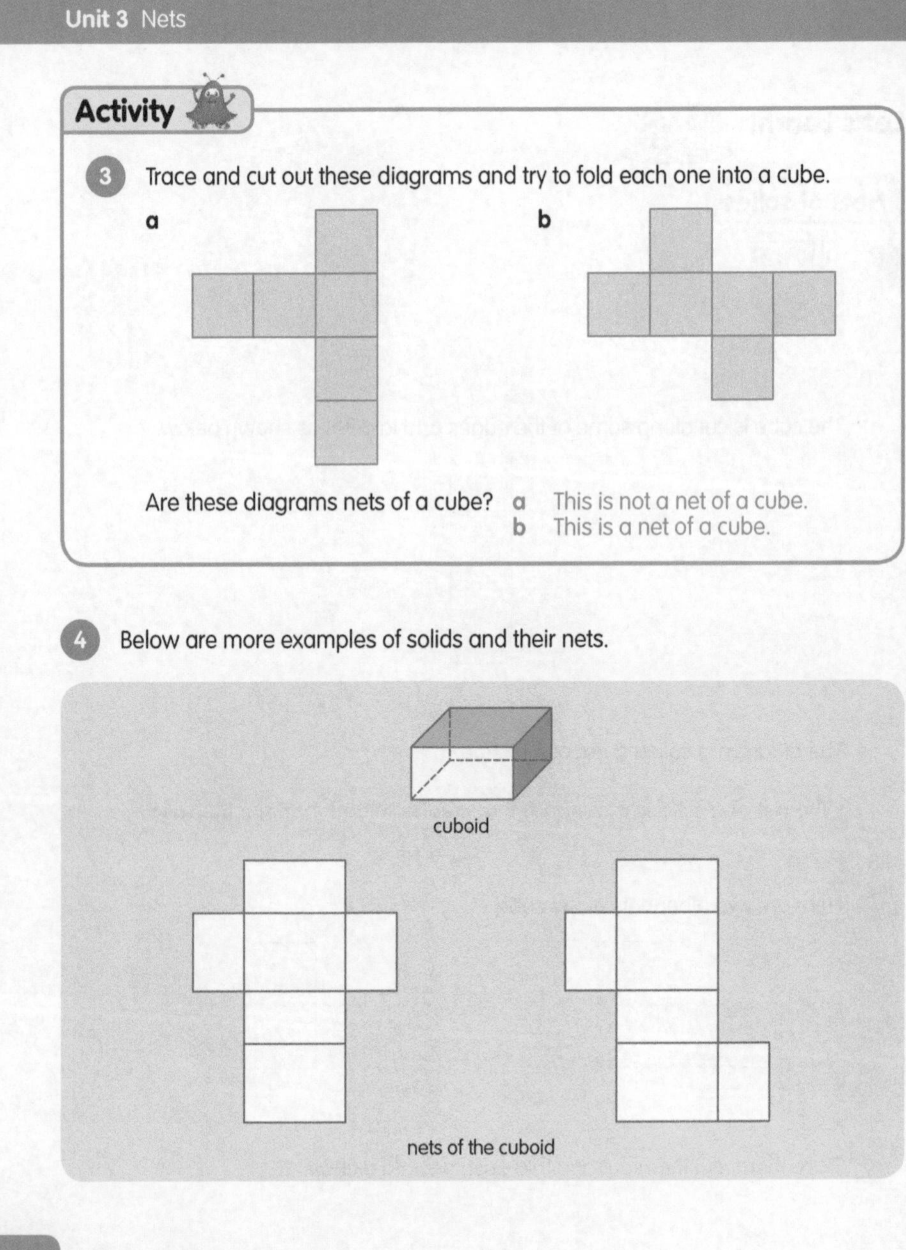

Unit 3 Nets

Activity

3 Trace and cut out these diagrams and try to fold each one into a cube.

a

b

Are these diagrams nets of a cube? **a** This is not a net of a cube.
b This is a net of a cube.

4 Below are more examples of solids and their nets.

44

What you will need

- Prisms made by folding the nets (see Photocopy master 7 on p 278)
- Pyramids made by folding the nets (see Photocopy master 8 on p 279)

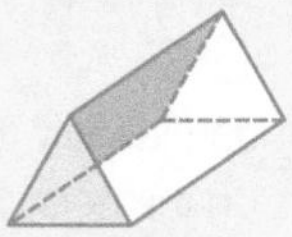

prism

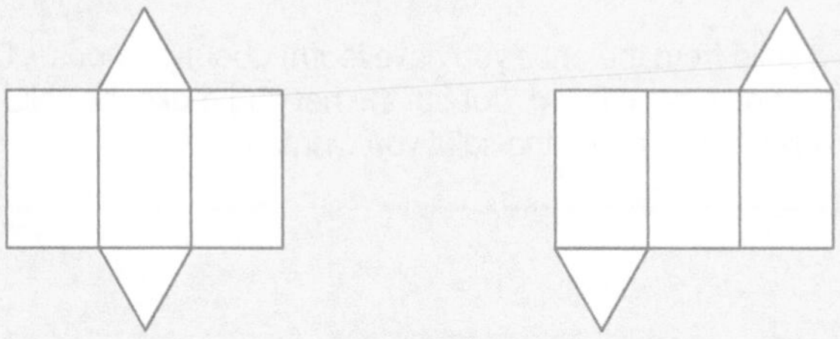

nets of the prism

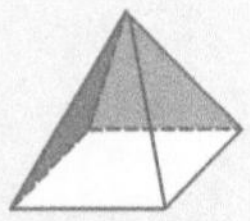

pyramid

nets of the pyramid

Home Maths

Give your child a cardboard box in the shape of a cube, cuboid, prism or pyramid. Help them to cut open the box to make a net of the solid.

45

Teaching sequence

- Show pupils some prisms and pyramids made by folding the nets provided on Photocopy masters 7 and 8. Open up the diagrams along the edges to obtain the nets for pupils to see.

What you will need

- Nets of a cuboid, a prism and a pyramid (see Photocopy masters 6 to 8 on pp 277 to 279)
- Squared paper
- Rulers
- Scissors

Objective of activity

Pupils will be able to explain why the diagrams shown are not nets of the given solids.

Thinking skill

Spatial visualisation

Additional activities

- Ask pupils, *"Do you think there are other possible nets of the cuboid, prism and pyramid shown in* 4*?"*
- Ask pupils to draw their nets. Invite a few pupils to draw their nets on the board. Discuss each diagram and agree whether it is a net.

Teaching sequence

5

- For this activity pupils can either be asked to trace the nets from 4 or you can provide them with these nets using Photocopy masters 6, 7 and 8.
- This activity enables pupils to use spatial visualisation to identify two faces of a solid on its nets.

6

- Ask pupils to draw a net of a solid.
- Use this activity to check that pupils can recognise nets of solids.

7 *Maths Journal*

- Pupils should be able to visualise that some of the faces of the diagrams will overlap, and so conclude that the diagrams are not nets of the given solids.

Unit 3 Nets

Activity

5 Trace the nets shown in 4 and identify the two coloured faces of each solid by shading these faces on the nets. Cut out the nets and fold them to make the solids. Did you shade the correct faces?

6 Choose a solid from the ones you have learnt about previously. Draw a net of the solid you have chosen. Cut out the net and make the solid. Does the net you have drawn make the solid you wanted?

Maths Journal

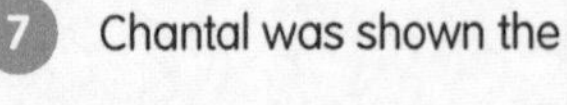

7 Chantal was shown the two solids below.

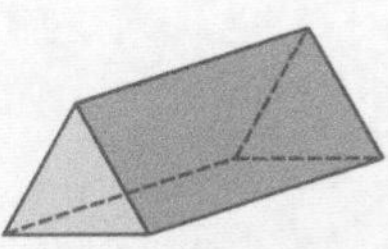

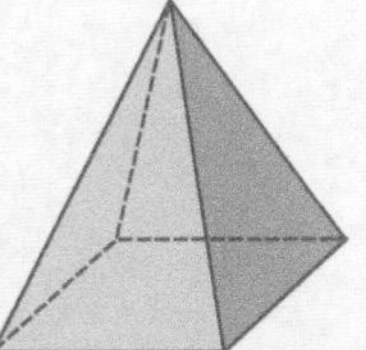

She drew the following diagrams. Are they the nets of the two solids above? Explain your answer. No, they are not the nets of the two solids above because they do not make the solids when folded.

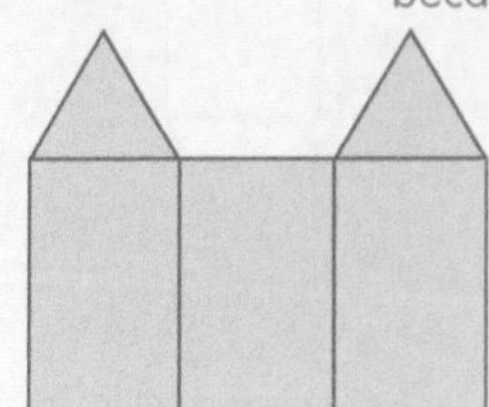

46

Independent work

Let's Practise!

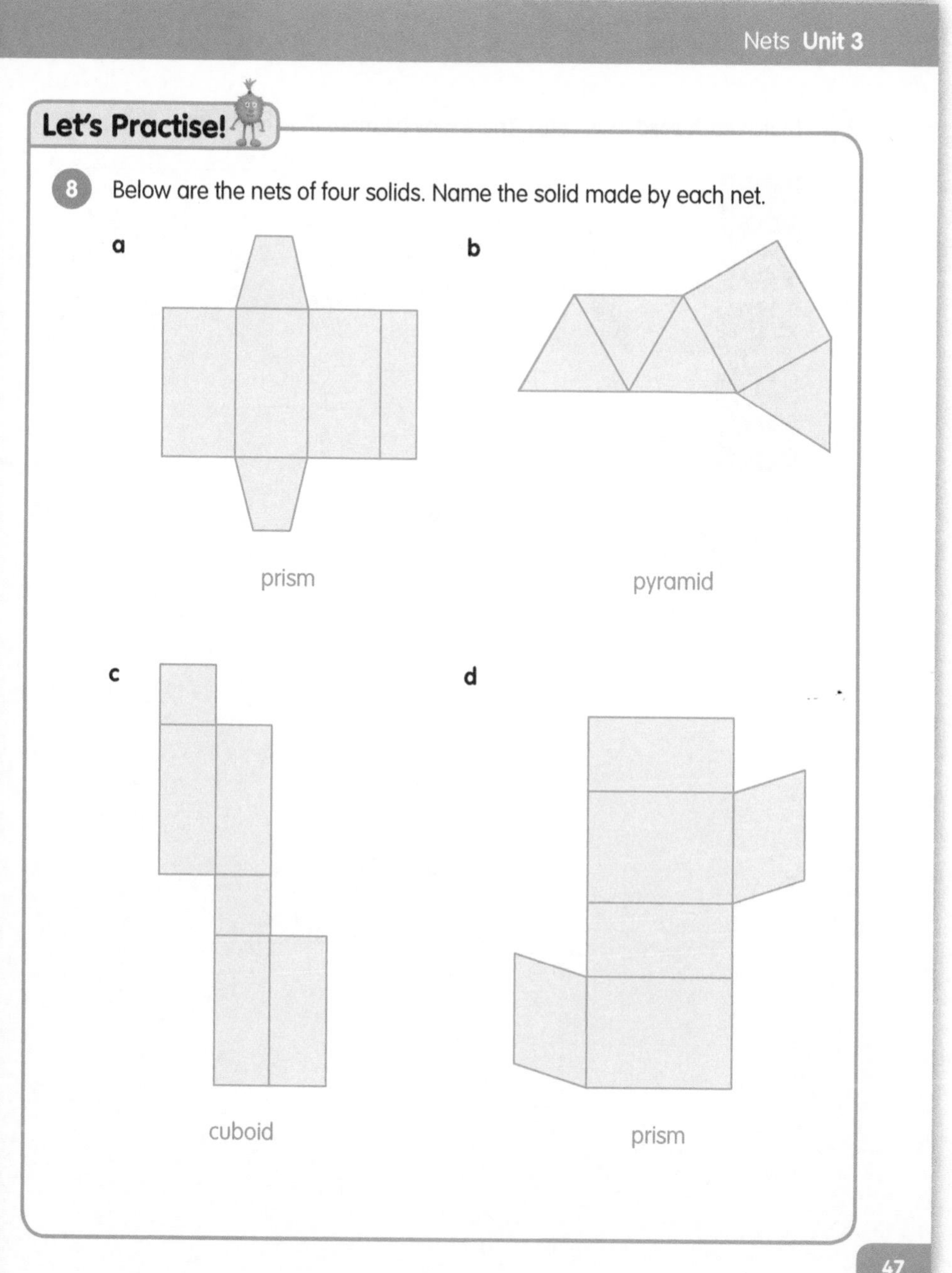

9 Match each solid to its net(s). There may be more than one net for each solid.

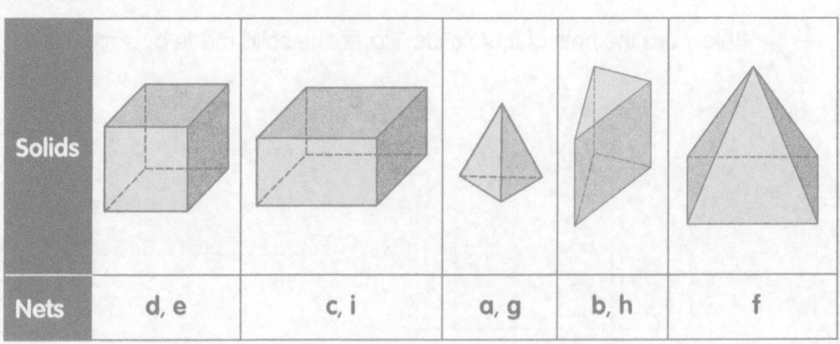

Solids					
Nets	d, e	c, i	a, g	b, h	f

a

b

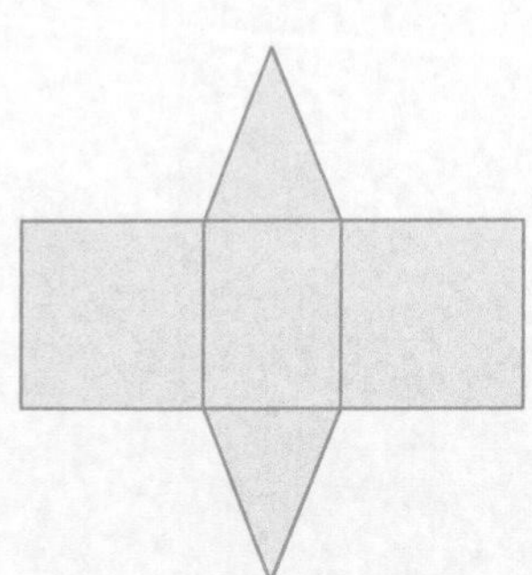

c

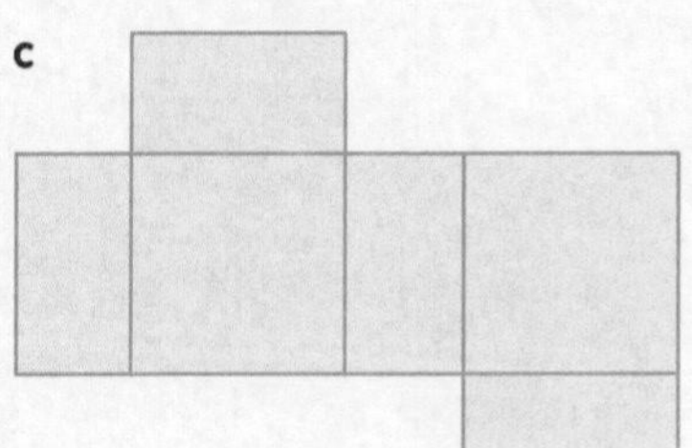

d

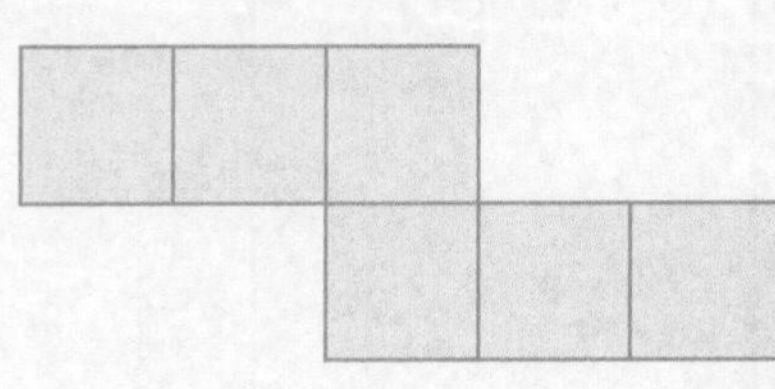

Independent work

Practice 2 in Practice Book 6A, pp 45 to 52.

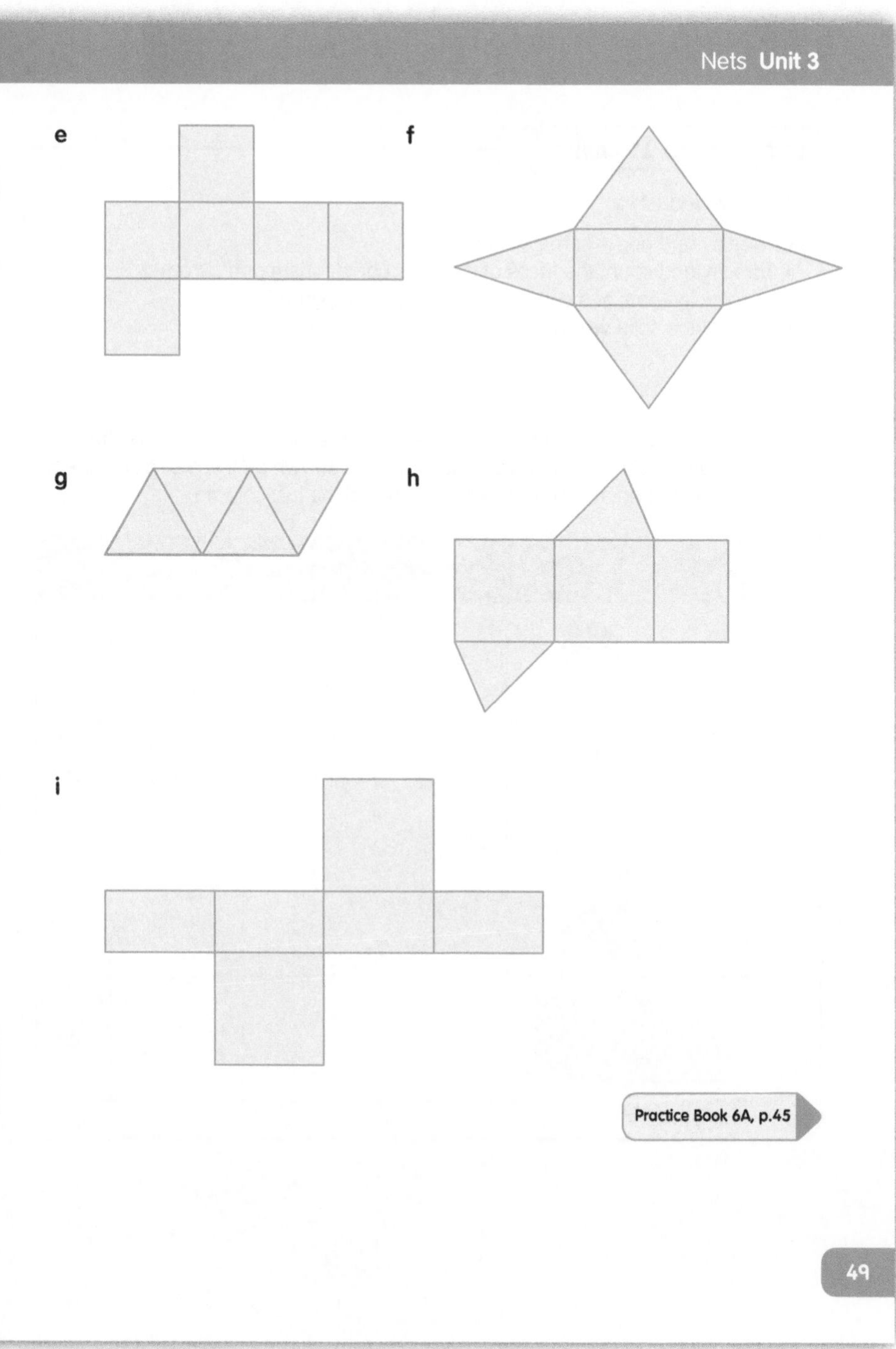

Teaching sequence

Let's Wrap It Up!

- Emphasise the key concepts, skills and processes that have been taught in the unit.

- Discuss the worked example with pupils to assess their understanding of these concepts, skills and processes.

Let's Wrap It Up!

You have learnt to:

- identify and name some solids
- identify and count the faces of a cube, cuboid, prism and pyramid
- identify the nets of a cube, cuboid, prism and pyramid
- identify the solid which is made from a net.

Let's Revise!

 The table below shows four solids. Copy the table and complete the first three empty columns. From the diagrams shown on the next page, identify the net of each solid and write its letter in the last column.

Solids	Name of Solid	Number of Faces	Shape(s) of Faces	Nets
	Prism	5	Triangle, Rectangle	f
	Cube	6	Square	a
	Pyramid	5	Square, Triangle	c
	Cuboid	6	Square, Rectangle	d

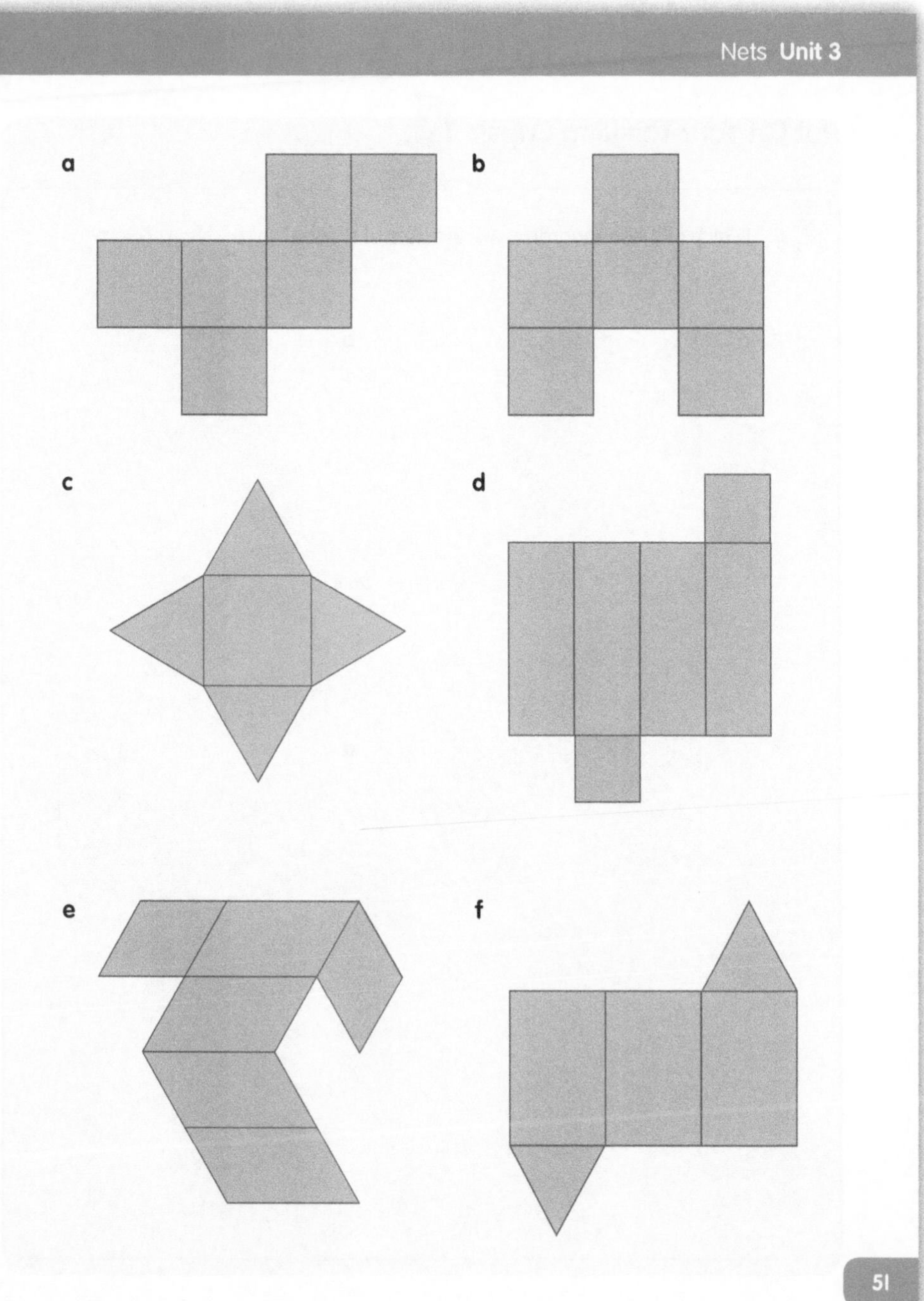
Nets Unit 3
a
b
c
d
e
f
51

Objective of activity

Pupils will be able to identify different nets of a cube in a given set of diagrams.

Thinking skill

Spatial visualisation

Heuristic for problem solving

Act it out

Independent work

- *Challenging Practice* and Review I in Practice Book 6A, pp 55 to 74.

Teaching sequence

11 *Put On Your Thinking Caps!*

- If pupils find it difficult to visualise folding the diagrams mentally, encourage them to confirm their predictions by tracing, cutting out and folding the diagrams for themselves.
- Ask pupils "*Which nets are easiest to visualise?*"

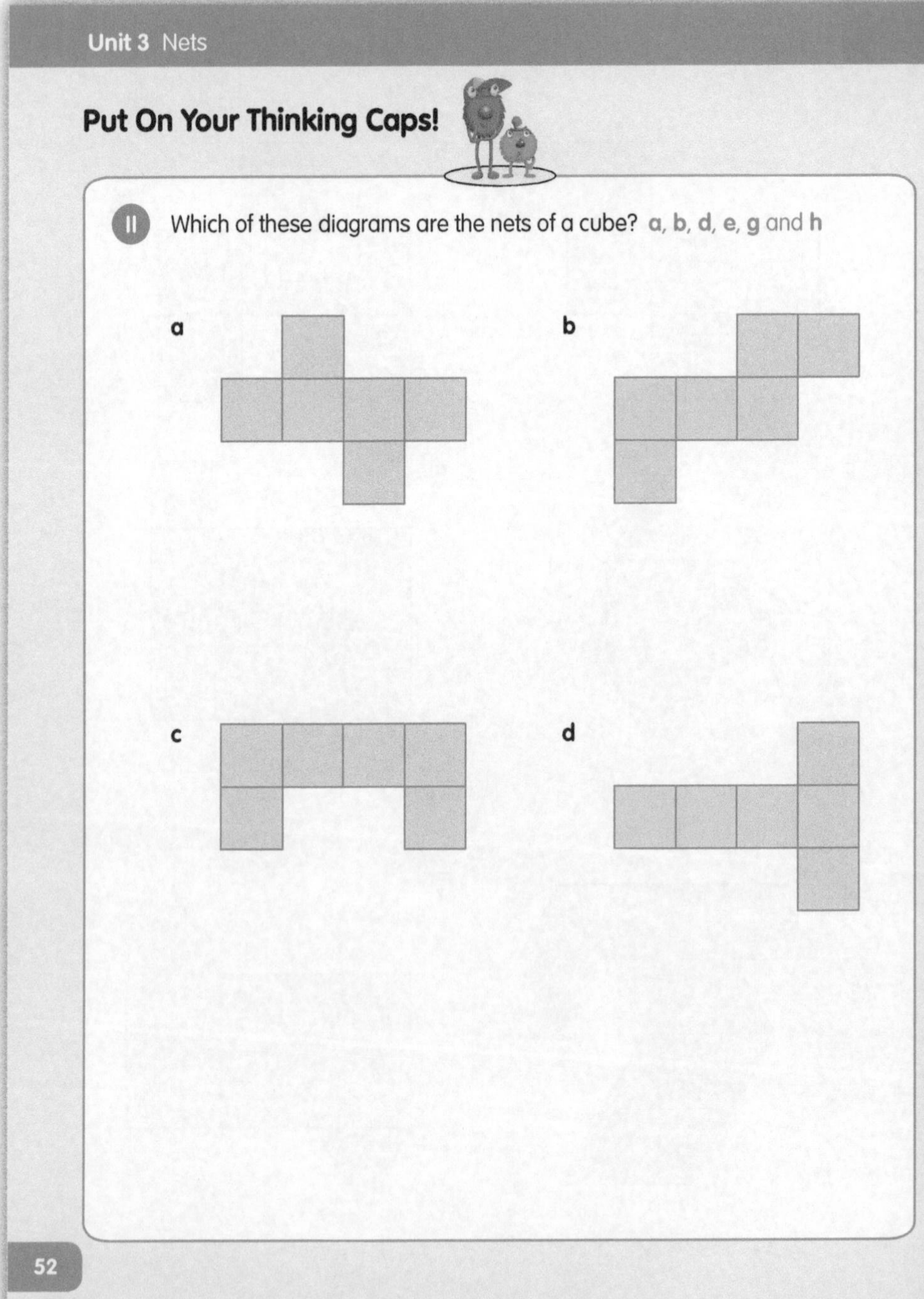

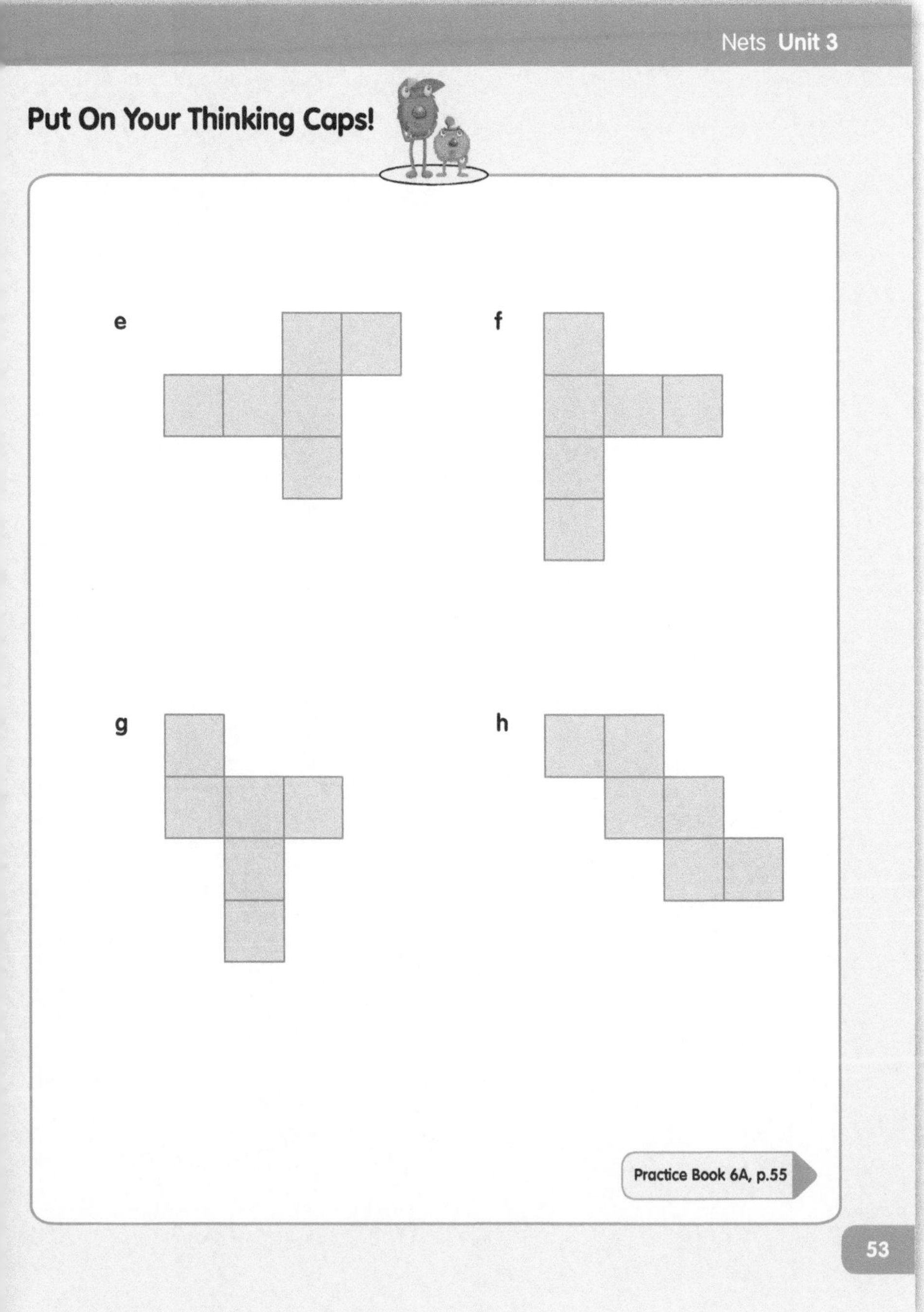
Nets Unit 3
Put On Your Thinking Caps!
e
f
g
h
Practice Book 6A, p.55
53

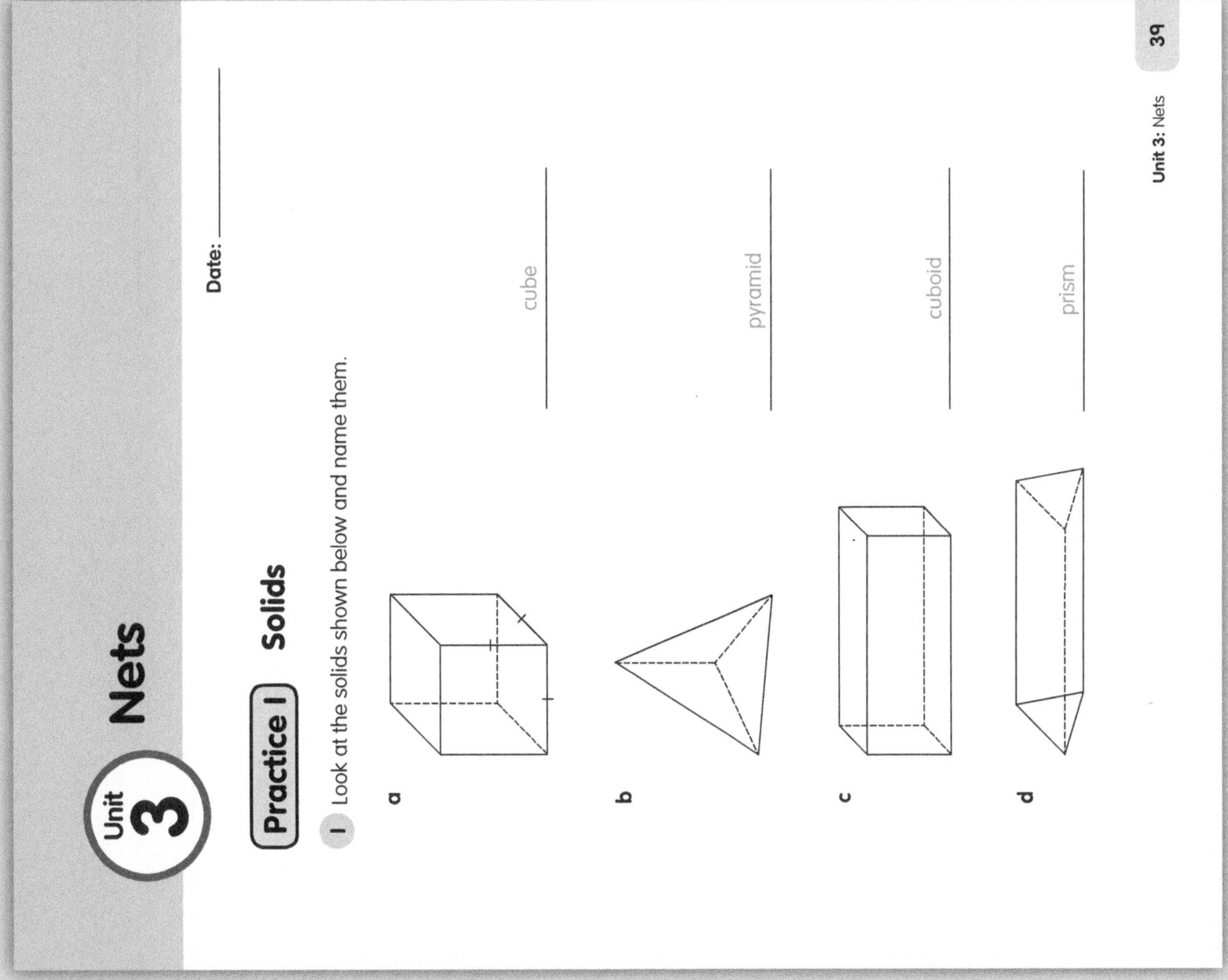

Unit 3 Nets

Practice 1 Solids

Date: ______

1 Look at the solids shown below and name them.

a cube

b pyramid

c cuboid

d prism

Unit 3: Nets 39

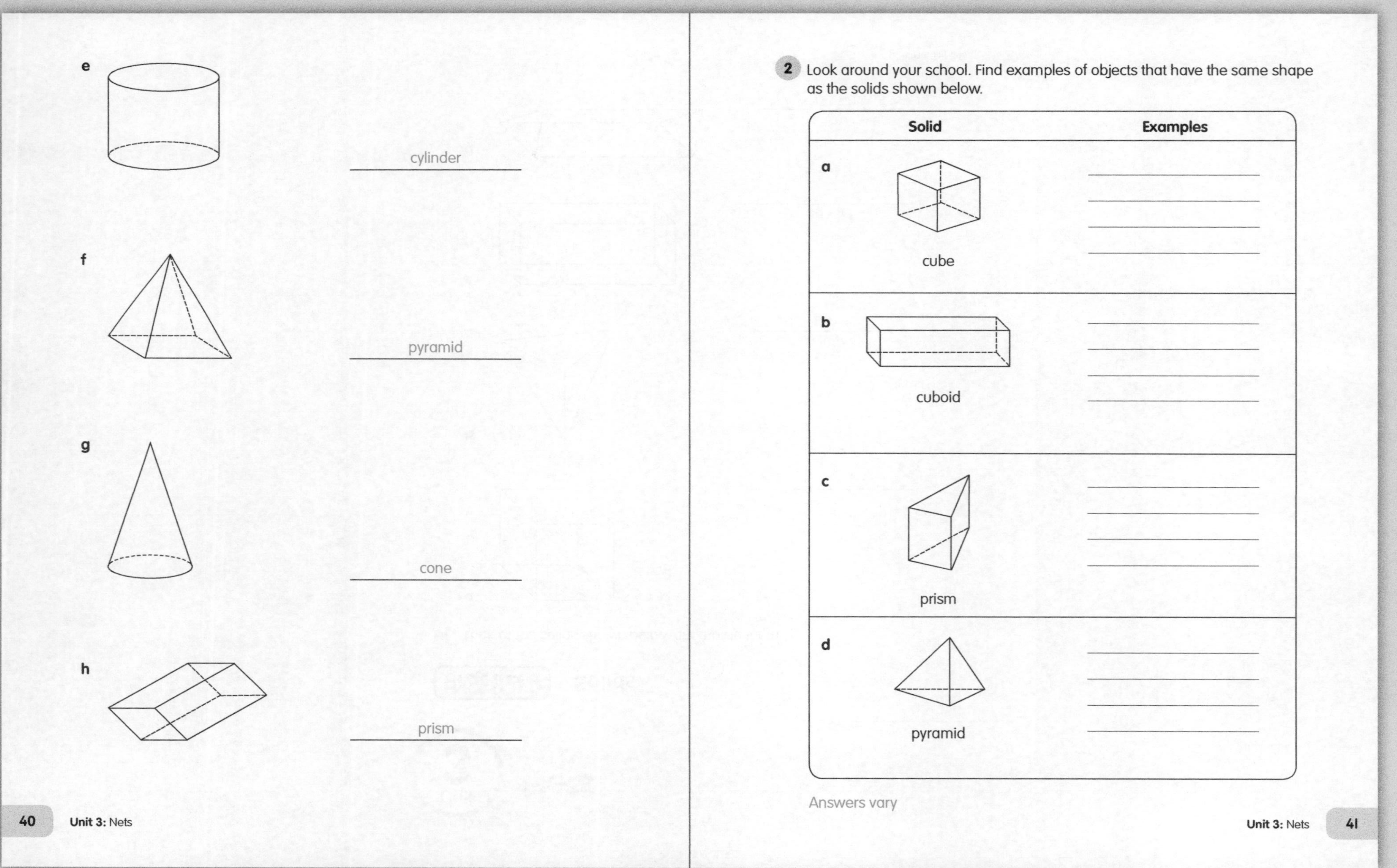

e cylinder

f pyramid

g cone

h prism

2 Look around your school. Find examples of objects that have the same shape as the solids shown below.

	Solid	Examples
a	cube	
b	cuboid	
c	prism	
d	pyramid	

Answers vary

3 Look carefully at the solids shown and complete the table.

Solid	Number of Faces	Shape of Faces
Example pyramid	5	1 rectangle/square 4 triangles
a cube	6	6 squares
b prism	5	3 rectangles 2 triangles
c pyramid	4	4 triangles
d cuboid	6	6 rectangles or 4 rectangles 2 squares

4 Read the statements below and identify the solid.

a It has 4 triangular faces. pyramid

b It has 6 square faces. cube

c It has 2 triangular faces and 3 rectangular faces. prism

d It has 4 triangular faces and a rectangular face. pyramid

Maths Journal

1 Name and draw some of the solids that you have learnt about.

Answers vary
Example:
Cube

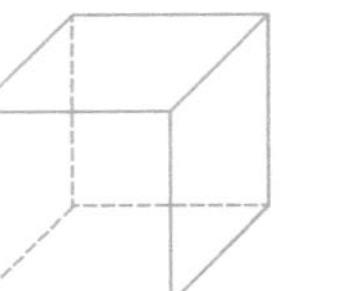

2 a How are a cube and a cuboid different?

Answers vary
Example:
A cuboid has 6 rectangular faces. If all these faces are square, then it is a cube.

b How are a pyramid and a cuboid different?

Answers vary
Example:
They have different number of faces.
A pyramid has triangular shaped faces but a cuboid does not.

Date: ____________

Practice 2 Nets of solids

1 Match each net to its solid.

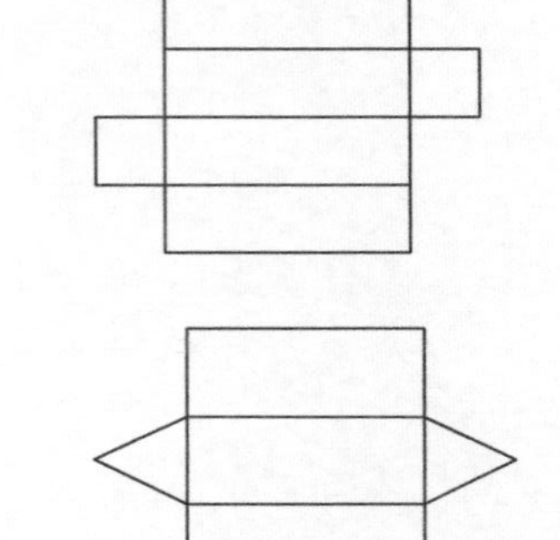

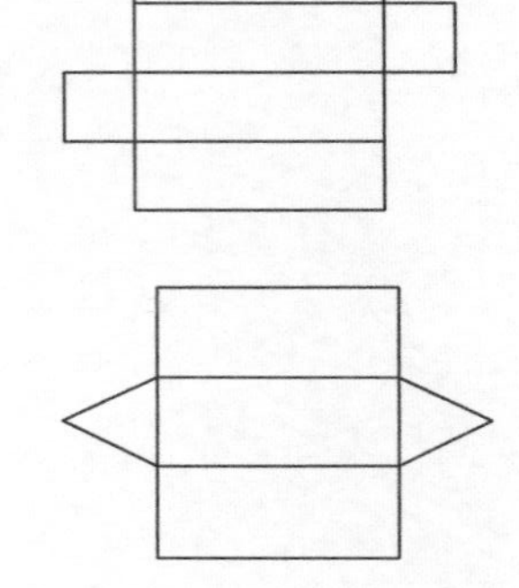

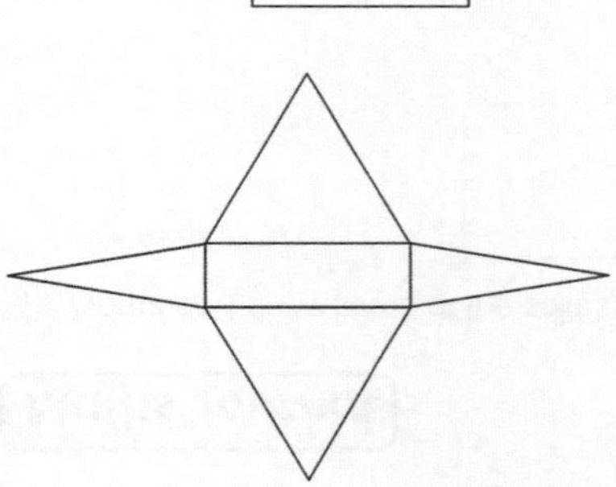

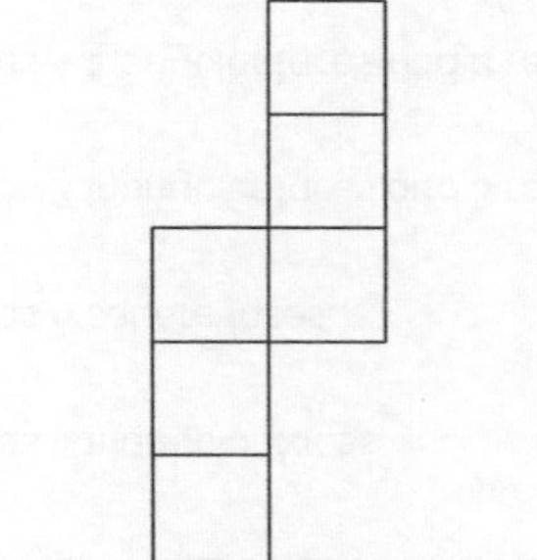

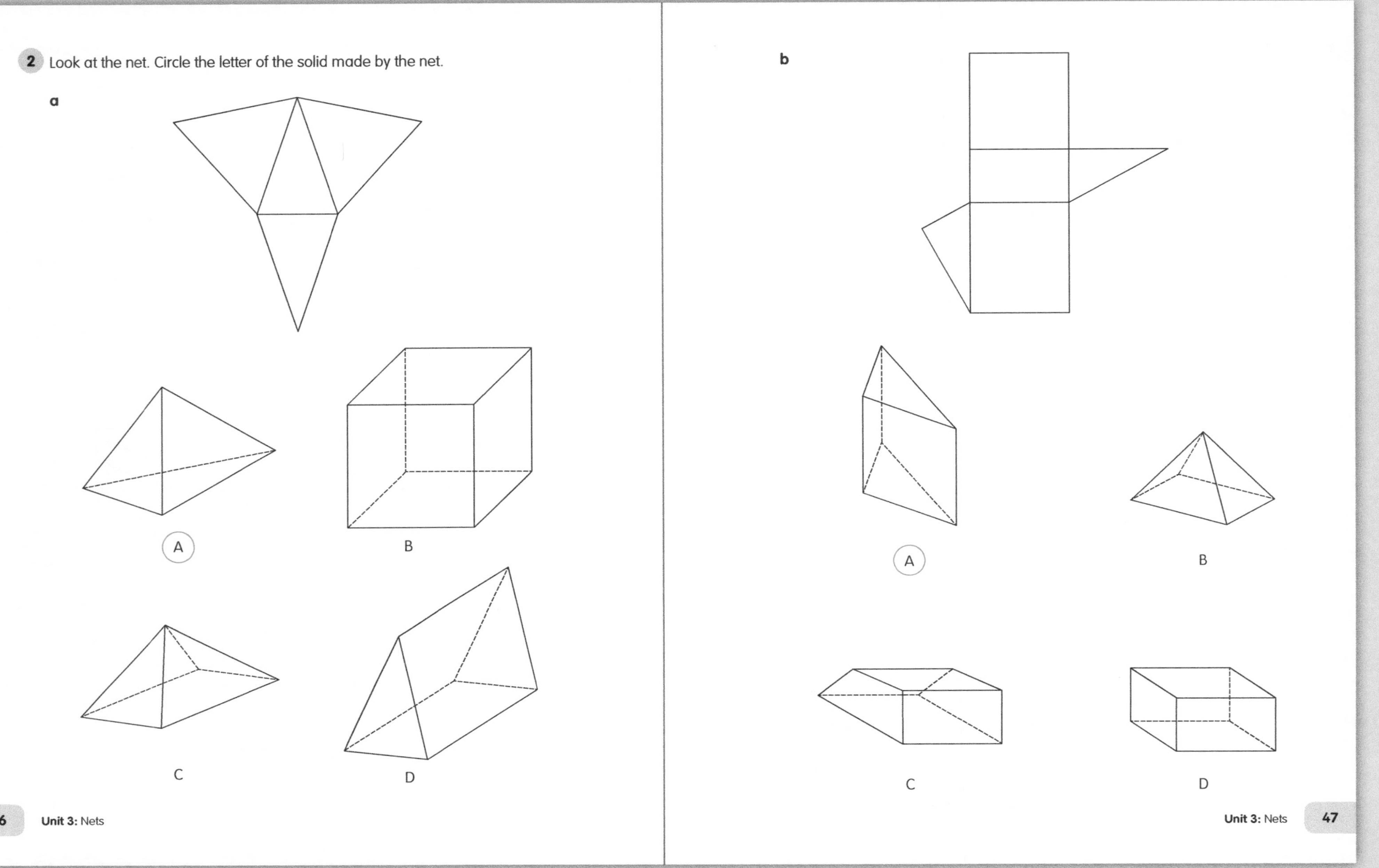
2 Look at the net. Circle the letter of the solid made by the net.

a

A B C D

(A) is circled.

b

A B C D

(A) is circled.

46 Unit 3: Nets

Unit 3: Nets 47

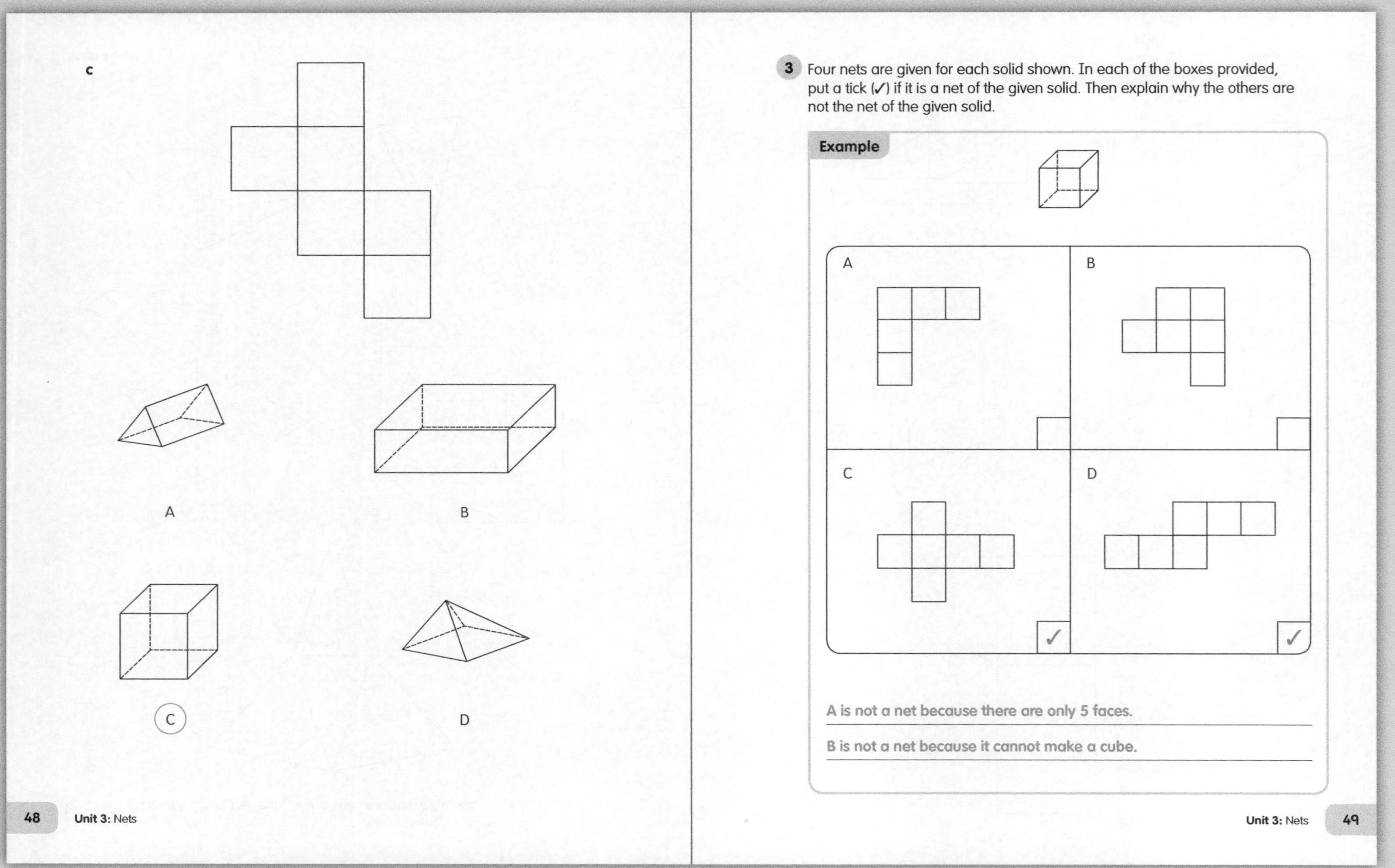

c

A

B

C

D

3 Four nets are given for each solid shown. In each of the boxes provided, put a tick (✓) if it is a net of the given solid. Then explain why the others are not the net of the given solid.

Example

A

B

C ✓

D ✓

A is not a net because there are only 5 faces.

B is not a net because it cannot make a cube.

a

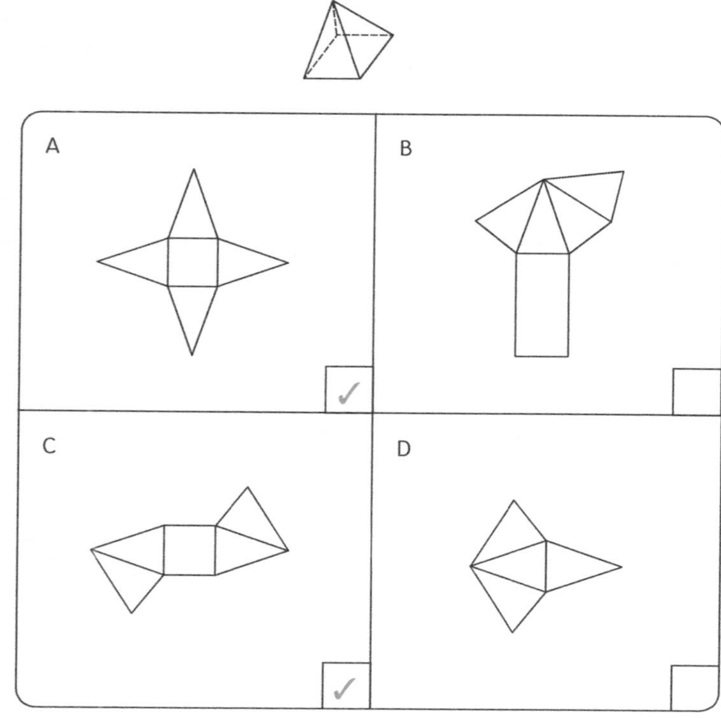

B is not the net because the sides of two of the triangles aren't long enough to attach to the two longer sides of the rectangle.

D is not the net because there are only 4 faces.

b

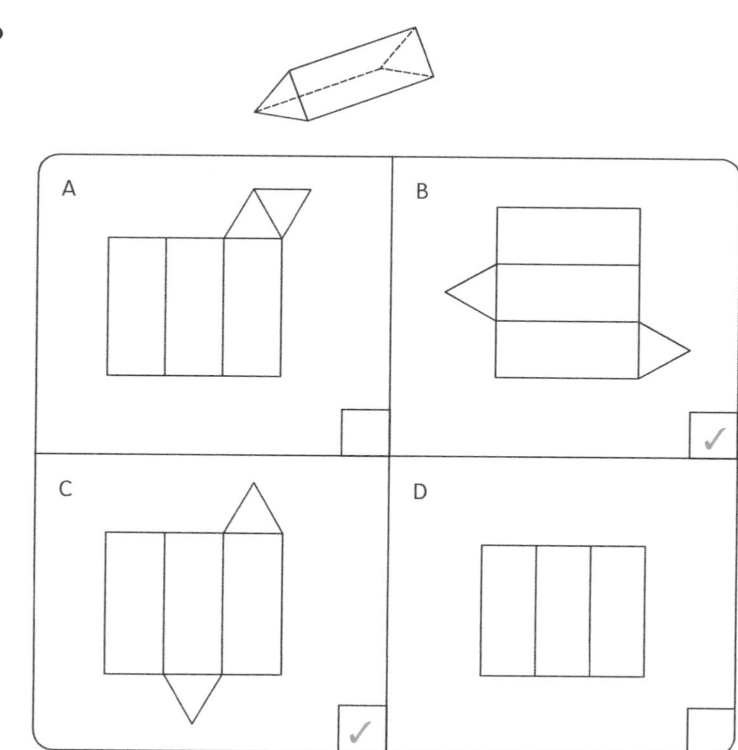

A is not the net because the two triangular faces are on the same side.

D is not the net because there are no triangular faces.

c

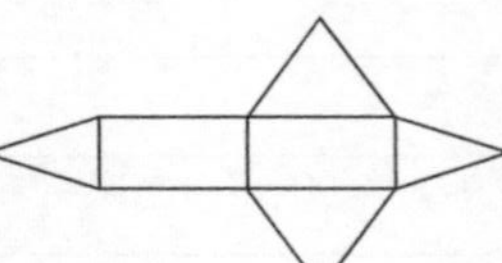

A B C D ✓ ✓

A is not the net because there are only five faces.

D is not the net because there are only five faces.

Date: ____________

Maths Journal

1 Miss Poole showed the class a pyramid and asked the pupils to draw the net of the pyramid. Omar drew the net below.

The net Omar drew does not make a pyramid.
What can be changed about the net above so that it will make a pyramid when folded?

Answers vary
Example:
The rectangular face on the left can be removed.

2 Peter baked a square cake for a party. Which of the following nets can Peter fold to make the most appropriate box for the cake? The box must cover the cake completely. Explain which nets cannot be used to make the most appropriate box for the cake.

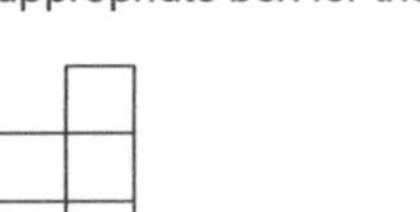

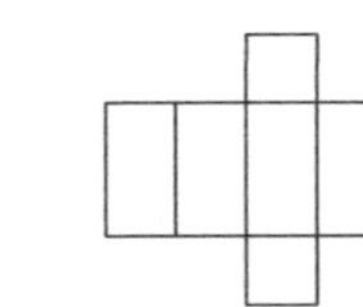

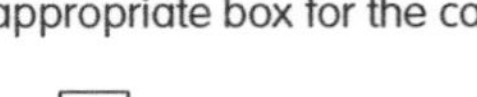

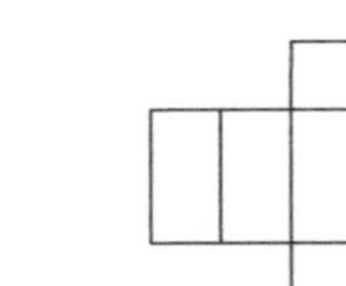

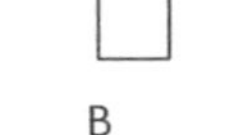

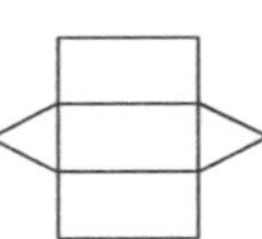

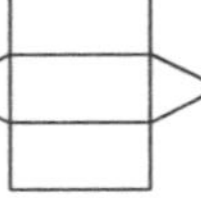

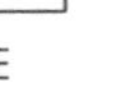

A B C

D E

Answers vary

Peter can use net C.

A cannot be used because it does not make a solid.

B, D and E make a cuboid, pyramid and prism respectively. These are not the most appropriate boxes for containing a square birthday cake.

Date: ______________

Challenging Practice

1 The net below each solid is not a net of the given solid because it has one extra face. Identify this extra face and put a cross (✗) on it.

a

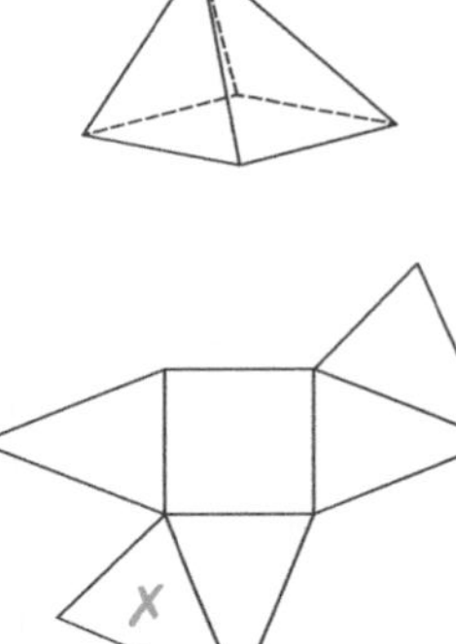

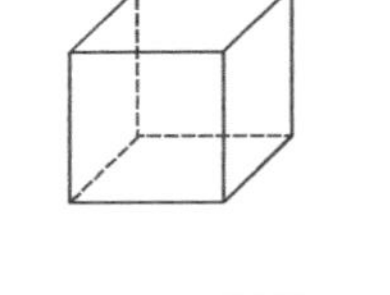

b

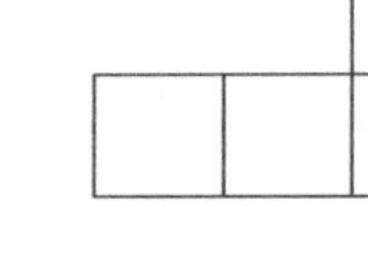

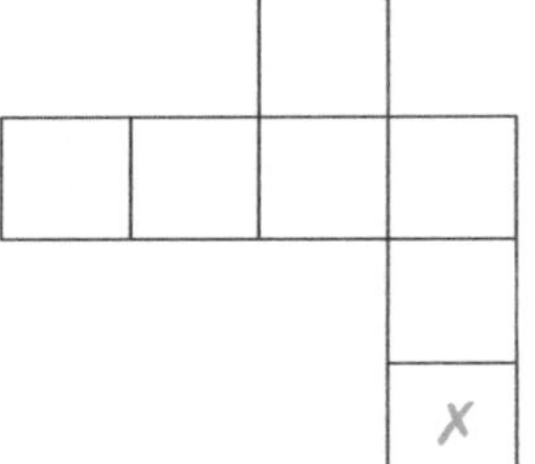

c

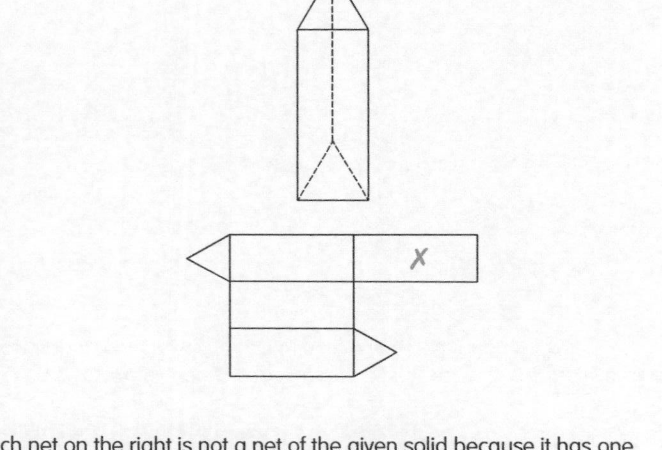

✗

2 Each net on the right is not a net of the given solid because it has one extra face. Identify this face and put a cross (✗) on it.

a

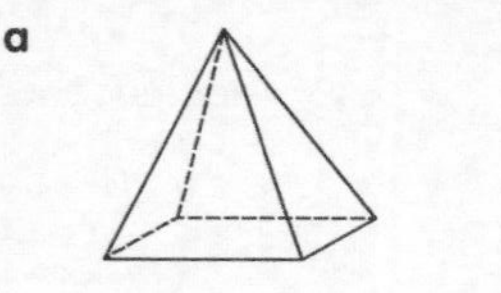

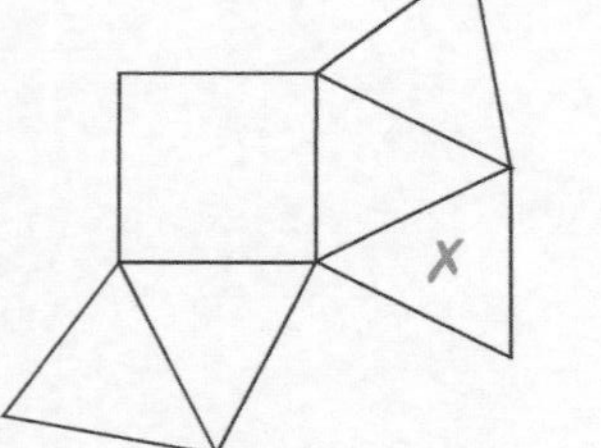

✗

b

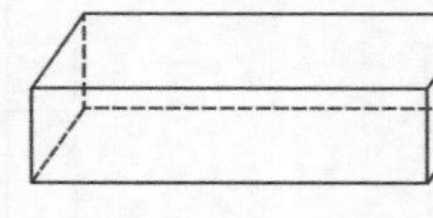

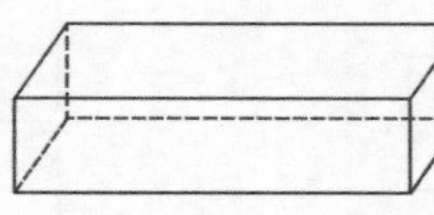

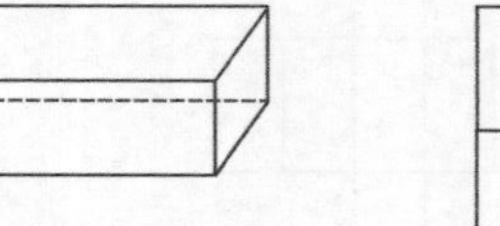

✗

Review 1

Date: ____________

Section A

Choose the correct answer for each question.
Write its letter in the box.

1 In 24 795, which digit is in the ten thousands place?

a 5 b 2
c 7 d 9

b

2 Express $1\frac{1}{5}$h in minutes.

a 61 b 65
c 72 d 120

c

3 4·324 = 4 + 0·3 + ☐. What is the number in the box?

a 0·024 b 0·24
c 0·324 d 24

a

4 36% as a fraction in the simplest form is ____________.

a $\frac{36}{100}$ b $\frac{16}{25}$
c $\frac{9}{25}$ d $\frac{9}{20}$

c

5 Mr James and Mrs Smith share £474. Mr James receives twice as much money as Mrs Smith. How much does Mr James receive?

a £118·50 b £158
c £237 d £316

d

6 Mr Hughes earns £950 a month. How much does he earn in a year?

a £9500 **b** £11 400
c £12 350 **d** £13 300

Answer: b

7 Which of the following is the net of this cuboid?

a **b** **c** **d**

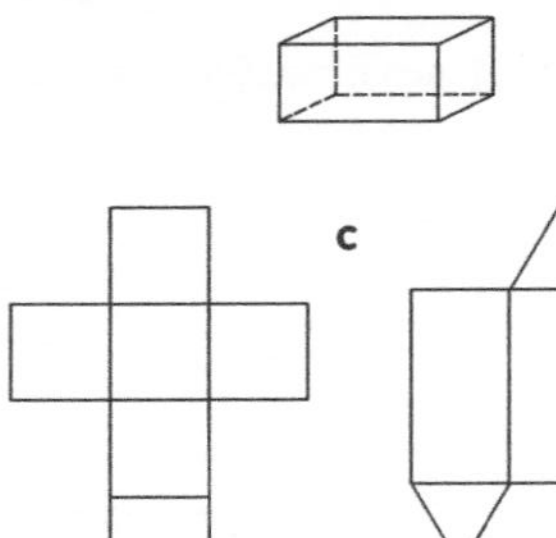

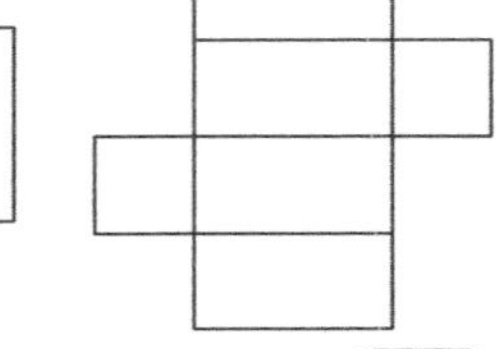

Answer: d

8 The diagram shows a square with a side of 38 cm. What is the area of the unshaded part?

a 152 cm²
b 361 cm²
c 1083 cm²
d 1444 cm²

Answer: c

9 The diagram below is not drawn to scale. AB and CD are straight lines.
Find $\angle x$.

a 45°
b 73°
c 118°
d 135°

Answer: b

10 The graph below shows the amount of fruit a shop owner sold in 5 weeks.

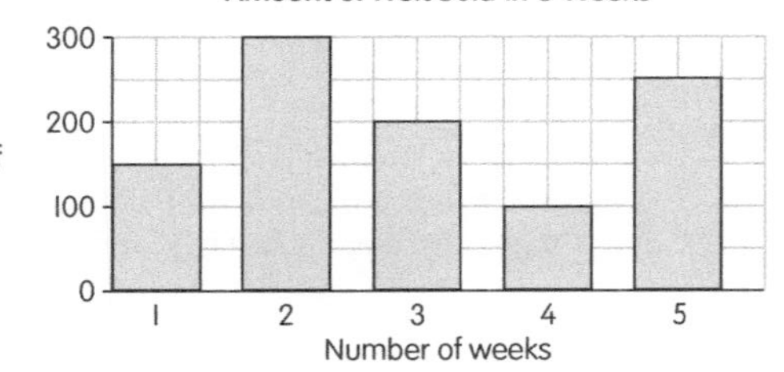

If the shop owner sold the pieces of fruit at £0·30 each, how much did he earn in five weeks?

a £300 **b** £900
c £1000 **d** £3000

Answer: a

11 The shape below is not drawn to scale. ABC is an isosceles triangle. AE and BD are straight lines. Find $\angle m$.

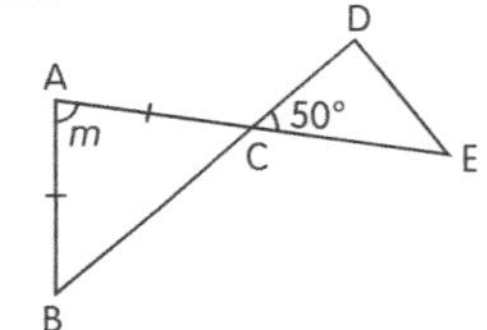

a 50° **b** 60°
c 80° **d** 100°

Answer: c

12 A pen costs twice as much as a ruler. Farha spends £6 on 3 pens and 2 rulers. How much does a pen cost?

a £0·75 **b** £1·50
c £2·25 **d** £4·50

Answer: b

13 The mean of two numbers is 81. The difference between the numbers is 26. What is the smaller number?

a 68 **b** 94
c 136 **d** 162

Answer: a

14 Hardeep and Ruby had some photographs in the ratio 1 : 5. If Ruby had 92 photographs more than Hardeep, how many photographs did they have altogether?

a 23 **b** 46
c 115 **d** 138

d

15 There are 2 books in a box. The mass of each book is r g. The box is 200 g lighter than each book. What is the total mass of the box and the two books?

a $2r$ g **b** $(2r - 200)$ g
c $3r$ g **d** $(3r - 200)$ g

d

Section B

Read the questions and fill in the answers.

16 Find the value of $129 - 85 \div 2 + 12$.

$129 - 85 \div 2 + 12 = 129 - 42{\cdot}5 + 12$
$= 86{\cdot}5 + 12$
$= 98{\cdot}5$

98·5

17 What is the sum of all the factors of 12?

$12 = 1 \times 12$
$= 2 \times 6$
$= 3 \times 4$

$1 + 2 + 3 + 4 + 6 + 12 = 28$

28

18 Arrange $\frac{5}{8}, \frac{3}{5}, \frac{3}{4}$ in order, beginning with the smallest.

$\frac{5}{8} = \frac{25}{40}, \frac{3}{5} = \frac{24}{40}, \frac{3}{4} = \frac{30}{40}$

$\frac{3}{5}, \frac{5}{8}, \frac{3}{4}$

19 $5{\cdot}79 \times \square = 5790$. What is the missing number in the box?

1000

20 What is the mass of the bag of plums?

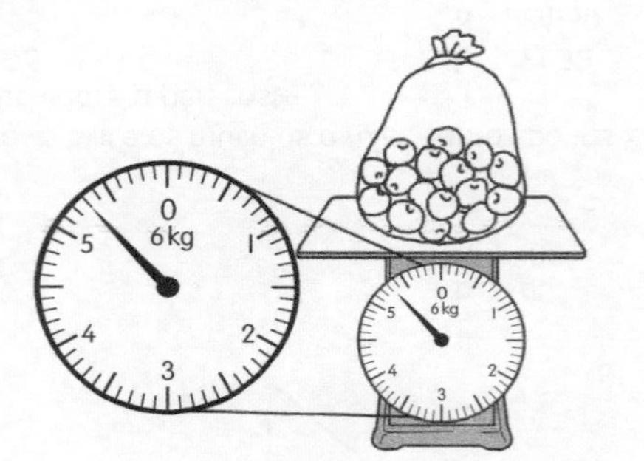

5 kg 300 g

21 How many faces are there on the solid below?

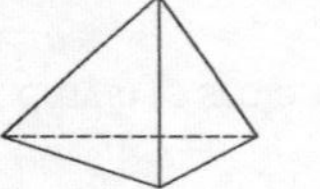

4

22 Simplify $3a + 5 - 2a + 6$.

$a + 11$

23 Mrs Wallace's salary is £3000 a month. She used 42% of it to pay bills and spent 16% of it on transport. How much did she have left?

$100\% - 42\% - 16\% = 42\%$

$\frac{42}{100} \times £3000 = £1260$

£ 1260

Look at the graph to answer question **24**.
The graph below shows the number of visitors to the Science Centre in a particular week. The Science Centre is closed on Monday.

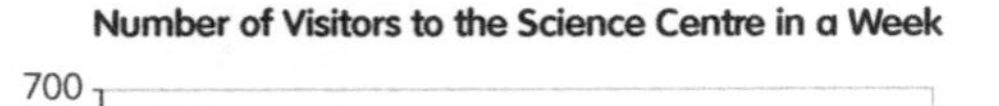

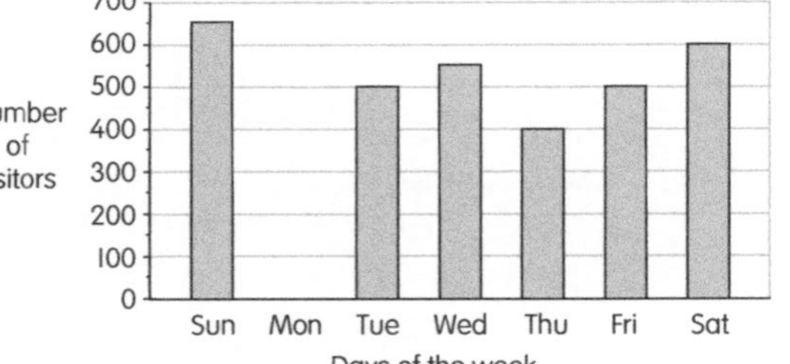

24 What fraction of all the visitors came on Thursday? Give your answer in the simplest form.

$650 + 500 + 550 + 400 + 500 + 600 = 3200$

$\frac{400}{3200} = \frac{4}{32} = \frac{1}{8}$

$\frac{1}{8}$

25 The diagram below is not drawn to scale. MNOP is a rhombus and MQ is a straight line. Find ∠POQ.

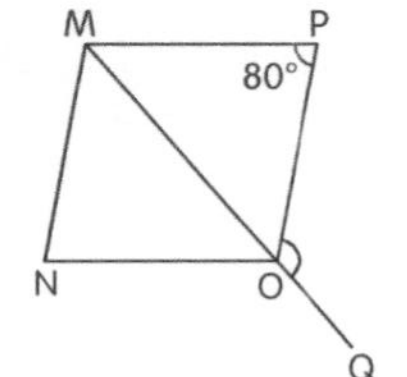

Since MP = PO, MPO is an isosceles triangle.

$\angle POM = (180° - 80°) \div 2$
$= 100° \div 2$
$= 50°$

$\angle POQ = 180° - 50°$
$= 130°$

130 °

26 A clothes factory produces 4500 hats a day. If the factory produces hats for 5 days every week, how many hats are produced in 3 weeks?

$4500 \times 5 = 22\,500$
$22\,500 \times 3 = 67\,500$

67 500 hats

27 Find the area of a triangle with a base of 24 cm and a height of 10 cm.

$\frac{1}{2} \times 24 \times 10 = 120\ cm^2$

120 cm^2

28 **a** Draw a line passing through point P that is parallel to line CD.
b Draw a line from point P that is perpendicular to line CD.

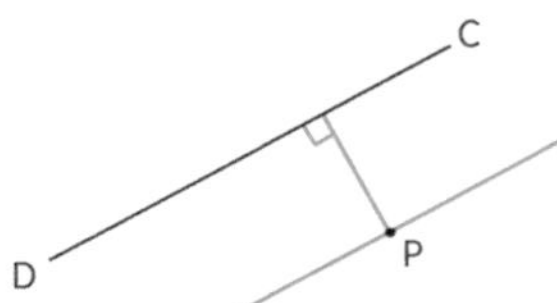

29 In the diagram below, what is the smallest number of squares that must be added so that line AB becomes a line of symmetry?

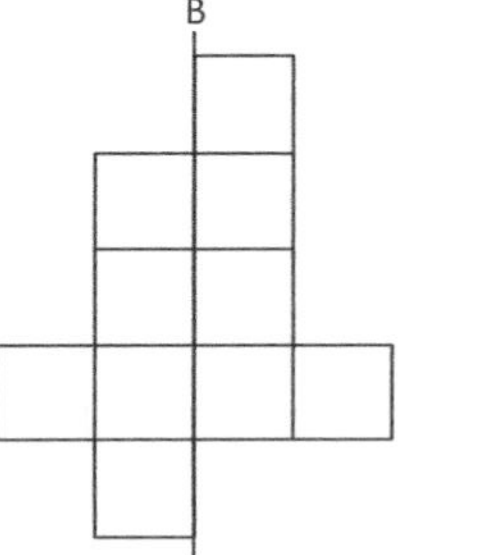

2

30 The perimeter of a rectangle is 40 cm. The ratio of its length to its width is 3 : 2. Find the length of the rectangle.

Total units = 3 + 2 + 3 + 2
= 10

10 units → 40 cm
1 unit → 4 cm
3 units → 12 cm

12 cm

31 $\frac{2}{5}$ of the T-shirts in a shop are yellow. $\frac{7}{13}$ of the remaining T-shirts are green. The rest of the T-shirts are black. If there are 32 more yellow T-shirts than black T-shirts, how many T-shirts are green?

$\frac{5}{5} - \frac{2}{5} = \frac{3}{5}$

$\frac{7}{13} \times \frac{3}{5} = \frac{21}{65}$ (green)

$\frac{6}{13} \times \frac{3}{5} = \frac{18}{65}$ (black)

$\frac{2}{5} - \frac{18}{65} = \frac{8}{65}$

8 units → 32 T-shirts
1 unit → 4 T-shirts
21 units → 84 T-shirts

84 T-shirts

32 Jake wrote 200 words in 15 mins and another 320 words in 25 mins. Find the mean number of words he wrote per minute.

200 + 320 = 520
He wrote a total of 520 words.

15 + 25 = 40
He took 40 minutes to write 520 words.

520 ÷ 40 = 13
He wrote a mean of 13 words per minute.

13 words

33 A game and 15 balloons cost £40.

a If the game costs £x, what is the cost of each balloon in terms of x?
b If the game costs £25·75, how much is each balloon?

a Cost of 15 balloons = £40 – £x
= £$(40 - x)$

Cost of 1 balloon = £$(40 - x) \div 15$
= £$\left(\frac{40 - x}{15}\right)$

b Cost of 1 balloon = £$\left(\frac{40 - 25{\cdot}75}{15}\right)$
= £0·95

a £ $\left(\frac{40 - x}{15}\right)$

b £ 0·95

34 A bag cost £36. During a sale, it was sold at $\frac{2}{3}$ of the usual price. Mr Roberts bought 3 bags during the sale. He used his shop card and got a further 5% discount on the bags. How much did he pay altogether?

$\frac{2}{3} \times$ £36 = £24

£24 × 3 = £72

£72 × 95% = £68·40

£68·40

Section C

Read the questions and write your answers in the spaces.
Show your workings clearly.

35 Jack had some football cards. His friend then gave him half the number of football cards Jack had at first. Jack then had 54 football cards. How many football cards did he have at first?

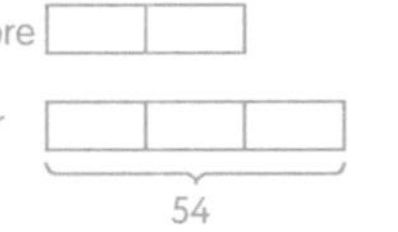

3 units → 54 football cards

1 unit → $\frac{54}{3}$ = 18 football cards

2 units → 18 × 2 = 36 football cards

Jack had 36 football cards at first.

36 The mass of a bottle completely filled with oil is 5 kg. When it is $\frac{1}{4}$ full, its mass is 1·4 kg. Find the mass of the empty bottle.

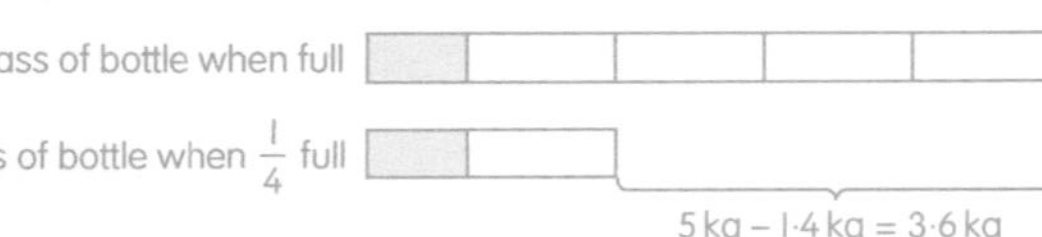

3 units → 3·6 kg
1 unit → 1·2 kg

Mass of empty bottle = 1·4 – 1·2
= 0·2 kg.

37 Find the area of the shaded triangle.

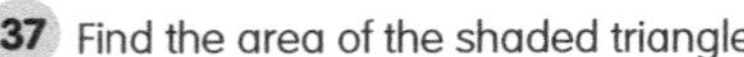

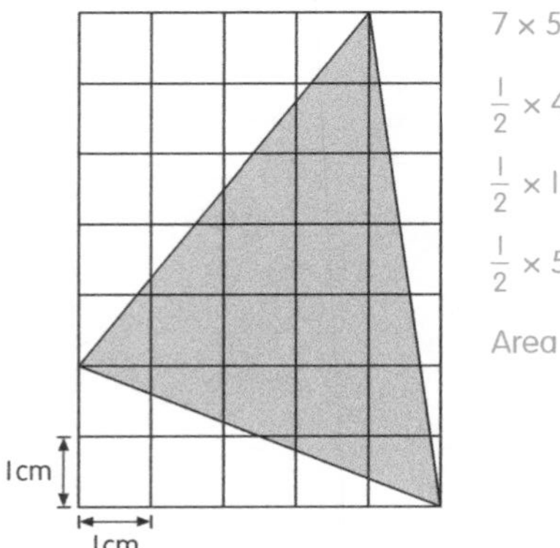

7 × 5 = 35

$\frac{1}{2}$ × 4 × 5 = 10

$\frac{1}{2}$ × 1 × 7 = 3·5

$\frac{1}{2}$ × 5 × 2 = 5

Area of shaded triangle = 35 – (10 + 3·5 + 5)
= 35 – 18·5
= 16·5 cm²

38 **a** Draw a triangle ABC in which BC = 7 cm, AB = 5 cm and ∠ABC = 55°. Line BC is given as shown.

b From the triangle you have drawn, measure ∠ACB.

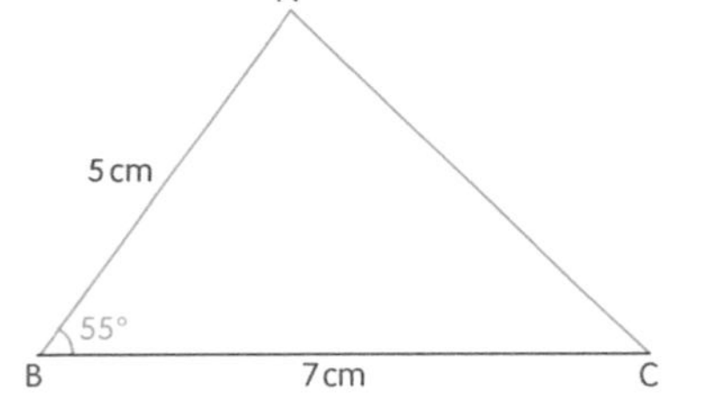

∠ACB = 45°

39 Miss Shaw has some counters. If she gives her pupils 3 counters each, she will have 12 counters left. If she gives them 4 counters each, she will need 24 more.

a How many pupils are there?
b How many counters does she have?

Number of Pupils	Number of Counters		
	If 3 Counters Each:	If 4 Counters Each:	
30	$30 \times 3 = 90$ $90 + 12 = 102$	$30 \times 4 = 120$ $120 - 24 = 96$	✗
36	$36 \times 3 = 108$ $108 + 12 = 120$	$36 \times 4 = 144$ $144 - 24 = 120$	✓

a There are 36 pupils.

b She has 120 counters.

40 A passenger travelled 41·8 km by taxi. How much did the passenger pay using the charges given below?

First 1 km	£2·80
Every additional 385 m or less	£0·20

First 1 km = £2·80

Remaining distance = 41·8 − 1
= 40·8 km
= 40 800 m

$\frac{40\,800}{385} = 105{\cdot}97 \approx 106$

106 × £0·20 = 106 × 20p
= 2120p
= £21·20

£2·80 + £21·20 = £24

The passenger paid £24.

41 Peter had a total of 300 coins in a box. 40% of them were Canadian coins and the rest were UK coins. He gave away 10% of the Canadian coins.

a How many Canadian coins did Peter have at first?
b How many coins are left in the box?

a $\frac{40}{100} \times 300 = 120$

Peter had 120 Canadian coins at first.

b $\frac{10}{100} \times 120 = 12$

Peter gave away 12 coins.

300 − 12 = 288
288 coins are left in the box.

42 A sports club had 63 members last year. The ratio of the number of boys to the number of girls in the club then was 5 : 4. This year, 2 new boys and 5 new girls joined the club. What was the ratio of the number of boys to the number of girls this year?

Total units = 5 + 4
= 9

9 units → 63 members
1 unit → $\frac{63}{9}$ = 7 members

5 units → 7 × 5 = 35 members (boys)
4 units → 7 × 4 = 28 members (girls)

Number of boys this year = 35 + 2
= 37

Number of girls this year = 28 + 5
= 33

The ratio of the number of boys to the number of girls this year was 37 : 33.

43 A computer game and a watch cost £70. A computer game and a camera cost £250. The camera cost 5 times as much as the watch.

a Find the cost of the watch.
b Find the cost of the computer game.

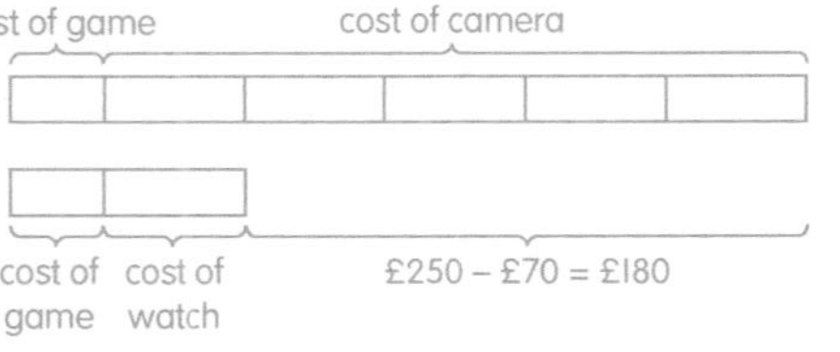

a 4 units → £180

1 unit → $£\left(\frac{180}{4}\right) = £45$

The cost of the watch is £45.

b £70 – £45 = £25
The cost of the computer game is £25.

44 The shape below is not drawn to scale. ABC is an equilateral triangle and ACDE is a rhombus. ∠ADE = 40°.

a Find ∠ACD.
b Find ∠AEB.

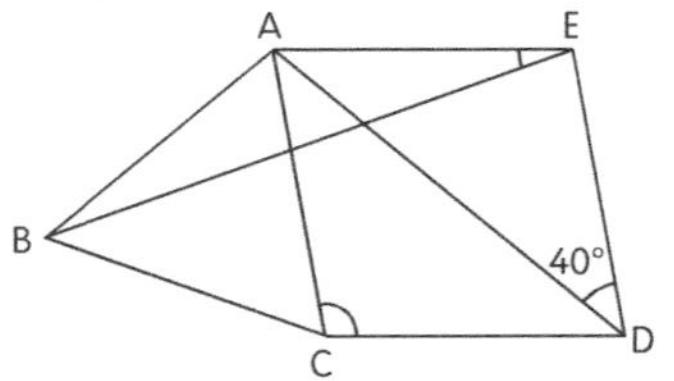

a Since AE = DE, ADE is an isosceles triangle.

∠DAE = ∠ADE
= 40°

∠AED = 180° – 40° – 40°
= 100°

∠ACD = ∠AED
= 100°

b ∠CAE = 180° – 100°
= 80°

∠BAC = 60°

∠BAE = 60° + 80°
= 140°

Since BA = AC and AC = AE, BA = AE and ABE is an isosceles triangle.

∠AEB
= (180° – 140°) ÷ 2
= 40° ÷ 2
= 20°

45 The mass of a bag of potatoes is 3·45 kg. The mass of a bag of carrots is $\frac{1}{3}$ of the mass of the bag of potatoes. A restaurant owner buys 4 bags of potatoes, 2 bags of carrots and 3 bags of tomatoes. The total mass of the bags is 23 kg. What is the mass of each bag of tomatoes?

Mass of a bag of potatoes = 3·45 kg

Mass of 4 bags of potatoes = 3·45 × 4
= 13·8 kg

Mass of a bag of carrots = 3·45 ÷ 3
= 1·15 kg

Mass of 2 bags of carrots = 1·15 × 2
= 2·3 kg

Mass of 4 bags of potatoes and 2 bags of carrots = 13·8 + 2·3
= 16·1 kg

Mass of 3 bags of tomatoes = 23 − 16·1
= 6·9 kg

Mass of a bag of tomatoes = 6·9 ÷ 3
= 2·3 kg

46 Mr Slade bought some pots and bowls. He paid £116 for them. The pots cost £12 each and a bowl was £5 cheaper than a pot. Mr Slade bought 3 more bowls than pots.

a How many pots did Mr Slade buy?
b How many bowls did Mr Slade buy?

Cost of 1 bowl = £12 − £5
= £7

Cost of 3 bowls = £7 × 3
= £21

Cost of 1 bowl and 1 pot = £7 + £12
= £19

a £116 − £21 = £95
£95 ÷ £19 = 5
Mr Slade bought 5 pots.

b 5 + 3 = 8
Mr Slade bought 8 bowls.

47 The graph below shows the number of people who went to the cinema in a particular week.

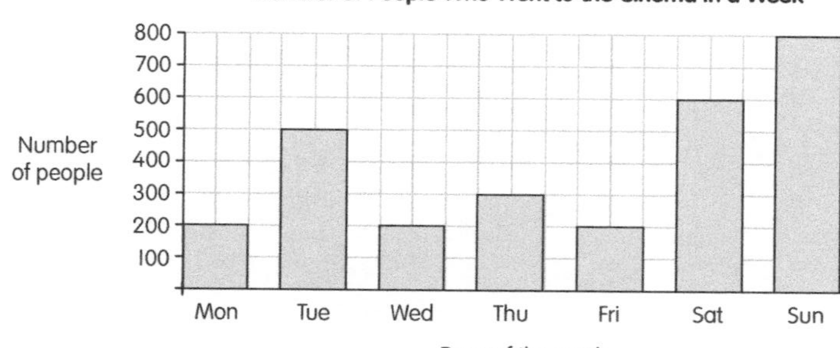

a What was the mean number of people who went to the cinema per day during that week?

b The mean number of people per day who went to the cinema in that week and the following week was 450. How many more people went to the cinema in the following week?

a Total number of people = 200 + 500 + 200 + 300 + 200 + 600 + 800
= 2800

Mean number of people = 2800 ÷ 7
= 400

b Total number of people for two weeks = 450 × 14
= 6300

Number of people who went in the following week = 6300 – 2800
= 3500

3500 – 2800 = 700
700 more people went to the cinema in the following week.

Unit 4: Fractions

Medium-term plan

Week	Learning Objectives	Thinking Skills	Resources
5	**(1) Four operations with fractions** Pupils will be able to: • add and subtract fractions or mixed numbers • multiply fractions • divide a fraction by a whole number • solve word problems on fractions		• Pupil Textbook 6A, pp 54 to 55 • Practice Book 6A, pp 75 to 76 • Teacher's Guide 6A, pp 106 to 107
5	**(2) Dividing by a proper fraction** Pupils will be able to: • interpret the division of a whole number by a proper fraction • interpret the division of a proper fraction by another proper fraction • find the quotient by multiplying the dividend by the reciprocal of the divisor	• Comparing • Deduction	• Pupil Textbook 6A, pp 56 to 67 • Practice Book 6A, pp 77 to 84 • Teacher's Guide 6A, pp 108 to 122

Unit 4: Fractions

Medium-term plan

Week	Learning Objectives	Thinking Skills	Resources
5	*Let's Explore!* Pupils will be able to observe that the numerators and denominators of the division calculations are swapped. *Maths Journal* Pupils will be able to: • explain what is found out when dividing by a proper fraction • explain the errors that have been made, based on their understanding of how to divide by a proper fraction	• Translating • Identifying relationships	• Pupil Textbook 6A, p 68 • Teacher's Guide 6A, p 120

Unit 4: Fractions

Medium-term plan

Week	Learning Objectives	Thinking Skills	Resources
5	**(3) Word problems** Pupils will be able to: • solve word problems involving division of a whole number or proper fraction by a proper fraction	• Translating	• Pupil Textbook 6A, pp 71 to 75 • Practice Book 6A, pp 85 to 92 • Teacher's Guide 6A, pp 123 to 127

Medium-term plan

Week	Learning Objectives	Thinking Skills	Resources
	Let's Wrap It Up! Emphasise the key concepts, skills and processes that have been taught in the unit. Discuss the worked examples with pupils to assess whether they have mastered these concepts, skills and processes. *Put On Your Thinking Caps!* Pupils will be able to draw a table and use guess and check to solve the problem.	• Translating Heuristics for problem solving: • Guess and check • Drawing a table	• Pupil Textbook 6A, pp 77 to 78 • Practice Book 6A, pp 93 to 94 • Teacher's Guide 6A, pp 129 to 130
Summative assessment opportunity			
Assessment Book 6, Test 4, pp 39 to 44			

Four
ons

Pupils will be able to:

- add and subtract fractions or mixed numbers
- multiply fractions
- divide a fraction by a whole number
- solve word problems on fractions

Key concepts

- A fraction is a part of a whole or set, a ratio or a quotient.
- Addition and subtraction of fractions or mixed numbers can be interpreted in the same way as addition and subtraction of whole numbers.
- Multiplication of fractions, e.g. $\frac{2}{3} \times \frac{3}{4}$, is interpreted as $\frac{2}{3}$ of $\frac{3}{4}$ or $\frac{3}{4}$ of $\frac{2}{3}$.
- Division of a fraction by a whole number is interpreted as partition (sharing).

Teaching sequence

 **a** and **b**

- Review the addition and subtraction of fractions.
- Remind pupils that only like fractions (same denominators) can be added or subtracted. The denominator of a fraction could be thought of in a similar way as the place of a digit in a whole number.

  Example:
  In the number 30, the value of the digit 3 is 3 tens. In the fraction $\frac{3}{5}$, the value of the digit 3 is 3 fifths.
- Just as only whole numbers in the same place can be added or subtracted, only like fractions can be added or subtracted.

  Example:
  3 (ones) + 4 (ones) = 7 (ones)
  3 + 4 = 7
  3 tens + 4 tens = 7 tens
  30 + 40 = 70
  3 fifths + 4 fifths = 7 fifths
  $\frac{3}{5} + \frac{4}{5} = \frac{7}{5}$

Unit 4

Fractions

Let's Learn!

Four operations with fractions

  Recall that:

a i $\frac{1}{4} + \frac{1}{8} = \frac{2}{8} + \frac{1}{8}$
$= \frac{3}{8}$

ii $\frac{2}{3} + \frac{1}{2} = \frac{4}{6} + \frac{3}{6}$
$= \frac{7}{6}$
$= 1\frac{1}{6}$

b i $\frac{5}{6} - \frac{1}{12} = \frac{10}{12} - \frac{1}{12}$
$= \frac{9}{12}$
$= \frac{3}{4}$

ii $\frac{4}{7} - \frac{1}{3} = \frac{12}{21} - \frac{7}{21}$
$= \frac{5}{21}$

c $\frac{2}{5} \times \frac{3}{4} = \frac{2 \times 3}{5 \times 4}$
$= \frac{6}{20}$
$= \frac{3}{10}$

I can also do this:
$\frac{2}{5} \times \frac{3}{4} = \frac{\cancel{2}^{1}}{5} \times \frac{3}{\cancel{4}_{2}}$
$= \frac{3}{10}$

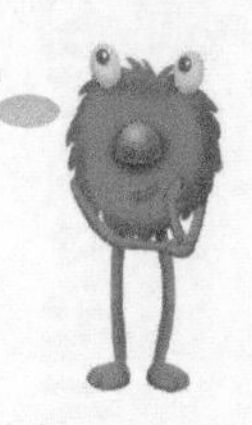

54

What you will need

Scientific calculator

Independent work

Practice 1 in Practice Book 6A, pp 75 to 76.

d $\frac{13}{4} \times \frac{4}{5} = \boxed{2}\frac{\boxed{3}}{\boxed{5}}$

e $\frac{6}{7} \div 3 = \frac{\cancel{6}^{2}}{7} \times \frac{1}{\cancel{3}_{1}}$

$= \frac{\boxed{2}}{\boxed{7}}$

f A gardener bought $2\frac{3}{4}$ kg of compost on Monday and another $4\frac{1}{6}$ kg on Tuesday. She filled 5 flower pots with $1\frac{1}{4}$ kg of compost each. How much compost did she have left?

$2\frac{3}{4} + 4\frac{1}{6} = \boxed{6}\frac{\boxed{11}}{\boxed{12}}$

She bought $\boxed{6}\frac{\boxed{11}}{\boxed{12}}$ kg of compost.

$1\frac{1}{4} \times 5 = \boxed{6}\frac{\boxed{1}}{\boxed{4}}$

She used $\boxed{6}\frac{\boxed{1}}{\boxed{4}}$ kg of compost.

$\boxed{6}\frac{\boxed{11}}{\boxed{12}} - \boxed{6}\frac{\boxed{1}}{\boxed{4}} = \frac{\boxed{2}}{\boxed{3}}$

She had $\frac{\boxed{2}}{\boxed{3}}$ kg of compost left.

Practice Book 6A, p.75

Teaching sequence

c and **d**

- Review multiplication of fractions:

  $\frac{2}{5} \times \frac{3}{4}$ is interpreted as

  $\frac{2}{5}$ of $\frac{3}{4}$ or $\frac{3}{4}$ of $\frac{2}{5}$.

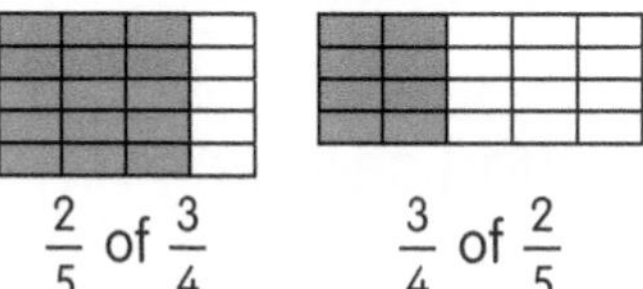

$\frac{2}{5}$ of $\frac{3}{4}$ $\quad$ $\frac{3}{4}$ of $\frac{2}{5}$

- In each case, the blue region represents the required product and is equal to $\frac{6}{20}$, that is, $\frac{2 \times 3}{5 \times 4}$ or $\frac{3 \times 2}{4 \times 5}$.

e

- Revise the division of a fraction by a whole number:

  $\frac{6}{7} \div 3$ is interpreted as partitioning $\frac{6}{7}$ into 3 equal parts: each part is $\frac{1}{3}$ of $\frac{6}{7}$.

  So $\frac{6}{7} \div 3 = \frac{1}{3}$ of $\frac{6}{7}$

  $= \frac{1}{3} \times \frac{6}{7} = \frac{1 \times 6}{3 \times 7} = \frac{2}{7}$

f

- Review the process of solving word problems, the addition and subtraction of mixed numbers and the multiplication of a mixed number by a whole number.

Learning objectives: Dividing by a proper fraction

Pupils will be able to:

- interpret the division of a whole number by a proper fraction
- interpret the division of a proper fraction by another proper fraction
- find the quotient by multiplying the dividend by the reciprocal of the divisor

Key concept

Division by a proper fraction is interpreted as measurement division; for example, $3 \div \frac{2}{3}$ or $\frac{3}{4} \div \frac{2}{3}$ is interpreted as the number of two-thirds in 3 or $\frac{3}{4}$.

Thinking skills

- Comparing
- Deduction

What you will need

Rectangular strips (see Photocopy master 9 on p 280)

Teaching sequence

- Introduce the division of 1 by $\frac{1}{2}$.
- Explain that $1 \div \frac{1}{2}$ means that we have to find how many halves there are in 1.
- Pupils can compare this concept with that of 6 divided by 2: encourage them to recall that $6 \div 2$ can be thought of as the number of twos in 6.
- Use the model to guide pupils to conclude that there are 2 halves in 1.

2

- The paper strips for this activity are provided on Photocopy master 9. Use this activity to reinforce the concept of division of 1 by a unit fraction.
- A unit fraction is a fraction with 1 as the numerator, e.g. $\frac{1}{2}$ or $\frac{1}{9}$.

Let's Learn!

Dividing by a proper fraction

Dividing a whole number by a proper fraction

Farha cut a rectangular paper strip into a number of pieces. Each piece was $\frac{1}{2}$ of the paper strip. How many pieces did Farha cut the paper strip into?

Number of pieces = $1 \div \frac{1}{2}$

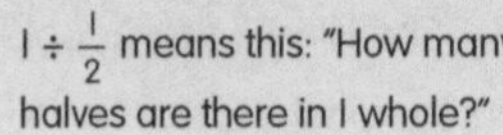

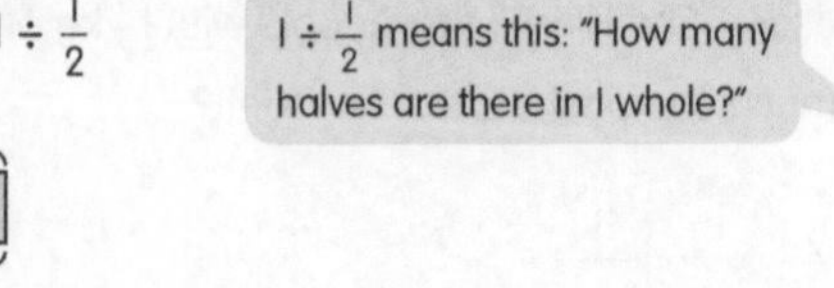

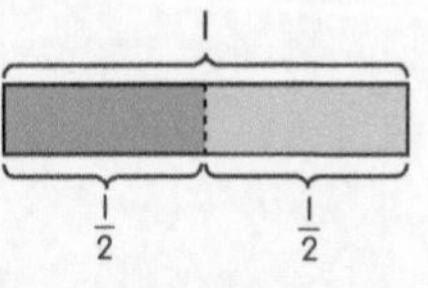

The model above shows that there are 2 halves in 1 whole.

So $1 \div \frac{1}{2} = 2$

Farha cut the rectangular paper strip into 2 pieces.

Activity

Work in pairs.
You will need 4 rectangular strips of paper. Each strip represents 1 whole.

a Use each strip to find:

i $1 \div \frac{1}{3}$ 3 **ii** $1 \div \frac{1}{4}$ 4

iii $1 \div \frac{1}{5}$ 5 **iv** $1 \div \frac{1}{6}$ 6

How many one-thirds, quarters, one-fifths and one-sixths are there in 1 whole?

What you will need

Scissors

Activity 

b How many one-tenths are there in 1 whole?

$1 \div \frac{1}{10} = 10$

c How many one-twelfths are there in 1 whole?

$1 \div \frac{1}{12} = 12$

3 Lee cut 2 oranges into a number of pieces. Each piece was $\frac{1}{4}$ of an orange. How many pieces did Lee cut the 2 oranges into?

Number of pieces = $2 \div \frac{1}{4}$

$2 \div \frac{1}{4}$ means this: "How many quarters are there in 2 wholes?"

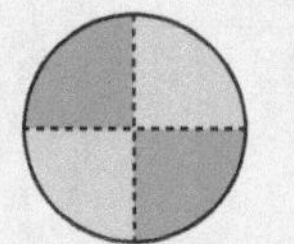

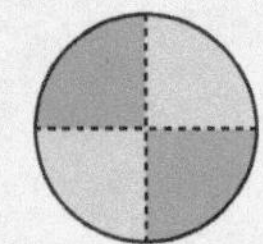

The model above shows that:

Number of quarters in 1 orange = 4

Number of quarters in 2 oranges = 2×4

So $2 \div \frac{1}{4} = 2 \times 4$
$= 8$

Dividing by $\frac{1}{4}$ is the same as multiplying by 4.

Lee cut the 2 oranges into 8 pieces.

Teaching sequence

3

- Using the unitary method, show that when dividing a whole number by a unit fraction the answer can be obtained by multiplying the whole number by the reciprocal of the unit fraction.

  Example:

  To find $2 \div \frac{1}{4}$, we can reason that:

  In 1 whole, there are 4 quarters. In 2 wholes, there are 2×4 quarters:

  $2 \div \frac{1}{4} = 2 \times 4 = 8$.

Teaching sequence

- Similarly, guide pupils to observe and then derive that $3 \div \frac{1}{6} = 3 \times 6 = 18$.

- Ask pupils to work on these questions as practice.

4 Sarah cut 3 square pieces of paper into a number of pieces. Each piece was $\frac{1}{6}$ of a square piece of paper. How many pieces did Sarah cut the 3 square pieces of paper into?

Number of pieces = $\boxed{3} \div \frac{\boxed{1}}{\boxed{6}}$

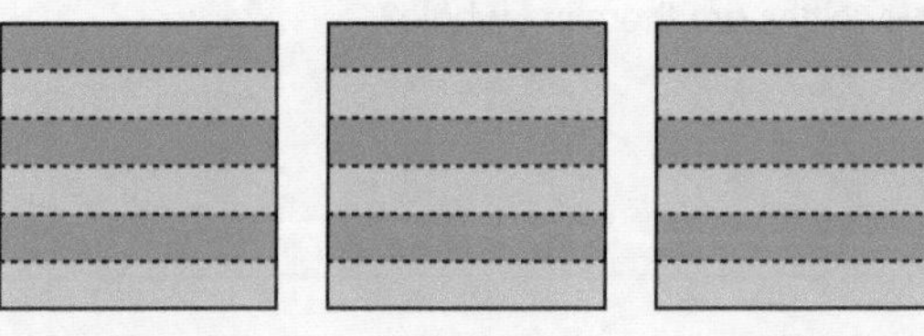

The model above shows that:
Number of one-sixths in 1 square piece of paper = $\boxed{6}$
Number of one-sixths in 3 square pieces of paper = $\boxed{3} \times \boxed{6}$

So $3 \div \frac{1}{6} = \boxed{3} \times \boxed{6}$
$= \boxed{18}$

Sarah cut the 3 square pieces of paper into $\boxed{18}$ pieces.

5 Find by multiplication.

a $3 \div \frac{1}{5} = \boxed{3} \times \boxed{5} = \boxed{15}$

b $7 \div \frac{1}{4} = \boxed{7} \times \boxed{4} = \boxed{28}$

c $4 \div \frac{1}{2} = \boxed{8}$

d $5 \div \frac{1}{3} = \boxed{15}$

e $6 \div \frac{1}{5} = \boxed{30}$

f $8 \div \frac{1}{8} = \boxed{64}$

What you will need

- Rectangular strips (see Photocopy master 9 on p 280)
- Scissors

Activity

6 Work in pairs.
You will need 5 identical rectangular strips of paper. Each strip represents 1 whole.

a Take 2 strips of paper. Divide each of them into one-thirds and place them as shown.
Then find $2 \div \frac{2}{3}$.

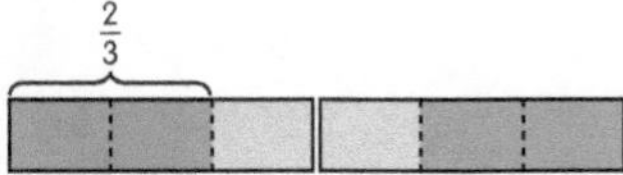

How many two-thirds are there in the 2 strips of paper?

There are 3 two-thirds in the 2 strips of paper.

So $2 \div \frac{2}{3} = 3$

b Divide each of the other 3 strips of paper into quarters and place them as shown.
Then find $3 \div \frac{3}{4}$.

How many three-quarters are there in the 3 strips of paper?

There are 4 three-quarters in the 3 strips of paper.

So $3 \div \frac{3}{4} = 4$

Teaching sequence

- The paper strips for this activity are provided on Photocopy master 9. Ask pupils to work in pairs and to use the concept of division by a unit fraction to work out $2 \div \frac{2}{3}$ and $3 \div \frac{3}{4}$.

Teaching sequence

- Use the unitary method to show that:

  In 2, there are 3 two-thirds.

  In 1, there are $\frac{3}{2}$ two-thirds.

  In 5, there are $5 \times \frac{3}{2}$ two-thirds:

  $5 \div \frac{2}{3} = 5 \times \frac{3}{2} = \frac{15}{2} = 7\frac{1}{2}$

- Ask pupils to work on this question as practice.

 What is $5 \div \frac{2}{3}$?

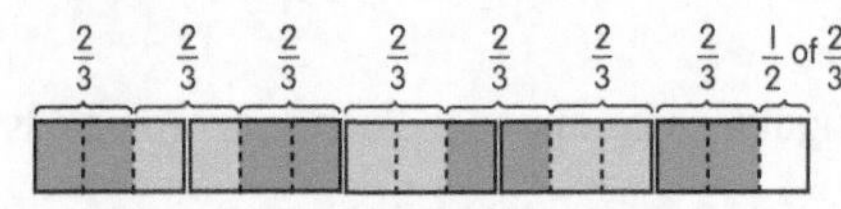

Number of two-thirds in 2 wholes = 3

Number of two-thirds in 1 whole = $\frac{3}{2}$

Number of two-thirds in 5 wholes = $5 \times \frac{3}{2}$

So $5 \div \frac{2}{3} = 5 \times \frac{3}{2}$

$= \frac{15}{2} = 7\frac{1}{2}$

8 What is $7 \div \frac{3}{4}$?

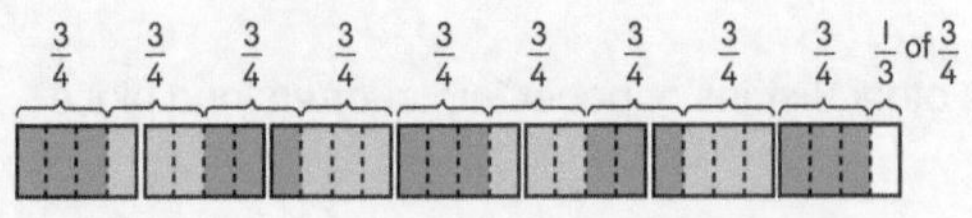

How many $\frac{3}{4}$ are there in 7 wholes?

Number of three-quarters in 3 wholes = 4

Number of three-quarters in 1 whole = $\frac{4}{3}$

Number of three-quarters in 7 wholes = $7 \times \frac{4}{3}$

So $7 \div \frac{3}{4} = 7 \times \frac{4}{3}$

$= \frac{28}{3}$

$= 9\frac{1}{3}$

Dividing by $\frac{3}{4}$ is the same as multiplying by $\frac{4}{3}$.

Activity

 A length of string is 3 m long.

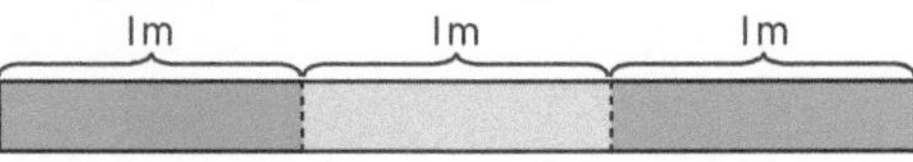

Copy the model and divide each metre of string into one-thirds.

How many $\frac{2}{3}$m long pieces can the string be cut into? 4

What is the length of the remaining string? $\frac{1}{3}$ m

Now find the answer by division. Express your answer as a mixed number.

Number of pieces $= 3 \div \frac{2}{3}$

$= 3 \times \frac{3}{2}$

$= \frac{9}{2}$

$= 4\frac{1}{2}$

The answer $4\frac{1}{2}$ means there are 4 pieces of string, each of length $\frac{2}{3}$m, and a remaining piece of string that is half of $\frac{2}{3}$m.

How many $\frac{2}{3}$m long pieces can the string be cut into? 4

What fraction of one piece of $\frac{2}{3}$m is the remaining string? $\frac{1}{2}$

What will be the length of the remaining string? $\frac{1}{2} \times \frac{2}{3} = \frac{1}{3}$ m

I can also find the remainder like this:

Total length of the 4 pieces of string $= 4 \times \frac{2}{3}$

$= 2\frac{2}{3}$m

Length of the remaining string $= 3 - 2\frac{2}{3}$

$= \frac{1}{3}$m

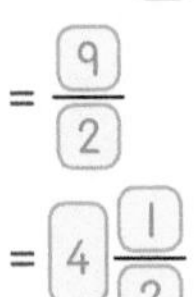

Teaching sequence

- This method enables pupils to interpret what the fractional part of the quotient means when a whole number is divided by a proper fraction.

What you will need

- Rectangular strips (see Photocopy master 9 on p 280)
- Scissors

Teaching sequence

10

- Ask pupils to work on these questions as an informal assessment.

11

- The paper strips for this activity are provided on Photocopy master 9. Guide pupils to recognise that a proper fraction can be divided by a proper fraction in the same way, by multiplying the dividend by the reciprocal of the divisor.

10 Find the value of each of the following.

a $4 \div \frac{4}{7}$ 7 b $6 \div \frac{2}{7}$ 21 c $9 \div \frac{3}{8}$ 24

d $5 \div \frac{10}{13}$ $6\frac{1}{2}$ e $10 \div \frac{5}{14}$ 28 f $12 \div \frac{9}{10}$ $13\frac{1}{3}$

Dividing a proper fraction by a proper fraction

Activity

11 Work in pairs.
You will need 2 identical rectangular strips of paper.
Each strip represents 1 whole.

a Take one strip of paper and divide it into halves.
Then find $\frac{1}{2} \div \frac{1}{4}$.

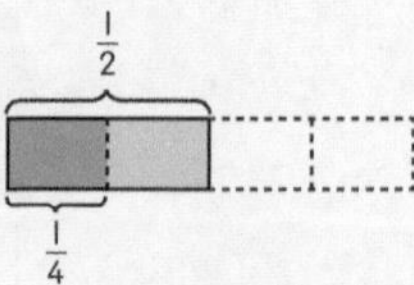

How many quarters are there in half?

So $\frac{1}{2} \div \frac{1}{4} = \boxed{2}$

How can you also find $\frac{1}{2} \div \frac{1}{4}$ by multiplication?

$\frac{1}{2} \div \frac{1}{4} = \frac{\boxed{1}}{\boxed{2}} \times \boxed{4}$

$= \boxed{2}$

What have you learnt about dividing by $\frac{1}{4}$?

Activity

b Divide the other strip of paper into one-thirds.

Then find $\frac{2}{3} \div \frac{1}{6}$.

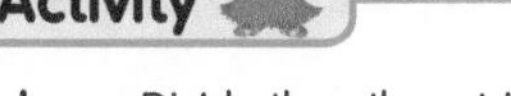

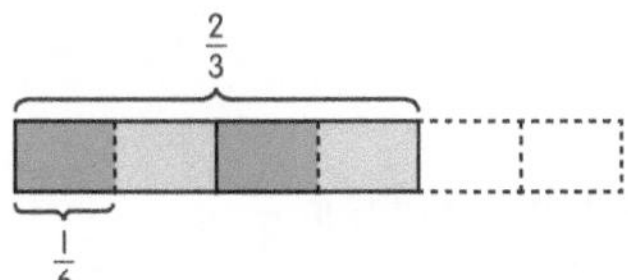

How many one-sixths are there in two-thirds?

So $\frac{2}{3} \div \frac{1}{6} = \boxed{4}$

How can you also find $\frac{2}{3} \div \frac{1}{6}$ by multiplication?

What have you learnt about dividing by $\frac{1}{6}$?

$\frac{2}{3} \div \frac{1}{6} = \frac{\boxed{2}}{\boxed{3}} \times \boxed{6}$

$= \boxed{4}$

Teaching sequence

12 and 13

- Reinforce the multiplication method of dividing a proper fraction by another proper fraction.
- Ask pupils to work on 13 as practice.

12 Ruby was given $\frac{3}{4}$ of a pizza. She cut it into a number of pieces. Each piece was $\frac{3}{8}$ of the pizza. How many pieces did Ruby cut it into?

Number of pieces = $\frac{3}{4} \div \frac{3}{8}$

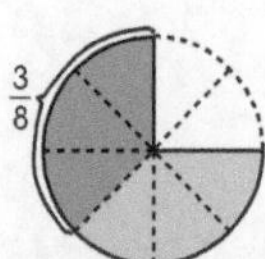

The model above shows that there are 2 three-eighths in $\frac{3}{4}$.

So $\frac{3}{4} \div \frac{3}{8} = 2$

We can now divide like this:

$\frac{3}{4} \div \frac{3}{8} = \frac{3}{4} \times \frac{8}{3}$

$= 2$

Ruby cut the pizza into 2 pieces.

Dividing by $\frac{3}{8}$ is the same as multiplying by $\frac{8}{3}$.

13 Hardeep had $\frac{5}{7}\ell$ of water. He poured the water into some cups. The capacity of each cup was $\frac{2}{7}\ell$. How many cups of water did Hardeep have?

Number of cups = $\frac{5}{7} \div \frac{2}{7}$

$= \frac{5}{7} \times \frac{7}{2}$

$= \frac{5}{2}$

$= 2\frac{1}{2}$

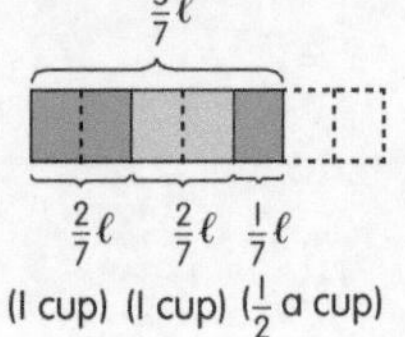

Hardeep had $2\frac{1}{2}$ cups of water.

Activity 

14 A jug contains $\frac{4}{5}\ell$ of orange juice.

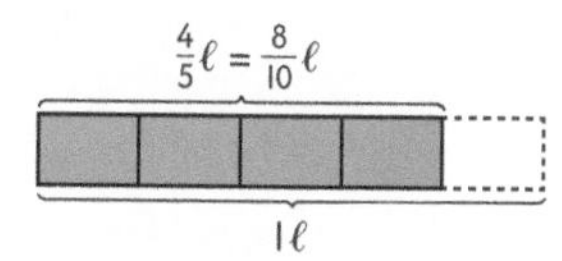

Copy the model above and divide it into one-tenths.

How many glasses, each containing $\frac{3}{10}\ell$, can the orange juice be poured into? 2

How many litres of orange juice will be left? $\frac{2}{10}\ell$

Now find the answer by division. Express your answer as a mixed number.

$$\text{Number of glasses} = \frac{4}{5} \div \frac{3}{10}$$
$$= \frac{4}{5} \times \frac{10}{3}$$
$$= \frac{8}{3}$$
$$= 2\frac{2}{3}$$

The answer $2\frac{2}{3}$ means there are 2 glasses of orange juice, each containing $\frac{3}{10}\ell$, and a remaining glass of orange juice that contains $\frac{2}{3}$ of $\frac{3}{10}\ell$.

How many glasses, each containing $\frac{3}{10}\ell$, can the orange juice be poured into? 2

What fraction of one glass of $\frac{3}{10}\ell$ is the orange juice left? $\frac{2}{3}$

How many litres of orange juice will be left? $\frac{2}{3} \times \frac{3}{10} = \frac{1}{5}\ell$

I can also find the remainder like this:

Total amount of orange juice in 2 glasses $= 2 \times \frac{3}{10}$
$= \frac{3}{5}\ell$

Amount of orange juice left $= \frac{4}{5} - \frac{3}{5}$
$= \frac{1}{5}\ell$

Teaching sequence

14

- This activity asks pupils to work through different methods for finding the amount of orange juice remaining when $\frac{4}{5}\ell$ are poured into cups each containing $\frac{3}{10}\ell$.
- The method involving division helps pupils to interpret what the fractional part of the quotient means when a proper fraction is divided by another proper fraction.

Teaching sequence

- Ask pupils to work on these questions as an informal assessment.

- Work through the first one-step word problem on the division of a whole number by a proper fraction with pupils.

- Ask pupils to work on this question as practice.

15 Find the value of:

a $\frac{2}{3} \div \frac{1}{9}$ 6 **b** $\frac{3}{5} \div \frac{1}{10}$ 6 **c** $\frac{3}{4} \div \frac{1}{2}$ $1\frac{1}{2}$

d $\frac{1}{6} \div \frac{2}{3}$ $\frac{1}{4}$ **e** $\frac{5}{8} \div \frac{15}{16}$ $\frac{2}{3}$ **f** $\frac{7}{16} \div \frac{5}{12}$ $1\frac{1}{20}$

16 A bottle contains 2 ℓ of sunflower oil. A cook uses $\frac{1}{12}$ ℓ of sunflower oil per day. How many days will the bottle of sunflower oil last?

2 ℓ

$\frac{1}{12}$ℓ $\frac{1}{12}$ℓ … $\frac{1}{12}$ℓ $\frac{1}{12}$ℓ

? days

Number of days $= 2 \div \frac{1}{12} = 2 \times 12$

$= 24$

The bottle of sunflower oil will last 24 days.

17 A chef buys 12 kg of spaghetti each day. He uses $\frac{2}{11}$ kg of spaghetti for each pot of spaghetti he cooks. When he has used up all the spaghetti, how many pots of spaghetti would he have cooked?

12 kg

$\frac{2}{11}$kg $\frac{2}{11}$kg … $\frac{2}{11}$kg $\frac{2}{11}$kg

? pots

Number of pots $= 12 \div \frac{2}{11}$

$= 12 \times \frac{11}{2}$

$= 66$

He would have cooked 66 pots of spaghetti.

18 A plank is $\frac{4}{5}$m in length. A worker cuts it into some pieces and each piece is $\frac{1}{10}$m long. How many pieces did he cut the plank into?

$\frac{4}{5}$m

$\frac{1}{10}$m | $\frac{1}{10}$m ... $\frac{1}{10}$m | $\frac{1}{10}$m

Number of pieces $= \frac{4}{5} \div \frac{1}{10}$

$= \frac{4}{5} \times 10$

$= 8$

He cut the plank into 8 pieces.

19 Lizzy had $\frac{2}{3}$ of a pizza. She cut it into a number of pieces. Each piece was $\frac{1}{9}$ of the whole pizza. How many pieces did she cut it into?

$\frac{2}{3}$ of a pizza

$\frac{1}{9}$ | $\frac{1}{9}$ ... $\frac{1}{9}$ | $\frac{1}{9}$

Number of pieces $= \frac{2}{3} \div \frac{1}{9}$

$= \frac{2}{3} \times 9$

$= 6$

She cut it into 6 pieces.

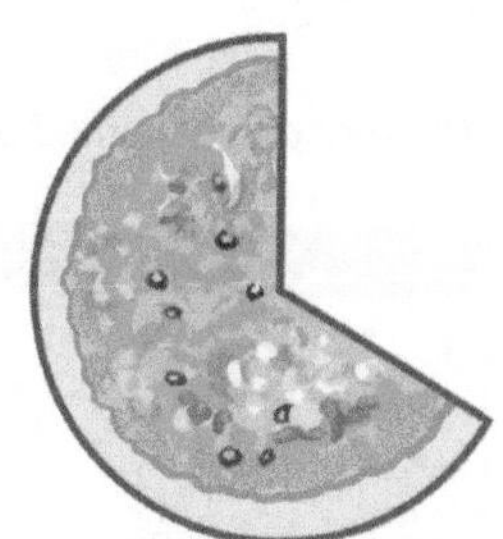

Teaching sequence

18

- Work through the first one-step word problem on the division of a proper fraction by another proper fraction with pupils.

19

- Ask pupils to work on this question as practice.

Objective of activity

Let's Explore!

Pupils will be able to observe that the numerators and denominators of the division calculations are swapped.

Thinking skills

- Translating
- Identifying relationships

Additional activities

- Starting at 0, how many steps of $\frac{2}{7}$ are needed to reach 4?

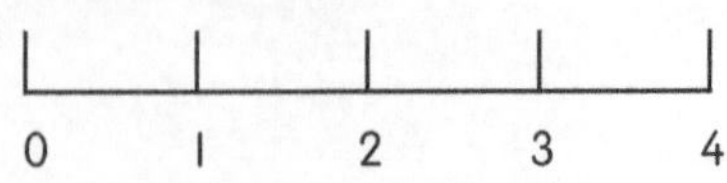

- Starting at 0, how many steps of $\frac{1}{12}$ are needed to reach $\frac{3}{4}$?

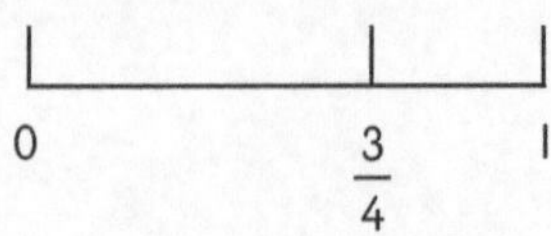

Teaching sequence

20 *Let's Explore!*

- Pupils should be able to predict the answer to a division calculation when the dividend and divisor are swapped.

21 *Maths Journal*

- This question allows pupils to express their understanding of division by a proper fraction in their own words.

22

- Pupils should be able to explain the errors that have been made, based on their understanding of how to divide by a proper fraction.

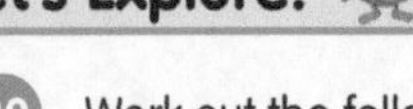

Let's Explore!

20 Work out the following:

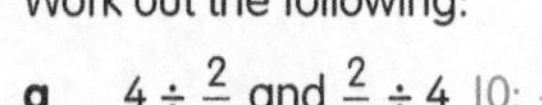

a $4 \div \frac{2}{5}$ and $\frac{2}{5} \div 4$ 10; $\frac{1}{10}$

b $\frac{1}{4} \div \frac{2}{3}$ and $\frac{2}{3} \div \frac{1}{4}$ $\frac{3}{8}$; $\frac{8}{3}$

c $\frac{4}{5} \div \frac{3}{10}$ and $\frac{3}{10} \div \frac{4}{5}$ $\frac{8}{3}$; $\frac{3}{8}$

d $\frac{5}{8} \div \frac{3}{4}$ and $\frac{3}{4} \div \frac{5}{8}$ $\frac{5}{6}$; $\frac{6}{5}$

What do you notice about the answers to each pair of divisions?
The answers for each pair of divisions have their numerators and denominators interchanged.

Given that $\frac{6}{7} \div 9 = \frac{2}{21}$ and $\frac{10}{11} \div \frac{5}{6} = \frac{12}{11}$, find without further workings:

i $9 \div \frac{6}{7}$ $\frac{21}{2}$

ii $\frac{5}{6} \div \frac{10}{11}$ $\frac{11}{12}$

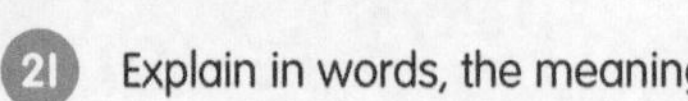

Maths Journal

21 Explain in words, the meaning of:

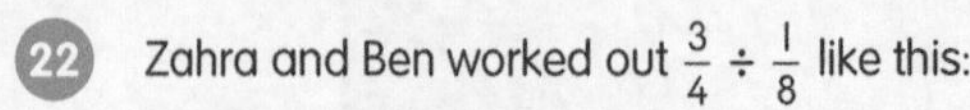

a $5 \div \frac{2}{5}$ How many $\frac{2}{5}$ are there in 5?

b $\frac{4}{7} \div \frac{1}{2}$ How many halves are there in $\frac{4}{7}$?

22 Zahra and Ben worked out $\frac{3}{4} \div \frac{1}{8}$ like this:

Zahra	Ben
$\frac{3}{4} \div \frac{1}{8} = \frac{4}{3} \times \frac{1}{8}$ $= \frac{4}{24}$ $= \frac{1}{6}$	$\frac{3}{4} \div \frac{1}{8} = \frac{4}{3} \times 8$ $= \frac{32}{3}$ $= 10\frac{2}{3}$

Explain what they did incorrectly. What should the answer be?
Zahra inverted the dividend instead of the divisor. Ben inverted both the dividend and the divisor instead of just the divisor.

Independent work

Let's Practise!

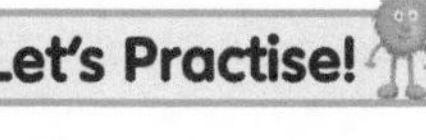

23 Use the models to find the answers.

a $1 \div \frac{1}{4}$ 4

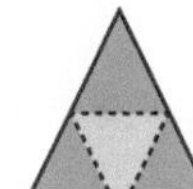

b $3 \div \frac{3}{5}$ 5

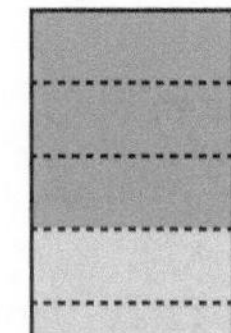

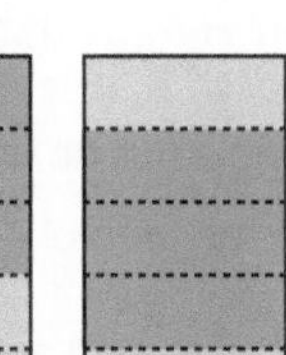

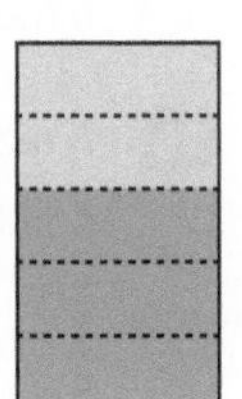

c $\frac{3}{4} \div \frac{1}{8}$ 6

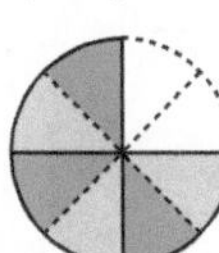

d $\frac{2}{3} \div \frac{2}{9}$ 3

24 Find by multiplication.

a $4 \div \frac{1}{7}$ 28

b $12 \div \frac{1}{3}$ 36

c $9 \div \frac{3}{4}$ 12

d $10 \div \frac{4}{5}$ $12\frac{1}{2}$

e $\frac{1}{2} \div \frac{1}{8}$ 4

f $\frac{1}{4} \div \frac{1}{2}$ $\frac{1}{2}$

g $\frac{3}{5} \div \frac{11}{15}$ $\frac{9}{11}$

h $\frac{2}{3} \div \frac{10}{13}$ $\frac{13}{15}$

Independent work

Practice 2 in Practice Book 6A, pp 77 to 84.

Let's Practise!

Solve these word problems. Show your workings clearly.

25 4 melons were shared among a group of children. Each child got $\frac{2}{9}$ of a melon. How many children were there in the group? 18 children

26 A rectangle has an area of 9 m^2. It is cut up into a number of parts. Each part has an area of $\frac{3}{8}$ m^2. How many parts has the rectangle been cut into? 24 parts

27 $\frac{5}{6}$ of a pie was left. Kate cut it into a number of pieces. Each piece was $\frac{1}{18}$ of the whole pie. How many pieces did Kate cut it into? 15 pieces

28 The tins of food in a pack have a total mass of $\frac{15}{16}$ kg. Each tin of food has a mass of $\frac{5}{32}$ kg. How many tins of food are there in the pack? 6 tins of food

29 A plank 4 m long is cut into a number of pieces. Each piece is $\frac{3}{5}$ m long.

- **a** How many pieces of length $\frac{3}{5}$ m has the plank been cut into? 6 pieces
- **b** What is the length of the remaining plank? $\frac{2}{5}$ m

30 A baker has $\frac{5}{6}$ kg of flour. She uses it to bake loaves of bread. Each loaf contains $\frac{2}{9}$ kg of flour.

- **a** How many loaves has she baked? 3 loaves
- **b** What is the mass of the remaining flour? $\frac{1}{6}$ kg

31 A roll of ribbon was 8 m long. Joe cut 6 pieces of ribbon, each of length $\frac{2}{3}$ m, to tie some presents. He then cut the remaining ribbon into some pieces, each of length $\frac{3}{4}$ m.

- **a** How many pieces of ribbon, each $\frac{3}{4}$ m in length, did Joe have? 5 pieces
- **b** What was the length of ribbon left over? $\frac{1}{4}$ m

Practice Book 6A, p.77

Learning objective: Word problems

Pupils will be able to solve word problems involving division of a whole number or proper fraction by a proper fraction.

Key concept

The process of problem solving in mathematics involves the application of concepts and strategies.

Thinking skill

Translating

What you will need

Scientific calculator

Let's Learn! 

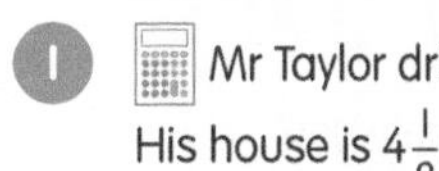

1 Mr Taylor drives from his house to his office and passes a library on the way. His house is $4\frac{1}{2}$ km away from the library. The distance between the library and his office is $2\frac{3}{8}$ km shorter than the distance between the library and his house. What is the distance between his house and his office?

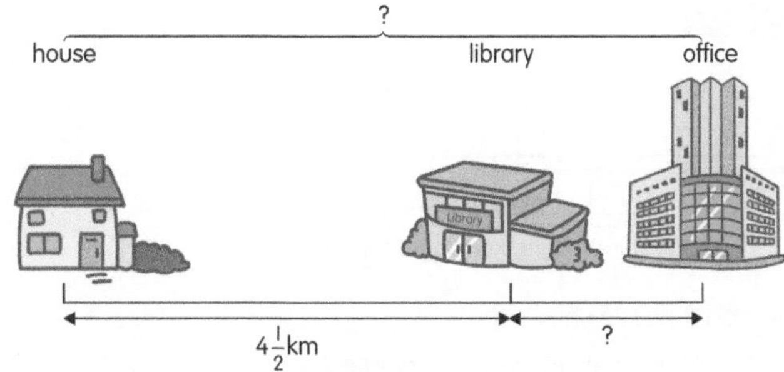

$4\frac{1}{2} - 2\frac{3}{8} = 2\frac{1}{8}$

The distance between the library and his office is $2\frac{1}{8}$ km.

$4\frac{1}{2} + 2\frac{1}{8} = 6\frac{5}{8}$

The distance between his house and his office is $6\frac{5}{8}$ km.

Teaching sequence

1

- Review the procedure for solving word problems with pupils:

  Step 1: *Read and understand*
  Ask pupils to read the problem. Guide them to identify the given and implied information through questioning:
  "What is the distance between Mr Taylor's house and the library?"
  "Since the distance between the library and his office is $2\frac{3}{8}$ km shorter, how can you find this distance?"
  "What are you required to find?"

  Step 2: *Think of a strategy*
  Ask pupils:
  "What number sentences should you write?"

  Step 3: *Solve the problem*
  Agree that, in this case, since pupils are able to write the relevant number sentences, they are able to solve the problem.

  Step 4: *Check the answer*
  Ask pupils to check the answer by working backwards.

What you will need

Scientific calculator

Teaching sequence

- Ask pupils to work on these questions as practice.

2 A school raises some money at a concert. The children chose to spend $\frac{1}{3}$ of the money on a trip, give $\frac{3}{8}$ of the reminder to the school fund and share the rest equally between 3 charities.

a What fraction of the money does each charity receive?

b If the concert raises £5400, how much does each charity get?

a **Method 1**

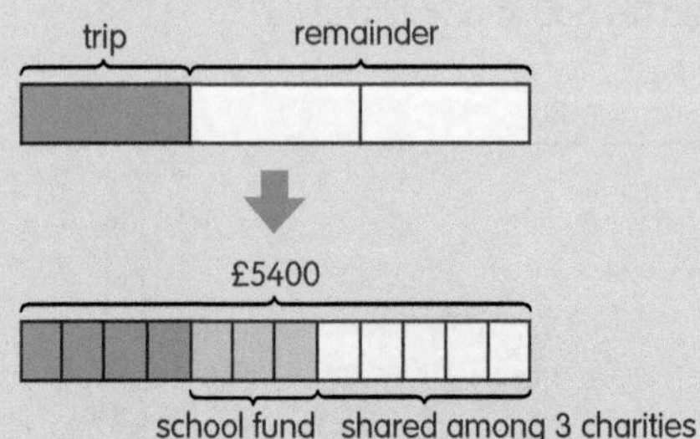

The model above shows that:

Number of units given away to charities = 5

Total number of units = 12

Fraction of money shared with charities = $\frac{5}{12}$

$\frac{5}{12} \div 3 = \frac{5}{12} \times \frac{1}{3}$

$= \frac{5}{36}$

Each charity receives $\frac{5}{36}$ of the money.

Method 2

$1 - \frac{1}{3} = \frac{2}{3}$ (remainder)

$\frac{3}{8} \times \frac{2}{3} = \frac{1}{4}$ (school fund)

$\frac{2}{3} - \frac{1}{4} = \frac{5}{12}$ (shared among 3 charities)

$\frac{5}{12} \div 3 = \frac{5}{12} \times \frac{1}{3}$

$= \frac{5}{36}$

Each charity receives $\frac{5}{36}$ of the money.

b $\frac{5}{36} \times £5400 = £750$

Each charity gets £750.

3 Miss Green used $\frac{2}{3}$ of her garden to plant tomatoes and another $\frac{1}{9}$ of it to plant lettuce. She then divided the rest of her garden into several small flower beds. Each small flower bed was $\frac{1}{18}$ of her garden.

a How many small flower beds were there?

b If the area of her garden was $72\,m^2$, what was the area of each small flower bed?

a Fraction of land divided $= 1 - \frac{2}{3} - \frac{1}{9} = \frac{2}{9}$

$\frac{2}{9} \div \frac{1}{18} = \frac{2}{9} \times 18$

$= 4$

There were 4 small flower beds.

b $\frac{1}{18} \times 72 = 4$

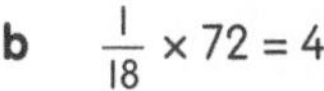

Each small flower bed was $4\,m^2$.

Teaching sequence

3

- Work through this word problem with pupils, using the steps outlined in .

Teaching sequence

4 and 5

- Ask pupils to work on these questions as practice.

Unit 4 Fractions

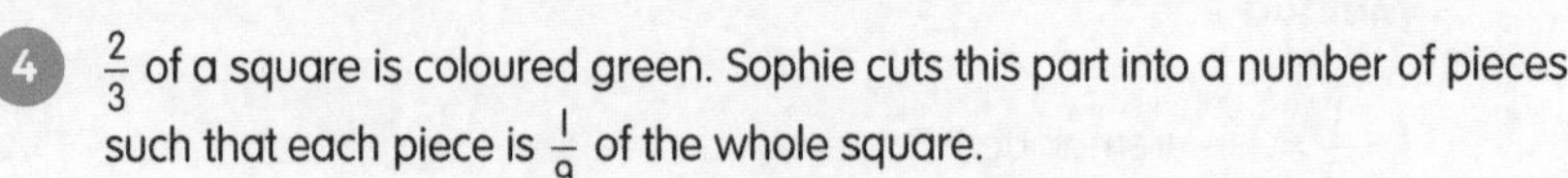

4 $\frac{2}{3}$ of a square is coloured green. Sophie cuts this part into a number of pieces such that each piece is $\frac{1}{9}$ of the whole square.

a Find the number of pieces Sophie has.

b If the area of the square is 45 cm², what is the area of each piece?

a Number of pieces $= \frac{2}{3} \div \frac{1}{9}$

$= \frac{2}{3} \times 9$

$= 6$

Sophie has 6 pieces.

b Area of green part $= \frac{2}{3} \times 45 = 30\,\text{cm}^2$

$30 \div 6 = 5$

The area of each piece is 5 cm².

5 $\frac{3}{5}$ of the pupils in a class were boys. The teacher divided the boys equally into groups such that each group of boys had $\frac{1}{10}$ of the number of pupils in the class. The teacher then divided the girls equally into groups such that each group of girls had $\frac{1}{5}$ of the number of pupils in the class.

a Find the number of groups of boys and the number of groups of girls.

b If there were 16 girls in the class, how many boys were there in each group?

74

Independent work

Let's Practise!

What you will need

Scientific calculator

a Number of groups of boys = $\frac{3}{5} \div \frac{1}{10}$

$= \frac{3}{5} \times 10$

$= 6$

Number of groups of girls = $\frac{2}{5} \div \frac{1}{5}$

$= \frac{2}{5} \times 5$

$= 2$

There were 6 groups of boys and 2 groups of girls.

b $\frac{2}{5}$ of the class ⟶ 16 pupils

$\frac{1}{5}$ of the class ⟶ 8 pupils

$\frac{3}{5}$ of the class ⟶ 24 pupils

$24 \div 6 = 4$

There were 4 boys in each group.

Let's Practise!

Solve these word problems. Draw models to help you where necessary.

6 A length of pipe was $2\frac{1}{3}$ m long. Another length of pipe was $\frac{5}{6}$ m shorter. A plumber joined the two pipes together. What was the total length of the pipe in the end? $3\frac{5}{6}$ m

7 A farmer picked some apples. She sold $\frac{2}{3}$ of them and gave $\frac{1}{5}$ of the remainder to her friend. She had 40 apples left. How many apples did she pick? 150 apples

Independent work

Practice 3 and *Maths Journal* in Practice Book 6A, pp 85 to 92.

Let's Practise!

8. Liam read the first $\frac{1}{6}$ of a book on Monday and another $\frac{1}{3}$ of it on Tuesday. He took another 4 days to finish reading the book. He read the same number of pages on each of these 4 days.

   a What fraction of the book did he read on each of these 4 days? $\frac{1}{8}$

   b If he read 30 pages on each of these 4 days, find the number of pages in the book. 240 pages

9. In June, Ella visited her aunt for a total of 8 hours. She spent $\frac{4}{5}$ hours at her aunt's house for each visit.

   a Find the number of visits she made in June. 10 visits

   b In July, she spent twice the amount of time she spent in June. How many visits did she make in July? 20 visits

10. A drama club spent $\frac{3}{10}$ of its budget on stage lights, $\frac{1}{5}$ of it on costumes and the rest on hiring a theatre. The theatre cost $\frac{1}{8}$ of the budget for each night of the show.

    a Find how many nights the show was performed. 4 nights

    b If the budget was £2400, how much money did the theatre cost each night? £300

11. Josh used $\frac{3}{8}$ of his money to buy some tennis balls and $\frac{2}{5}$ of the remainder to buy 2 tennis rackets. A tennis racket costs 3 times as much as a tennis ball. How many tennis balls did he buy? 9 tennis balls

Practice Book 6A, p.85

Let's Wrap It Up!

You have learnt to:

- divide a whole number by a proper fraction
- divide a proper fraction by another proper fraction.

Let's Revise!

12 $12 \div \frac{3}{8} = 12 \times \frac{8}{3}$
$= 32$

13 $\frac{5}{6} \div \frac{10}{11} = \frac{5}{6} \times \frac{11}{10}$
$= \frac{11}{12}$

14 A square piece of cardboard has an area of $\frac{4}{9}$ m^2. Nick cut it into a number of pieces, each with an area of $\frac{2}{27}$ m^2. How many pieces did Nick cut the cardboard into?

Number of pieces $= \frac{4}{9} \div \frac{2}{27}$
$= \frac{4}{9} \times \frac{27}{2}$
$= 6$

Nick cut the cardboard into 6 pieces.

Teaching sequence

Let's Wrap It Up!

- Emphasise the key concepts, skills and processes that have been taught in the unit.

12 to 14

- Discuss the worked examples with pupils to assess whether they have mastered these concepts, skills and processes.

Objective of activity

Pupils will be able to draw a table and use guess and check to solve the problem.

Thinking skill

Translating

Heuristics for problem solving

- Guess and check
- Drawing a table

Independent work

- *Challenging Practice* and *Problem Solving* in Practice Book 6A, pp 93 to 94.

Teaching sequence

15 *Put On Your Thinking Caps!*

- Ask pupils to work in pairs to solve the problem by translating the statements into symbolic representations.

Put On Your Thinking Caps!

15 Mr Carson cooked a stew. He divided the stew equally into portions of $\frac{1}{5}$ kg each. If he divided it equally into portions of $\frac{1}{8}$ kg each, he will get 12 more portions of stew. How many kilograms of stew did he cook? (Assume that the mass of stew is a whole number.)

Practice Book 6A, p.93 Practice Book 6A, p.94

Mass of Stew (kg)	Number of $\frac{1}{5}$ kg Portions	Number of $\frac{1}{8}$ kg Portions	Difference in Number of Portions
1	$1 \div \frac{1}{5} = 5$	$1 \div \frac{1}{8} = 8$	3
2	$2 \div \frac{1}{5} = 10$	$2 \div \frac{1}{8} = 16$	6
3	$3 \div \frac{1}{5} = 15$	$3 \div \frac{1}{8} = 24$	9
4	$4 \div \frac{1}{5} = 20$	$4 \div \frac{1}{8} = 32$	12

Mr Carson cooked 4 kg of stew.

Heuristic: Use guess and check, make a table
Thinking skill: Deduction

Unit 4

Fractions

Date: ______________

Practice 1 Four operations with fractions

1 There were some people at a concert. $\frac{1}{7}$ of them were men and $\frac{3}{5}$ of them were women. The rest were children. What fraction of the people were children?

$\frac{1}{7} + \frac{3}{5} = \frac{26}{35}$

$1 - \frac{26}{35} = \frac{9}{35}$

$\frac{9}{35}$ of the people were children.

2  James drove from London to York. He took 4 h for the whole journey. He drove for $2\frac{1}{2}$ h and rested for $\frac{1}{4}$ h before completing the rest of the journey. How long did he take for the rest of the journey?

$2\frac{1}{2} + \frac{1}{4} = 2\frac{3}{4}$

$4 - 2\frac{3}{4} = 1\frac{1}{4}$

He took $1\frac{1}{4}$ h for the rest of the journey.

3 Mr Bell bought 2 kg of chicken. He put $\frac{3}{4}$ kg in his fridge and packed 2 bags, each containing $\frac{1}{4}$ kg of chicken to put in the freezer.
He used the rest to make dinner.
How many kilograms of chicken did he use for dinner?

$\frac{1}{4} \times 2 = \frac{1}{2}$

$\frac{3}{4} + \frac{1}{2} = 1\frac{1}{4}$

$2 - 1\frac{1}{4} = \frac{3}{4}$

He used $\frac{3}{4}$ kg of chicken for dinner.

4 A total of 9 ℓ of orange squash was poured equally into 6 jugs.
Ella poured $\frac{2}{5}$ ℓ of orange squash from a jug into a glass and drank it.
She found the juice too sweet, so she added $\frac{4}{5}$ ℓ of water into the jug she had.
Find the total amount of orange squash in the jug after she added $\frac{4}{5}$ ℓ of water.

$9 \div 6 = 1\frac{1}{2}$

$1\frac{1}{2} - \frac{2}{5} = 1\frac{1}{10}$

$1\frac{1}{10} + \frac{4}{5} = 1\frac{9}{10}$

The amount of orange squash in the jug was $1\frac{9}{10}$ ℓ.

Date: ____________

Practice 2 Dividing by a proper fraction

1 Use the models to find the answers.

a $1 \div \frac{1}{9} = 9$

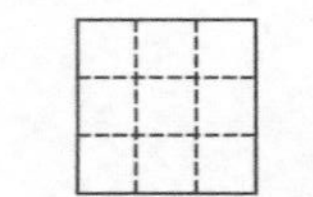

b $3 \div \frac{1}{4} = 12$

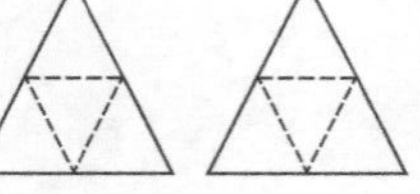

c $2 \div \frac{1}{6} = 12$

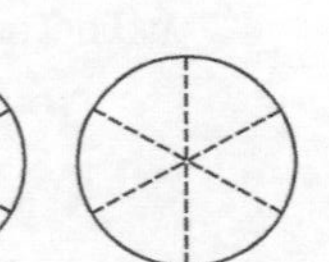

d $2 \div \frac{3}{8} = 5\frac{1}{3}$

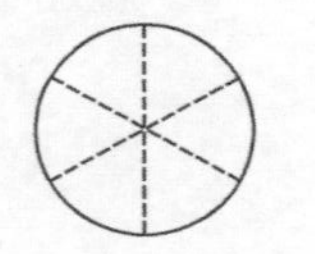

e $4 \div \frac{5}{6} = 4\frac{4}{5}$

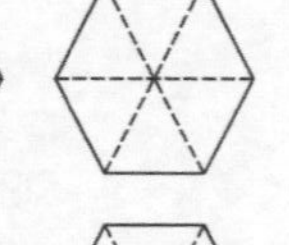

f $4 \div \frac{2}{5} = 10$

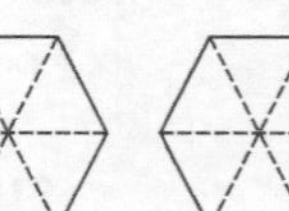

2 Divide. Express your answer in its simplest form where necessary.

a $4 \div \frac{1}{5} = 4 \times 5$
$= 20$

b $6 \div \frac{1}{3} = 6 \times 3$
$= 18$

c $12 \div \frac{1}{4} = 12 \times 4$
$= 48$

d $18 \div \frac{1}{8} = 18 \times 8$
$= 144$

e $1 \div \frac{3}{4} = 1 \times \frac{4}{3}$
$= 1\frac{1}{3}$

f $6 \div \frac{3}{8} = 6 \times \frac{8}{3}$
$= 16$

g $10 \div \frac{4}{5} = 10 \times \frac{5}{4}$
$= 12\frac{1}{2}$

h $12 \div \frac{2}{3} = 12 \times \frac{3}{2}$
$= 18$

i $16 \div \frac{3}{8} = 16 \times \frac{8}{3}$
$= 42\frac{2}{3}$

j $15 \div \frac{5}{7} = 15 \times \frac{7}{5}$
$= 21$

3 Use the models to find the answer.

a $\frac{3}{4} \div \frac{1}{4} = 3$

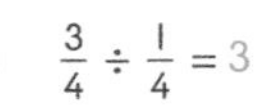
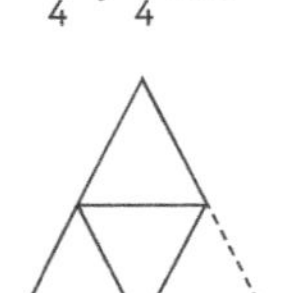

b $\frac{4}{5} \div \frac{2}{5} = 2$

c $\frac{5}{6} \div \frac{1}{12} = 10$

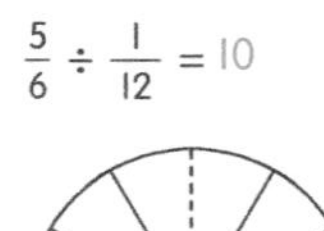
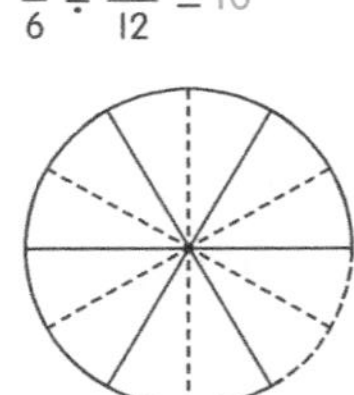

d $\frac{1}{2} \div \frac{1}{3} = 1\frac{1}{2}$

e $\frac{3}{4} \div \frac{1}{2} = 1\frac{1}{2}$

f $\frac{7}{10} \div \frac{1}{5} = 3\frac{1}{2}$

4 Divide. Express your answer in its simplest form where necessary.

a $\frac{1}{4} \div \frac{1}{3} = \frac{1}{4} \times 3$

$= \frac{3}{4}$

b $\frac{1}{2} \div \frac{1}{5} = \frac{1}{2} \times 5$

$= 2\frac{1}{2}$

c $\frac{1}{8} \div \frac{1}{4} = \frac{1}{8} \times 4$

$= \frac{1}{2}$

d $\frac{1}{9} \div \frac{1}{6} = \frac{1}{9} \times 6$

$= \frac{2}{3}$

e $\frac{5}{7} \div \frac{1}{7} = \frac{5}{7} \times 7$

$= 5$

f $\frac{3}{4} \div \frac{5}{8} = \frac{3}{4} \times \frac{8}{5}$

$= 1\frac{1}{5}$

g $\frac{2}{3} \div \frac{3}{4} = \frac{2}{3} \times \frac{4}{3}$

$= \frac{8}{9}$

h $\frac{8}{9} \div \frac{1}{12} = \frac{8}{9} \times 12$

$= 10\frac{2}{3}$

i $\frac{4}{15} \div \frac{3}{4} = \frac{4}{15} \times \frac{4}{3}$

$= \frac{16}{45}$

j $\frac{6}{7} \div \frac{9}{14} = \frac{6}{7} \times \frac{14}{9}$

$= 1\frac{1}{3}$

Solve these word problems. Show your workings clearly.

5 16 pizzas were shared among some guests at a party. Each guest received $\frac{2}{5}$ of a pizza. How many guests were there at the party?

$16 \div \frac{2}{5} = 16 \times \frac{5}{2}$

$= 40$

There were 40 guests at the party.

6 $\frac{3}{4}$ of a cake was shared by a group of children. Mrs Rahman gave each child $\frac{1}{8}$ of the cake. How many children were there in the group?

$\frac{3}{4} \div \frac{1}{8} = \frac{3}{4} \times 8$

$= 6$

There were 6 children in the group.

7 There is $\frac{2}{5}\ell$ of water in a jug. The water is poured into some glasses. Each glass contains $\frac{2}{15}\ell$ of water. How many glasses are there?

$\frac{2}{5} \div \frac{2}{15} = \frac{2}{5} \times \frac{15}{2}$

$= 3$

There are 3 glasses.

8 Mr Bateman bought $\frac{9}{11}$ kg of cherries. He repacked the cherries into some bags, each containing $\frac{3}{11}$ kg of cherries. How many bags of cherries were there?

$\frac{9}{11} \div \frac{3}{11} = \frac{9}{11} \times \frac{11}{3}$

$= 3$

There were 3 bags of cherries.

9 Millie bought 3 m of ribbon and cut the ribbon into smaller pieces. Each piece of ribbon was $\frac{3}{5}$ m long. How many pieces were there?

$3 \div \frac{3}{5} = 5$

There were 5 pieces.

10 Mrs Smith made 24 muffins. She gave each of her students $\frac{3}{4}$ of a muffin. How many students did she have?

$24 \div \frac{3}{4} = 32$

She had 32 students.

11 Mrs Wright bought a $\frac{3}{4}$ kg cake. She divided it among her children. Each child received $\frac{3}{16}$ kg of the cake. How many children did she have?

$\frac{3}{4} \div \frac{3}{16} = 4$

She had 4 children.

12 A container is $\frac{5}{6}$ full of apple juice. Omar pours the apple juice into some cups. Each cup contains $\frac{1}{18}$ of the apple juice. How many cups are there?

$\frac{5}{6} \div \frac{1}{18} = 15$

There are 15 cups.

Date: ____________

Practice 3 Word problems

Solve these word problems. Show your workings clearly.

1 Miss Thomas receives £180 every month. She spends $\frac{1}{5}$ of the money on transport. She spends $\frac{3}{4}$ of the remainder on food. She saves the remaining amount of money. How much does she save?

$1 - \frac{1}{5} = \frac{4}{5}$

$1 - \frac{3}{4} = \frac{1}{4}$

$\frac{1}{4} \times \frac{4}{5} = \frac{1}{5}$ (fraction of monthly money saved)

$\frac{1}{5} \times £180 = £36$

Miss Thomas saves £36 a month.

2 Miss Pierce wins £4200 on a game show. Mr Green wins $\frac{6}{7}$ as much as Miss Pierce. Miss Pierce saves $\frac{1}{5}$ of her winnings and Mr Green saves $\frac{1}{8}$ of his winnings. How much do they save altogether?

$\frac{6}{7} \times £4200 = £3600$ (amount Mr Green wins)

$\frac{1}{5} \times £4200 = £840$ (amount Miss Pierce saves)

$\frac{1}{8} \times £3600 = £450$ (amount Mr Green saves)

£840 + £450 = £1290

They save £1290 altogether.

3 Mrs Lake has 4 dogs. Each dog eats $1\frac{1}{2}$ bowls of dog food every day. How many bowls of dog food do the dogs eat altogether in a day?

$1\frac{1}{2} \times 4 = 6$

The dogs eat 6 bowls of dog food altogether in a day.

4 Miss Green had 25 kg of fruit. She kept 1 kg of fruit and packed the remaining fruit into some bags to sell. Each bag contained $\frac{1}{2}$ kg of fruit. If each bag of fruit was bought by one person, how many people bought fruit?

$25 - 1 = 24$ (amount of fruit sold)

$24 \div \frac{1}{2} = 24 \times 2$

$= 48$

48 people bought fruit.

5 Ella had some paper stars. $\frac{2}{5}$ of her paper stars were yellow and $\frac{1}{10}$ of her paper stars were blue. The remaining paper stars were red. Ella gave away all her red paper stars to her friends. She gave away $\frac{1}{8}$ of her red stars to each friend. How many friends were there?

$1 - \frac{2}{5} - \frac{1}{10} = \frac{1}{2}$ (fraction of red paper stars)

$\frac{1}{2} \div \frac{1}{8} = 4$

There were 4 friends.

6 A group of people had a bag of assorted fruit to share. $\frac{1}{3}$ of the pieces of fruit were apples and the rest were pears. The apples were shared among the adults so that each adult received $\frac{1}{9}$ of the pieces of fruit. The pears were shared among the children so that each child received $\frac{1}{6}$ of the pieces of fruit. Find the number of adults and the number of children.

$\frac{1}{3} \div \frac{1}{9} = 3$

$\frac{2}{3} \div \frac{1}{6} = 4$

There were 3 adults and 4 children.

7 Mrs Sharma had £459 and Miss Evans had £1560. After both of them spent an equal amount of money, Mrs Sharma had $\frac{1}{4}$ as much as Miss Evans.

How much did Miss Evans spend?

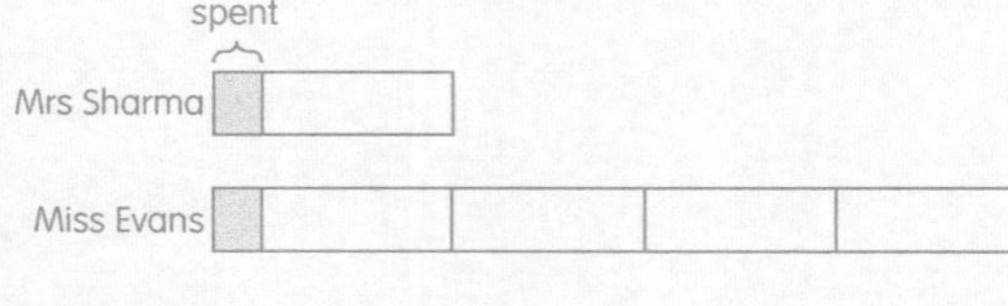

£1560 – £459 = £1101

£1101 ÷ 3 = £367

£459 – £367 = £92

Miss Evans spent £92.

8 At a school play, $\frac{2}{3}$ of the audience were women. $\frac{1}{5}$ of them were men. The rest were children. If there were 48 more women than children, how many people were there?

$1 - \frac{2}{3} - \frac{1}{5} = \frac{2}{15}$

$\frac{2}{15}$ of the audience were children.

$\frac{2}{3} - \frac{1}{15} = \frac{8}{15}$

8 units → 48 people
1 unit → 6 people
15 units → 90 people

There were 90 people.

9 The shape below is made up of a square with sides of 8 cm and a rectangle measuring 12 cm by 7 cm. What fraction of the shape is shaded?

7 cm
12 cm
8 cm
8 cm

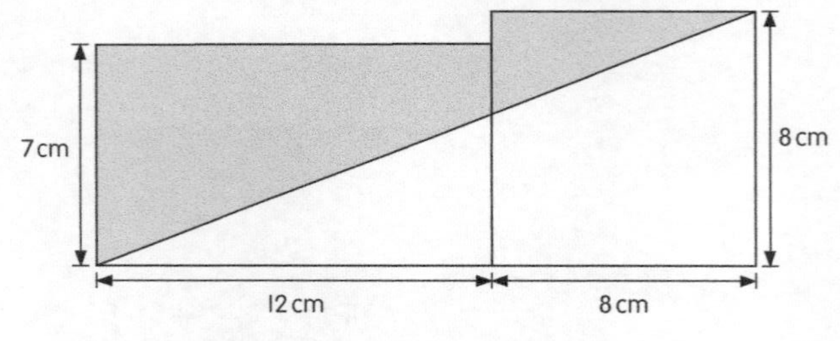

8 × 8 = 64 (area of square)
12 × 7 = 84 (area of rectangle)
64 + 84 = 148 (total area of shape)

$\frac{1}{2} \times 20 \times 8 = 80$ (area of unshaded part)

148 – 80 = 68 (area of shaded part)

$\frac{68}{148} = \frac{17}{37}$

$\frac{17}{37}$ of the shape is shaded.

10 There were 25 people in a cookery class. They made 135 biscuits altogether. $\frac{2}{5}$ of the people were children. They made the same number of biscuits each. The remaining people were adults. Each adult made $\frac{1}{3}$ as many biscuits as each child. How many biscuits did each child make?

$\frac{2}{5} \times 25 = 10$

There were 10 children.

$25 - 10 = 15$

There were 15 adults.

$15 + (10 \times 3) = 45$

45 units → 135 biscuits
1 unit → 3 biscuits
3 units → 9 biscuits

Each child made 9 biscuits.

11 Tai and Miya shared some stickers. If Tai gave $\frac{1}{3}$ of his share to Miya, Miya would have 70 more than Tai. If Tai gave $\frac{1}{5}$ of his share to Miya, Miya would have 10 more than Tai. How many stickers did Tai have at first?

$\frac{1}{3} - \frac{1}{5} = \frac{2}{15}$

$70 - 10 = 60$

2 units → 60 stickers
1 unit → 30 stickers
15 units → 450 stickers

Tai had 450 stickers at first.

Date: ____________

Maths Journal

1 The answer George gave for each of the following is incorrect. Explain the mistakes he could have made. Then show the correct workings and answer.

a $\frac{3}{5} \div \frac{1}{2} = \frac{3}{10}$

He multiplied the two fractions together. He should have inverted the second fraction before multiplying.

$\frac{3}{5} \div \frac{1}{2} = \frac{3}{5} \times 2 = 1\frac{1}{5}$

b $\frac{3}{5} \div \frac{2}{7} = \frac{10}{21}$

He inverted the first fraction instead of inverting the second fraction.

$\frac{3}{5} \div \frac{2}{7} = \frac{3}{5} \times \frac{7}{2} = 2\frac{1}{10}$

Date: ____________

Challenging Practice

1 During the school holidays, Omar read 312 pages of a book at first. He read the remaining pages in 20 days, by reading the same number of pages each day. During these 20 days, he read $\frac{1}{12}$ of the book in 6 days. How many pages of the book did he read in the 6 days?

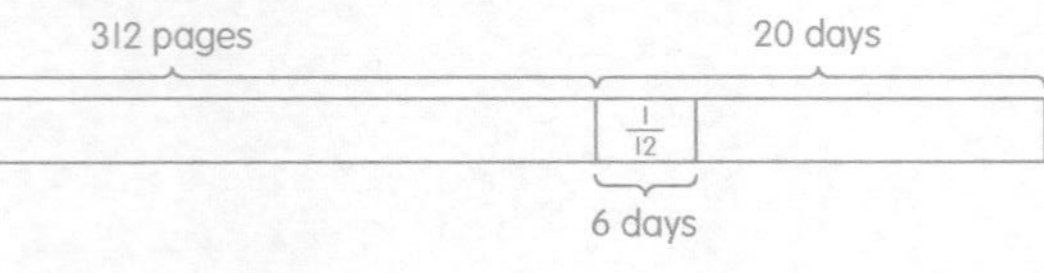

6 days → $\frac{1}{12}$

1 day → $\frac{1}{72}$

20 days → $\frac{20}{72}$

72 – 20 = 52 units

52 units → 312 pages
1 unit → 6 pages
72 units → 432 pages

$\frac{1}{12} \times 432 = 36$ pages

He read 36 pages in the 6 days.

Date: ______________

Problem Solving

1 Miss Ward had some money. She spent $\frac{1}{6}$ of her money on Saturday. On Sunday, she spent $\frac{1}{2}$ of the remaining money and gave £20 to her niece. She spent the rest of her money at a mean amount of £15 per day for the next 5 days. How much money did Miss Ward have at first?

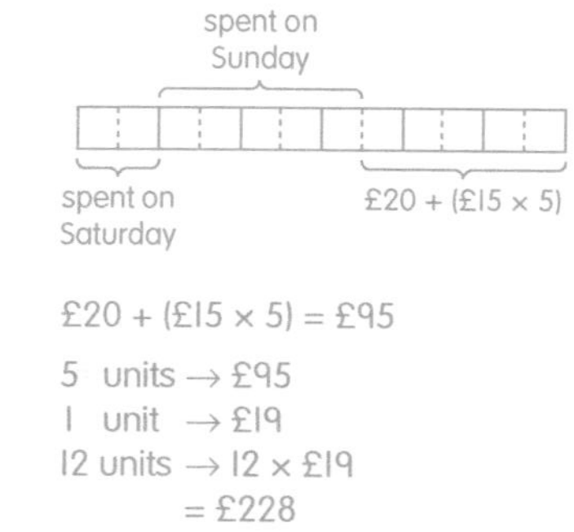

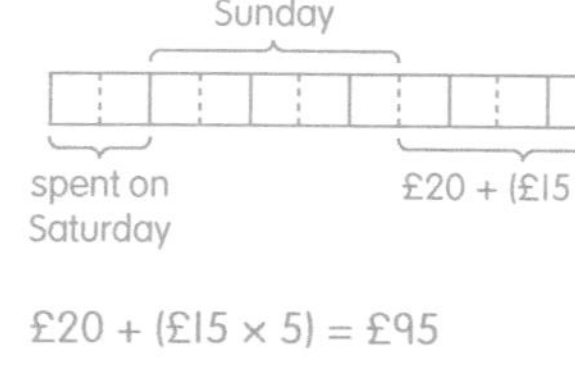

£20 + (£15 × 5) = £95

5 units → £95
1 unit → £19
12 units → 12 × £19
= £228

She had £228 at first.

Unit 5: Ratio

Medium-term plan

Week	Learning Objectives	Thinking Skills	Resources
6	**(1) Ratio and fraction** Pupils will be able to: • write the ratio of one quantity to another quantity in terms of (i) the actual number, and (ii) the number of groups • express one quantity as a fraction of another quantity given their ratio • find how many times larger one value is compared to another, given their ratio *Let's Explore!* Pupils will be able to recognise the relationship of the first and second quantities in a ratio to the numerator and denominator of a fraction. *Maths Journal* Pupils will be able to express the ratio statements as equivalent fraction statements.	• Comparing • Analysing parts and wholes	• Pupil Textbook 6A, pp 79 to 84 • Practice Book 6A, pp 95 to 102 • Teacher's Guide 6A, pp 145 to 150

Week	Learning Objectives	Thinking Skills	Resources
6	**(2) Word problems (1)** Pupils will be able to: • express fractions and comparative statements as models • interpret a model and use the unitary method to solve word problems • solve word problems by applying the common multiple concept • apply the ratio concept to solve geometrical problems using the unitary method	• Analysing parts and wholes • Identifying patterns and relationships	• Pupil Textbook 6A, pp 87 to 94 • Practice Book 6A, pp 103 to 108 • Teacher's Guide 6A, pp 153 to 160
7	**(3) Comparing ratios** Pupils will be able to: • recognise that a set of ratios can be expressed in their simplest form as the same ratio and that their corresponding values are multiples of the units in this ratio • apply these concepts and equivalent ratios to solve simple word problems • apply these concepts and the unitary method (together with models) to solve word problems	• Comparing	• Pupil Textbook 6A, pp 95 to 102 • Practice Book 6A, pp 109 to 112 • Teacher's Guide 6A, pp 161 to 168
7	**(4) Word problems (2)** Pupils will be able to solve higher-order word problems involving ratios using model drawing, the 'before-after' concept and the strategy of working backwards.	• Analysing parts and wholes	• Pupil Textbook 6A, pp 103 to 108 • Practice Book 6A, pp 113 to 118 • Teacher's Guide 6A, pp 169 to 174

Unit 5: Ratio

Medium-term plan

Week	Learning Objectives	Thinking Skills	Resources
7	*Let's Explore!* Pupils will be able to use the concept of equivalent ratios to solve the problems.		• Pupil Textbook 6A, p 109 • Teacher's Guide 6A, p 175
7	*Let's Wrap It Up!* Emphasise the key concepts, skills and processes that have been taught in the unit. Discuss the worked examples with pupils to assess whether they have mastered these concepts, skills and processes. *Put On Your Thinking Caps!* Pupils will be able to use the heuristics and hints provided in the question to solve the problem.	• Sequencing Heuristics for problem solving: • Make a systematic list • Before-after concept • Guess and check	• Pupil Textbook 6A, pp 109 to 112 • Practice Book 6A, pp 119 to 120 • Teacher's Guide 6A, pp 175 to 178
Summative assessment opportunity			
Assessment Book 6, Test 5, pp 45 to 50			

Ratio

Learning objectives: Ratio and fraction

Pupils will be able to:

- write the ratio of one quantity to another quantity in terms of
  (i) the actual number, and
  (ii) the number of groups
- express one quantity as a fraction of another quantity given their ratio
- find how many times larger one value is compared to another, given their ratio

Key concepts

- The ratio of one quantity to another quantity may not represent the actual number of items in each group.
- A simplified ratio of two quantities shows the relative amount of each quantity with respect to the other.

Thinking skills

- Comparing
- Analysing parts and wholes

Unit 5

Ratio

Let's Learn!

Ratio and fraction

1  Omar has 9 pencils. Millie has 15 pencils.

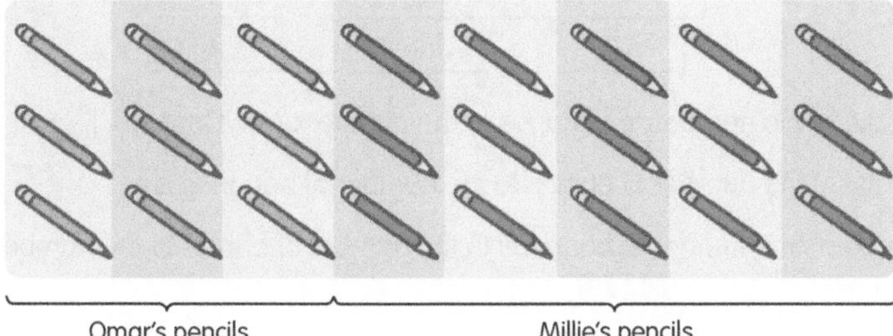

We can show the number of pencils both children have by using a model.

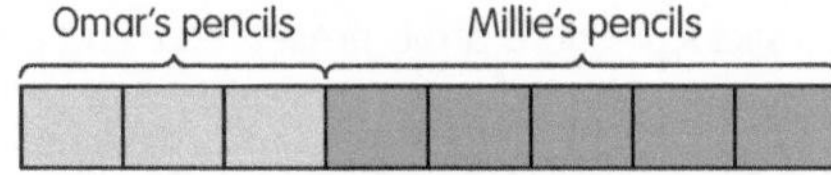

We can also arrange the model in another way.

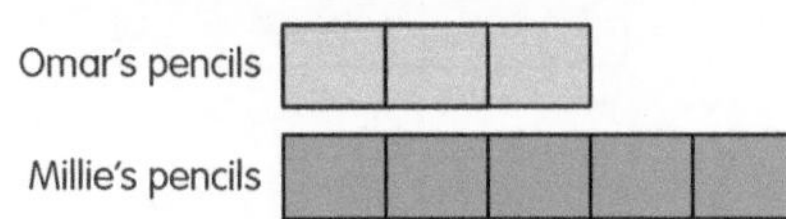

The ratio of the number of Omar's pencils to the number of Millie's pencils is 3 : 5.

The ratio of the number of Millie's pencils to the number of Omar's pencils is 5 : 3.

Teaching sequence

1

- Show pupils that the ratio of the number of items in one group to the number of items in another group can be expressed in a simpler form using a common factor. In , the common factor of 9 and 15 is 3, so we divide the number in each group by 3.
- Using a model to represent the two groups of items, explain and show pupils that there are two ways of drawing the model as shown in the textbook.

Teaching sequence

- Ask pupils to work on this question as an informal assessment to gauge whether they are able to interpret the model and write various ratios based on it.

- Show pupils how to find the ratio of one quantity (length of stick A) to another quantity (length of stick B) and the ratio of one quantity (length of stick A or B) to the whole (total length of both sticks).
- Explain how to interpret the ratio and write the length of one stick as a fraction of the length of the other stick.

Unit 5 Ratio

2  There are 4 bananas, 6 apples and 8 kiwi fruit in a basket.

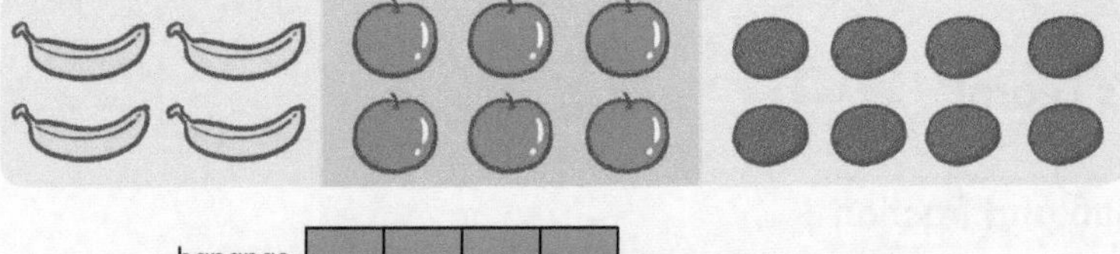

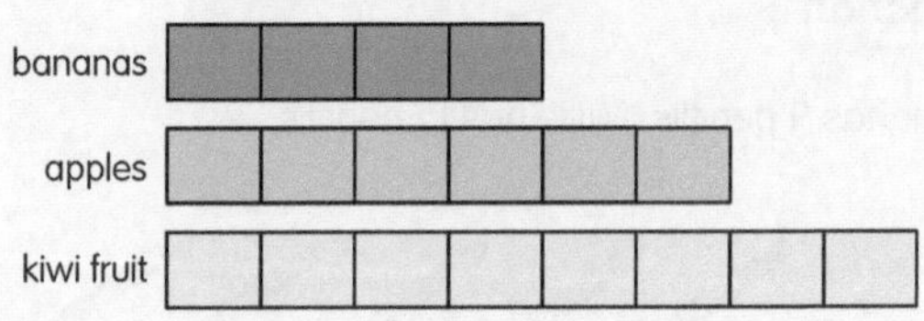

The ratio of the number of bananas to the number of kiwi fruit is [1] : [2]. or 2:
or 4:

The ratio of the number of apples to the number of bananas is [3] : [2]. or 6:

The ratio of the number of bananas to the number of apples to the number of kiwi fruit is [2] : [3] : [4]. or 4 : 6 : 8

The ratio of the number of kiwi fruit to the number of bananas to the number of apples is [4] : [2] : [3]. or 8 : 4 : 6

3 The lengths of two sticks, A and B are represented using a model.

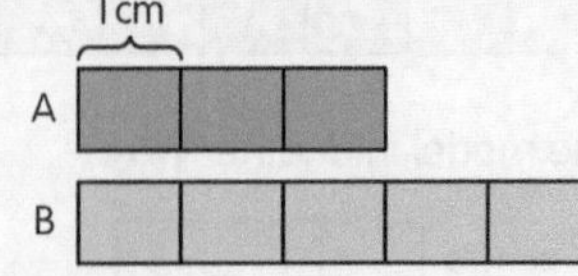

Total length of the two sticks = 3 + 5 = 8 cm

The ratio of the length of Stick A to the total length of the two sticks is 3 : 8.
So the length of Stick A is $\frac{3}{8}$ of the total length of the two sticks.

The ratio of the length of Stick A to the length of Stick B is 3 : 5. So the length of Stick A is $\frac{3}{5}$ of the length of Stick B.

The ratio of the length of Stick B to the length of Stick A is 5 : 3. So the length of Stick B is $\frac{5}{3}$ of the length of Stick A.

4 The masses of a rabbit, a chicken and a sheep are shown below.

1 unit

rabbit

chicken

sheep

The ratio of the mass of the chicken to the mass of the sheep is 4 : 11.

The mass of the chicken is $\frac{4}{11}$ of the mass of the sheep.

The mass of the sheep is $\frac{11}{4}$ of the mass of the chicken.

The ratio of the mass of the rabbit to the mass of the sheep is 3 : 11.

The mass of the rabbit is $\frac{3}{11}$ of the mass of the sheep.

The mass of the sheep is $\frac{11}{3}$ of the mass of the rabbit.

The ratio of the mass of the rabbit to the total mass of the three animals is 1 : 6.

The mass of the rabbit is $\frac{1}{6}$ of the total mass of the three animals.

Teaching sequence

- Ask pupils to work on this question as an informal assessment. Encourage pupils to notice that three items are involved here, rather than two.
- The ratio 1 : 6 needs to be a result of simplifying 3 : 18.

Teaching sequence

- Ask pupils to complete this question without the use of models.

- Work with pupils to interpret the model to find a ratio, then simplify the ratio.

- Ask pupils to work on this question to check whether they are able to find and simplify a ratio, then express it as a fraction.

5 The ratio of Sam's height to his little brother's height is 5 : 2.

a The ratio of Sam's height to the total height of the two boys is 5 : 7.

b His brother's height is $\frac{2}{5}$ of Sam's height.

c Sam's height is $\frac{5}{2}$ of his brother's height.

6 The number of adults and children watching a film is represented by this model.

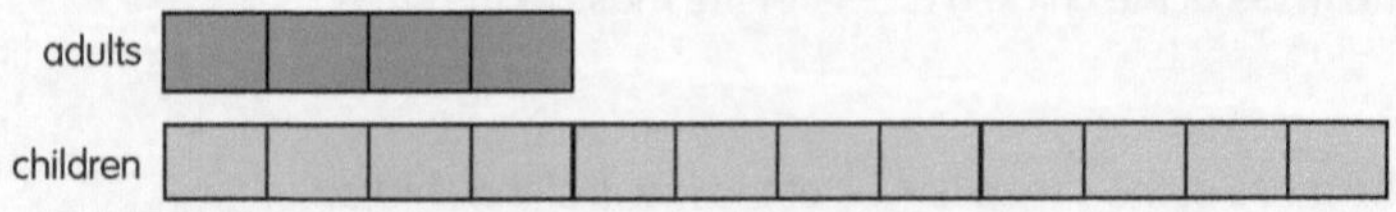

adults [4 boxes]

children [12 boxes]

a The ratio of the number of adults to the number of children is 4 : 12 = 1 : 3.

b The ratio of the number of children to the number of adults is 3 : 1.

c The number of adults is $\frac{1}{3}$ of the number of children.

d The number of children is $\frac{3}{1}$ of the number of adults.
So the number of children is 3 times as many as the number of adults.

7 Miss Taylor spent £21 and Mr Jackson spent £42.

a The ratio of the amount of money Miss Taylor spent to the amount of money Mr Jackson spent is 1 : 2.

b The amount of money Miss Taylor spent is $\frac{1}{2}$ of the amount of money Mr Jackson spent.

c The amount of money Mr Jackson spent is 2 times the amount of money Miss Taylor spent.

Additional activity

Ask pupils to work in pairs. Pupil A writes a fraction statement and draws the corresponding model. Pupil B writes related ratio and fraction statements. Pupils A and B swap roles.

8 Michael saved $\frac{3}{4}$ as much money as Poppy.

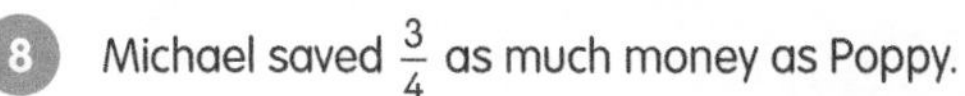

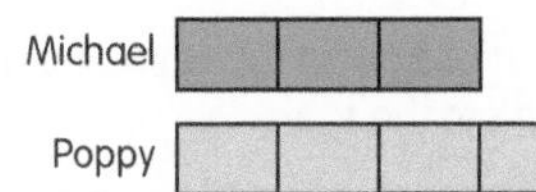

a The ratio of Michael's savings to Poppy's savings is 3 : 4.

b The ratio of Poppy's savings to their total savings is 4 : 7.

c Poppy's savings were $\frac{4}{7}$ of their total savings.

9 Peter cut a rope into two pieces. The length of the first piece was $\frac{4}{7}$ of the length of the second piece.

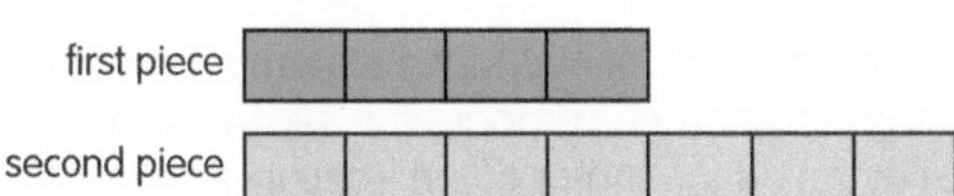

a The ratio of the length of the first piece to that of the second piece was 4 : 7.

b The ratio of the length of the second piece to the total length was 7 : 11.

c The length of the second piece was $\frac{7}{11}$ of the total length.

Teaching sequence

8

- Explain to pupils how to interpret the statement *"A has $\frac{3}{4}$ as much as B"* Discuss how to apply the statement to 8.
- Guide pupils to recognise the pattern: the numerator of the fraction refers to the first quantity in the ratio and the denominator refers to the second quantity. Agree that they can use this observation to draw the model.

9

- Ask pupils to work on these questions as an informal assessment.

Objectives of activities

Let's Explore!

Pupils will be able to recognise the relationship of the first and second quantities in a ratio to the numerator and denominator of a fraction.

Maths Journal

Pupils will be able to express the ratio statements as equivalent fraction statements.

Thinking skills

- Comparing
- Analysing parts and wholes

Teaching sequence

10 *Let's Explore!*

- Pupils should be able to describe the pattern following their work on **8** and **9**.

11 *Maths Journal*

- This task helps pupils to reflect on the ratio concepts they have learnt. They should be able to write three of the following fraction statements:

(i) $\frac{\text{Quantity 1}}{\text{Quantity 2}}$

(ii) $\frac{\text{Quantity 2}}{\text{Quantity 1}}$

(iii) $\frac{\text{Quantity 1}}{\text{Total}}$

(iv) $\frac{\text{Total}}{\text{Quantity 1}}$

(v) $\frac{\text{Quantity 2}}{\text{Total}}$

(vi) $\frac{\text{Total}}{\text{Quantity 2}}$

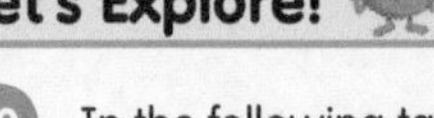

Let's Explore!

10 In the following table, you are given the ratio of a quantity to another quantity. Copy and complete the table.

Ratio Statement	Fraction Statement
A : B = 3 : 8	A is $\frac{3}{8}$ of B
C : D = 4 : 7	C is $\frac{4}{7}$ of D
E : F = 5 : 9	E is $\frac{5}{9}$ of F

Compare the first quantity of each ratio statement with the numerator of the fraction statement. Then compare the second quantity of each ratio statement with the denominator of the fraction statement.

What do you notice after comparing? Do you observe a pattern? Write a statement about the pattern that you have observed.
The first quantity of the ratio is always the numerator and the second quantity is always the denominator.

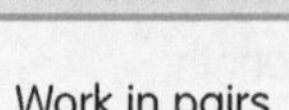

Maths Journal

11 Work in pairs.
Write three fraction statements for each of the following.

a The ratio of the number of apples to the number of oranges is 4 : 7.

Example

The number of apples is $\frac{4}{7}$ of the number of oranges.

b Mrs Lee saved £450 per month while Mr Lee saved £150 per month.
Accept all correct answers.

Independent work

Let's Practise!

12 X represents 2 units of stamps and Y represents 7 units of stamps.

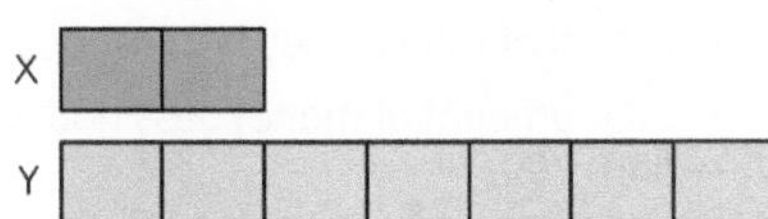

a Find the ratio of X to Y. 2 : 7

b X is $\frac{2}{7}$ of Y. **c** Y is $\frac{7}{2}$ of X.

13 The ratio of the length of Pole A to the length of Pole B is 4 : 5.

Pole A

Pole B

a Find the ratio of the length of Pole A to the total length of the two poles. 4 : 9

b What fraction of the length of Pole A is the length of Pole B? $\frac{5}{4}$

c What fraction of the length of Pole B is the length of Pole A? $\frac{4}{5}$

d What fraction of the total length of the two poles is the length of Pole A? $\frac{4}{9}$

e What fraction of the total length of the two poles is the length of Pole B? $\frac{5}{9}$

14 A cat's mass is $\frac{3}{5}$ of a dog's mass.

a What is the ratio of the dog's mass to the cat's mass? 5 : 3

b What is the ratio of the cat's mass to their total mass? 3 : 8

c Express the cat's mass as a fraction of their total mass. $\frac{3}{8}$

d What fraction of the total mass is the dog's mass? $\frac{5}{8}$

Independent work

Practice 1 in Practice Book 6A, pp 95 to 102.

Unit 5 Ratio

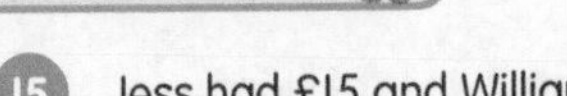

Let's Practise!

15 Jess had £15 and William had £21.

- **a** Find the total amount of money they had altogether. £36
- **b** Find the ratio of the amount of money Jess had to the amount of money that William had. 5 : 7
- **c** Express the amount of money Jess had as a fraction of the amount of money that William had. $\frac{5}{7}$
- **d** Express the amount of money William had as a fraction of the amount of money that Jess had. $\frac{7}{5}$
- **e** Find the ratio of the amount of money Jess had to the total amount of money that they had altogether. 5 : 12
- **f** Express the amount of money Jess had as a fraction of the total amount of money that they had altogether. $\frac{5}{12}$

16 Three children, Anna, Bella and Cheng, share some beads in the ratio 2 : 3 : 4.

- **a** Express the number of beads Anna has as a fraction of the total number of beads. $\frac{2}{9}$
- **b** Express the number of beads Cheng has as a fraction of the number of beads Bella has. $\frac{4}{3}$
- **c** What fraction of the total number of beads Anna and Cheng have is the number of beads Bella has? $\frac{1}{2}$
- **d** How many times the number of beads Anna has is the number of beads Cheng has? 2 times

17 Steven bought a loaf of bread and cut it into three pieces. The mass of the first piece of bread was $\frac{5}{8}$ of the mass of the second piece of bread. The mass of the second piece of bread was $\frac{4}{7}$ of the mass of the third piece of bread.

- **a** Find the ratio of the mass of the first piece of bread to that of the second piece of bread to that of the third piece of bread. 5 : 8 : 14
- **b** What is the ratio of the mass of the second piece of bread to the total mass of the 3 pieces of bread? 8 : 27
- **c** What fraction of the total mass of the 3 pieces of bread was the mass of the third piece of bread? $\frac{14}{27}$

Practice Book 6A, p.95

86

Learning objectives: Word problems (1)

Pupils will be able to:

- express fractions and comparative statements as models
- interpret a model and use the unitary method to solve word problems
- solve word problems by applying the common multiple concept
- apply the ratio concept to solve geometrical problems using the unitary method

Key concepts

- Fractions and ratios can be used to show the relative amounts of two quantities.
- The multiple concept in multiplication is another comparative tool to show the relative amount of two quantities.

Thinking skills

- Analysing parts and wholes
- Identifying patterns and relationships

Let's Learn!

Word problems (1)

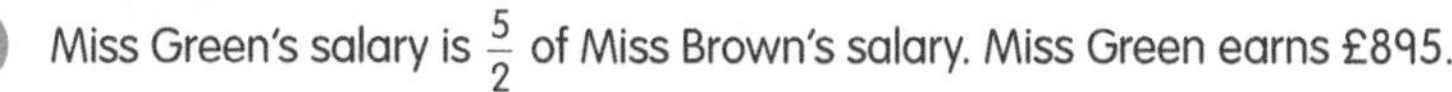

1 Miss Green's salary is $\frac{5}{2}$ of Miss Brown's salary. Miss Green earns £895.

a Find the ratio of Miss Green's salary to Miss Brown's salary.

b How much do they earn altogether?

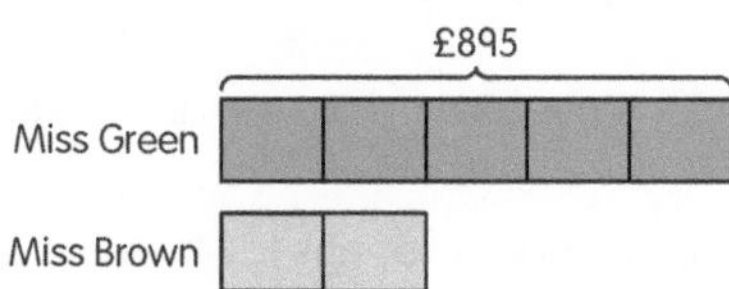

Total number of units = 5 + 2 = 7

The model above shows that:

a The ratio of Miss Green's salary to Miss Brown's salary is 5 : 2.

b 5 units ⟶ £895
1 unit ⟶ £895 ÷ 5 = £179
7 units ⟶ £179 × 7 = £1253

They earn £1253 altogether.

2 The number of pupils School A has is $\frac{7}{3}$ of the number of pupils School B has. School A has 896 pupils.

a Find the ratio of the number of pupils School B has to the number of pupils School A has to the total number of pupils they have.

b How many pupils do they have altogether?

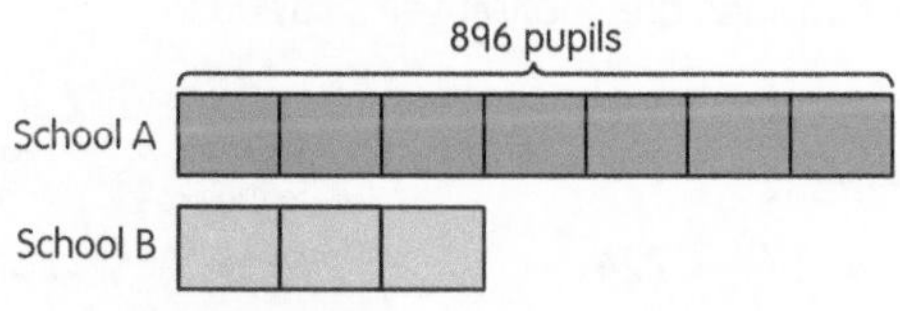

Total number of units = [7] + [3] = [10] units

Teaching sequence

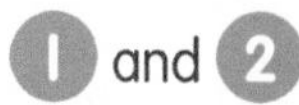

1 and 2

- These two problems will help pupils to revise their understanding and skills relating to the relationship between fractions and ratios.
- Review the following fraction relationship:

  A ⟶ $\frac{x}{y}$ ⟵ B

  For example, A and B are two different amounts of money where A is $\frac{x}{y}$ of B. Expressed as the ratio of A to B, this becomes $x : y$.
- Ask pupils to work on 2 as practice.
- Remind pupils to use the unitary method to find the total number of pupils.

Teaching sequence

- The main idea here is the multiple concept '4 times as much as'.
- Explain to pupils how to interpret the information and draw a model to show the multiple concept, then interpret it in terms of ratio.
- Guide pupils to use the unitary method in solving the last part of the word problem, by relating the parts to the amount.

The model on the previous page shows that:

a The ratio of the number of pupils School B has to the number of pupils School A has to the total number of pupils they have is 3 : 7 : 10.

b 7 units → 896 pupils

1 unit → 896 ÷ 7 = 128 pupils

10 units → 128 × 10 = 1280 pupils

They have 1280 pupils altogether.

3 Mr Lee's savings are 4 times as much as Mr Clark's savings. Both people save a total of £120.

a What is the ratio of Mr Lee's savings to Mr Clark's savings to their total saving

b What fraction of their total savings are Mr Lee's savings?

c What fraction of Mr Lee's savings are Mr Clark's savings?

d How much does Mr Lee save?

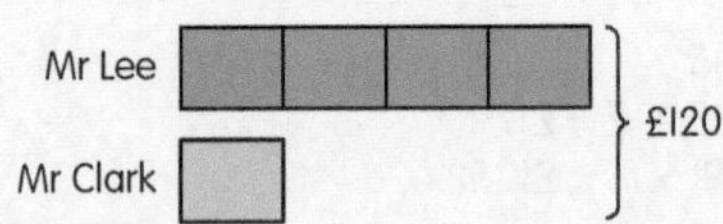

a Total number of units = 5

The ratio of Mr Lee's savings to Mr Clark's savings to their total savings is 4 : 1 : 5

b The ratio of Mr Lee's savings to their total savings is 4 : 5.

Mr Lee's savings are $\frac{4}{5}$ of the total savings.

c The ratio of Mr Clark's savings to Mr Lee's savings is 1 : 4.

Mr Clark's savings are $\frac{1}{4}$ of Mr Lee's savings.

d The model above shows that:

5 units → £120

1 unit → £$\frac{120}{5}$ = £24

4 units → 4 × £24 = £96

Mr Lee saves £96.

The ratio of Mr Lee's savings to their total savings is 4 : 5.
Mr Lee's savings are $\frac{4}{5}$ of their total savings.
So Mr Lee's savings = $\frac{4}{5}$ × £120
= £96

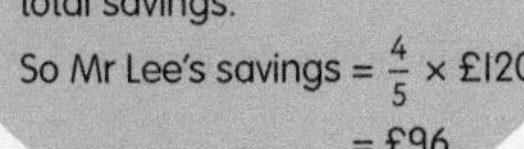

What you will need

Scientific calculator

 Mr Green spent 5 times as much money as Miss Lim. Mr Green spent £13 448 more than Miss Lim.

a What is the ratio of the amount of money Mr Green spent to the amount of money Miss Lim spent to the total amount of money spent?

b What fraction of the total amount of money spent is the amount of money Mr Green spent?

c How much did each person spend?

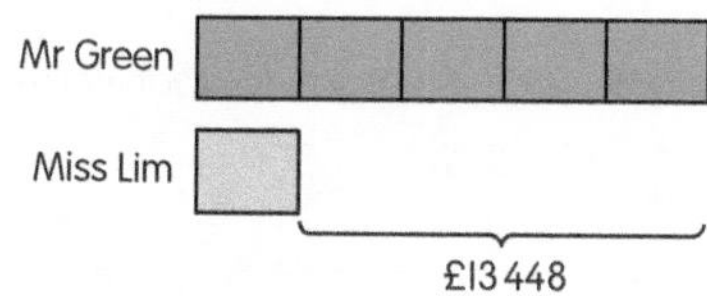

The model above shows that:

a The ratio of the amount of money Mr Green spent to the amount of money Miss Lim spent to the total amount of money spent is 5 : 1 : 6.

b $\frac{\text{Amount Mr Green spent}}{\text{Total amount spent}} = \frac{5}{6}$

The amount of money Mr Green spent is $\frac{5}{6}$ of the total amount of money spent.

c 4 units → £ 13 448

1 unit → £ 3362

5 units → £ 16 810

Mr Green spent £ 16 810 and Miss Lim spent £ 3362.

Teaching sequence

- Ask pupils to work on these questions as practice.
- Strategies pupils might use for part **c** include:
  - dividing by 4 through halving and then halving again
  - multiplying by 5 by multiplying by 10 and then halving
  - finding the value of 5 units by adding the values of 1 unit and 4 units.

What you will need

Scientific calculator

Teaching sequence

- Highlight the key pieces of information in this question:
  - (i) There are two ratios.
  - (ii) One of the quantities is common to both ratios.
- Guide pupils to recognise that the problem can be solved by giving the common quantity the same unit in both ratios. **a** can be solved only when this is done. It might help to set the problem out in the following way. The 'middle share' is placed in the middle to show how the parts compare.

  M : G : S
  3 : 2
  4 : 5

  To compare the ratios, the second number in the first ratio needs to be the same as the first number in the second ratio because they relate to George's share. The lowest common multiple of 2 and 4 is 4, so we make this share 4 in each ratio by multiplying the parts in the first ratio by 2, so the ratios become:

  M : G : S
  6 : 4
  4 : 5

  Therefore the ratio M : G : S is 6 : 4 : 5 and any ratio can now be obtained by choosing the correct parts.
- Work through the two methods for solving **b** with pupils: the unitary method (Method 1) and the fraction method (Method 2).

5 The ratio of the number of football cards Meena has to the number of football cards George has is 3 : 2. The ratio of the number of football cards George has to the number of football cards Sarah has is 4 : 5. Meena, George and Sarah have 75 football cards altogether.

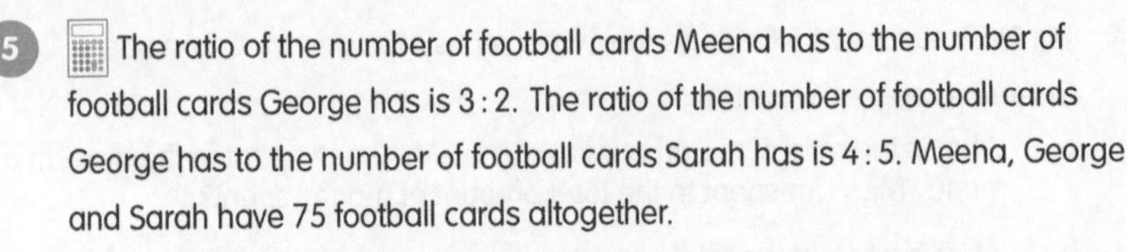

a Find the ratio of the number of football cards Meena has to the number of football cards Sarah has.

b How many football cards does Sarah have?

a Meena's football cards : George's football cards

× 2 (3 : 2 / 6 : 4) × 2

George's football cards : Sarah's football cards
4 : 5

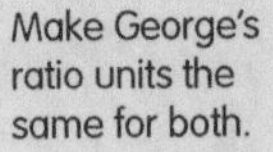

The ratio of the number of football cards Meena has to the number of football cards Sarah has is 6 : 5.

b **Method 1**

Total number of units = 6 + 4 + 5 = 15
15 units ⟶ 75 football cards
1 unit ⟶ $\frac{75}{15}$ = 5 football cards
5 units ⟶ 5 × 5 = 25 football cards

Sarah has 25 football cards.

Method 2

The ratio of the number of football cards Sarah has to the total number of football cards is 5 : 15 = 1 : 3.

Sarah's football cards = $\frac{1}{3} \times 75$
= 25

Sarah has 25 football cards.

6 Anna, Ben and Jacob keep fish as pets. The ratio of the number of fish Anna has to the number of fish Ben has is 2 : 1. The ratio of the number of fish Ben has to the number of fish Jacob has is 2 : 3.

a Find the ratio of the number of fish Anna has to the number of fish Ben has to the number of fish Jacob has.

b If they have a total of 27 fish, how many fish do Anna and Ben have altogether?

a

Anna's fish : Ben's fish	Ben's fish : Jacob's fish
× 2 (2 : 1 → 4 : 2) × 2	2 : 3

The ratio of the number of fish Anna has to the number of fish Ben has to the number of fish Jacob has is 4 : 2 : 3.

b **Method 1**

Total number of units = 9

9 units → 27 fish

1 unit → $\frac{27}{9}$ = 3 fish

6 units → 6 × 3 = 18 fish

Anna and Ben have 18 fish altogether.

Method 2

Anna's fish : Total number of fish = 4 : 9

Anna's fish = $\frac{4}{9}$ × 27

= 12

Ben's fish : Total number of fish = 2 : 9

Ben's fish = $\frac{2}{9}$ × 27

= 6

Anna and Ben have 18 fish altogether.

Teaching sequence

- Ask pupils to work on these questions as practice.
- For further explanation of what is being done in part **a** you could provide the following details:

2 : 1
2 : 3

become:

4 : 2
2 : 3

Therefore the ratio A : B : J is 4 : 2 : 3.

What you will need

Scientific calculator

Teaching sequence

- Note that this question involves applying the ratio concept in geometry. The sum of the ratio units can be equated to the perimeter of the triangle.

- Ask pupils to work on this question as practice.
- You could allow pupils who are confident in performing calculations without a calculator to do so for this question. One strategy they might use for finding 1 unit could be to divide the numerator and denominator by 2 and then by 9, to discover that $\frac{144}{18} = \frac{72}{9} = 8$.

 The sides of a triangle are in the ratio 2 : 3 : 4. The sum of all the sides of the triangle is 162 cm. Find the length of the longest side of the triangle.

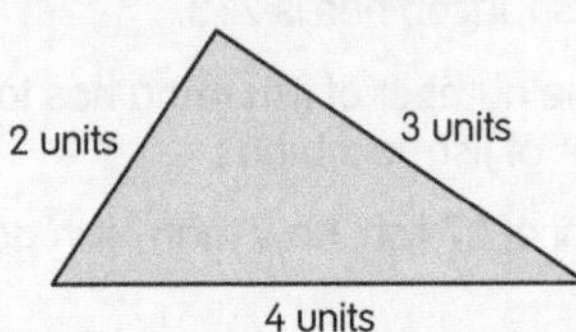

Sum of the three sides = 9 units

9 units ⟶ 162 cm

1 unit ⟶ 162 ÷ 9 = 18 cm

4 units ⟶ 4 × 18 = 72 cm

The length of the longest side of the triangle is 72 cm.

8 The sides of a right-angled triangle are in the ratio 5 : 12 : 13. The sum of the shortest side and the longest side is 144 cm. Find the length of the third side of the triangle.

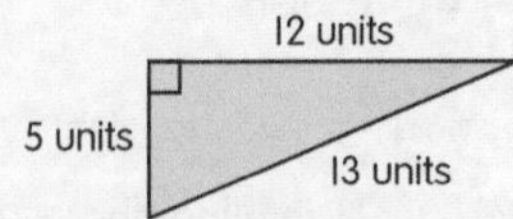

Sum of the shortest side and the longest side = 5 + 13

= [18] units

18 units ⟶ [144] cm

1 unit ⟶ $\frac{144\ [\ ]}{[18]}$ = [8] cm

12 units ⟶ 12 × [8] = [96] cm

The length of the third side of the triangle is [96] cm.

Independent work

Let's Practise!

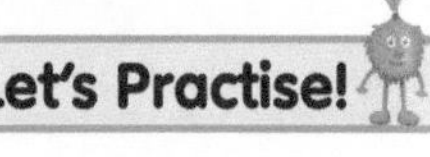

9 A vet weighed 2 dogs. Lucky's mass was $\frac{3}{2}$ of Rusty's mass. Their total mass was 90 kg.

a Find the ratio of Lucky's mass to Rusty's mass. 3 : 2

b What fraction of the total mass of the two dogs was Rusty's mass? $\frac{2}{5}$

c What fraction of the total mass of the two dogs was Lucky's mass? $\frac{3}{5}$

d Find the mass of each dog. Rusty : 36 kg Lucky : 54 kg

10 The mass of potatoes used by Mr Wood in his cooking was $\frac{5}{2}$ of the mass of carrots used. He used 9 kg more potatoes than carrots.

a Find the ratio of the mass of potatoes used to the mass of carrots used to the total mass of both ingredients. 5 : 2 : 7

b What fraction of the total mass of both ingredients was the mass of the potatoes? $\frac{5}{7}$

c Find the total mass of both ingredients. 21 kg

11 A wall has an area of 7·2 m^2. It was painted yellow and brown. The area of the wall painted yellow was 3 times as large as the area painted brown.

a What was the ratio of the area painted yellow to the area painted brown? 3 : 1

b What was the ratio of the area painted yellow to the area of the entire wall? 3 : 4

c What fraction of the area of the entire wall was painted brown? $\frac{1}{4}$

d Find the area of the wall painted yellow. 5·4 m^2

What you will need

Scientific calculator

Independent work

Practice 2 and *Maths Journal* in Practice Book 6A, pp 103 to 108.

Teaching sequence

14 *Let's Practise!*

- You could allow pupils who are confident about performing long division by 13 without a calculator to do so for this question. These pupils could use a calculator to check their answer.

- You could allow pupils who are confident about performing the calculations without a calculator to do so for this question. One strategy they could use is to work out 746·1 ÷ 3 = 248·7. Then 248·7 × 22 could be calculated by multiplying by 10, doubling this (i.e. working out 248·7 × 20) and then adding double 248·7 (i.e. 248·7 × 2). These pupils could use a calculator to check their answer.

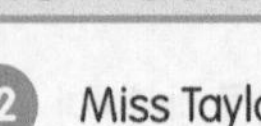

Let's Practise!

12 Miss Taylor and Mr Green won some money on a game show. Miss Taylor won 5 times as much money as Mr Green. Mr Green won £4200 less than Miss Taylor.

a What was the ratio of the amount of money Miss Taylor won to the amount of money Mr Green won to the total amount of money both people won? 5 : 1 : 6

b What fraction of the total amount of money both people won did Miss Taylor win? $\frac{5}{6}$

c What fraction of the total amount of money both people won did Mr Green win? $\frac{1}{6}$

d How much money did each person win?
Mr Green: £1050, Miss Taylor: £5250

13 The ratio of the number of pupils in Group A to the number of pupils in Group B is 2 : 5. The ratio of the number of pupils in Group B to the number of pupils in Group C is 10 : 3.

a Find the ratio of the number of pupils in Group A to the number of pupils in Group B to the number of pupils in Group C. 4 : 10 : 3

b If there are 70 pupils in Group A and Group C altogether, how many pupils are there in Group B? 100 pupils

c However if Group B has 40 pupils, how many pupils are there in Group A and Group C altogether? 28 pupils

14 The ratio of the length of a rectangle to its width is 9 : 4. If the perimeter of the rectangle is 104 cm, find the area of the rectangle. 576 cm^2

15 The ratio of the length of a parallelogram to that of its width is 7 : 4. The length is longer than the width by 746·1 cm. Find the perimeter of the parallelogram. 5471·4 cm

Practice Book 6A, p.103

Learning objectives: Comparing ratios

Pupils will be able to:

- recognise that a set of ratios can be expressed in their simplest form as the same ratio and that their corresponding values are multiples of the units in this ratio
- apply these concepts and equivalent ratios to solve simple word problems
- apply these concepts and the unitary method (together with models) to solve word problems

Key concept

The quantities in fixed ratios increase or decrease by the same multiple.

Thinking skill

Comparing

Let's Learn!

Comparing ratios

 Mr Smith made five mixtures of orange and pineapple juice using different amounts of juice. He recorded them in a table.

Mixture	A	B	C	D	E
Amount of orange juice (ml)	300	450	600	750	900
Amount of pineapple juice (ml)	200	300	400	500	600

Find the ratio of the amount of orange juice to the amount of pineapple juice in each mixture.

Mixture	A	B	C	D	E
Amount of orange juice : Amount of pineapple juice	3 : 2	3 : 2	3 : 2	3 : 2	3 : 2

What can you say about the ratios?
We say that the ratio of the amount of orange juice used to the amount of pineapple juice used is the **same** in each mixture.

We can also say that the amount of orange juice used and the amount of pineapple juice used are in a **fixed ratio**.

Teaching sequence

- Ensure that pupils understand that in fixed ratios, the ratio of one quantity to the other quantity must be consistently the same, even when different amounts of the corresponding quantities are used.
- Work through the example with pupils. Emphasise that the ratio of the amount of orange juice to the amount of pineapple juice is always the same, even though the amounts themselves change.

Teaching sequence

- Ask pupils to work on this question as practice.
- Encourage pupils to notice the relationship between the ratios in their simplest form and the corresponding fraction.

Mr Khan uses the following table to prepare four different mixtures of cement and sand. Complete the table.

Number of buckets of cement	4	8	12	16
Number of buckets of sand	3	6	9	12
Number of buckets of cement : number of buckets of sand	4:3	8:6	12 : 9	16 : 12
Number of buckets of cement : number of buckets of sand (simplest form)	4:3	4:3	4 : 3	4 : 3
$\frac{\text{Number of buckets of cement}}{\text{Number of buckets of sand}}$	$\frac{4}{3}$	$\frac{4}{3}$	$\frac{4}{3}$	$\frac{4}{3}$

What can you say about the ratios in the fourth row of the table?

Are all the ratios the same? Yes

What can you say about the fractions in the fifth row of the table?

Are all the fractions the same? Yes

So the number of buckets of cement used and the number of buckets of sand used are in a fixed ratio.

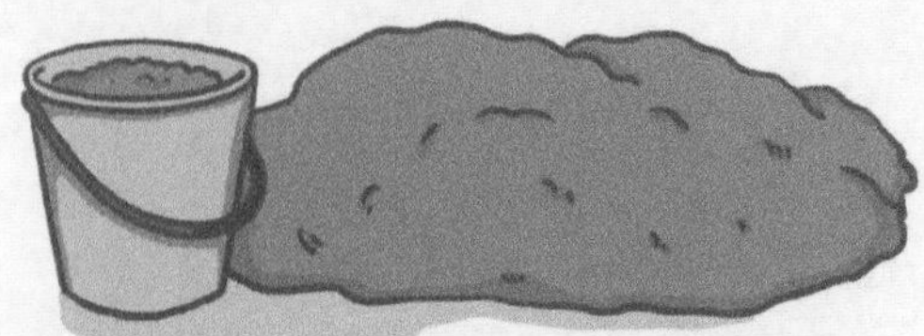

3 To make some dough, Amina mixes 5 cups of flour with every 3 cups of water.

a Find the ratio of the amount of flour used to the amount of water used.

b If Amina wants to make 5 times the amount of dough as above, how many cups of water and how many cups of flour does she need?

c If she uses 21 cups of water, how many cups of flour are needed to make the same type of dough?

a The ratio of the amount of flour used to the amount of water used is 5 : 3.

b

$$\frac{\text{Number of cups of flour}}{\text{Number of cups of water}} = \frac{5}{3} = \frac{25}{15} \quad (\times 5)$$

5 × 5 = 25
3 × 5 = 15

Amina needs 15 cups of water and 25 cups of flour.

c **Method 1**

$$\frac{\text{Number of cups of flour}}{\text{Number of cups of water}} = \frac{5}{3} = \frac{35}{21} \quad (\times 7)$$

3 × 7 = 21
5 × 7 = 35

35 cups of flour are needed.

Method 2

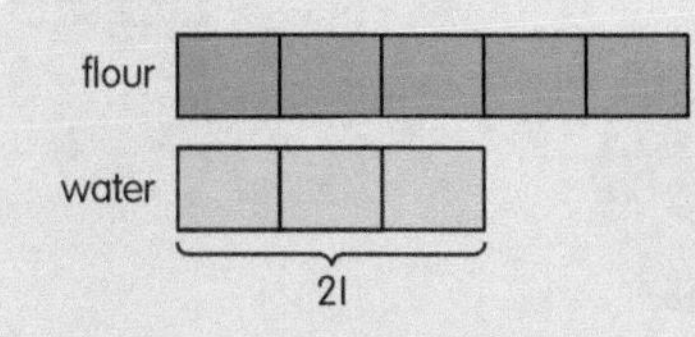

3 units ⟶ 21 cups
1 unit ⟶ 21 ÷ 3 = 7 cups
5 units ⟶ 5 × 7 = 35 cups

35 cups of flour are needed.

Teaching sequence

3

- Method 1 uses the equivalent ratio method to obtain the required value.
- Method 2 uses a model and the unitary method. The underlying concept here is that the '1 unit' representing the number of cups is the same in all cases.

Teaching sequence

- Ask pupils to work on these questions as practice.

 Mr Lee prepares porridge for his family. For each bowl of porridge, he always uses 3 cups of water for every 2 cups of oats.

a Find the ratio of the number of cups of water used to the number of cups of oats used.

b If he wants to prepare 5 bowls of porridge, how many cups of water and how many cups of oats does he need?

c If he uses 18 cups of oats, how many cups of water does he need?

a The ratio of the number of cups of water used to the number of cups of oats used is 3 : 2.

b $\frac{\text{Number of cups of water used}}{\text{Number of cups of oats used}} = \frac{3}{2} = \frac{15}{10}$

Mr Lee needs 15 cups of water and 10 cups of oats.

c $\frac{\text{Number of cups of water used}}{\text{Number of cups of oats used}} = \frac{3}{2} = \frac{27}{18}$

Mr Lee needs 27 cups of water.

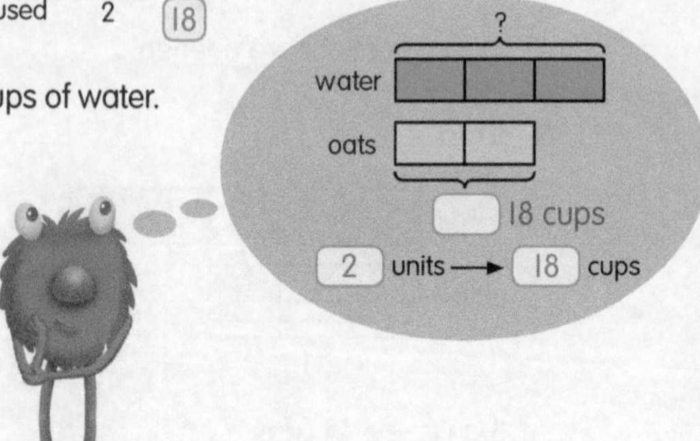

5 Omar mixed 200 ml of squash with every 500 ml of water to make a drink for a party.

a Complete the table if the ratio of the amount of squash to the amount of water is the same.

Amount of squash (ml)	200	600	1000	1400	1800
Amount of water (ml)	500	1500	2500	3500	4500
Amount of squash : amount of water	2 : 5				

b Based on the table in **a**, how much water is needed if 800 ml of squash is used?

c Based on the table in **a**, how much squash is needed if 400 ml of water is used?

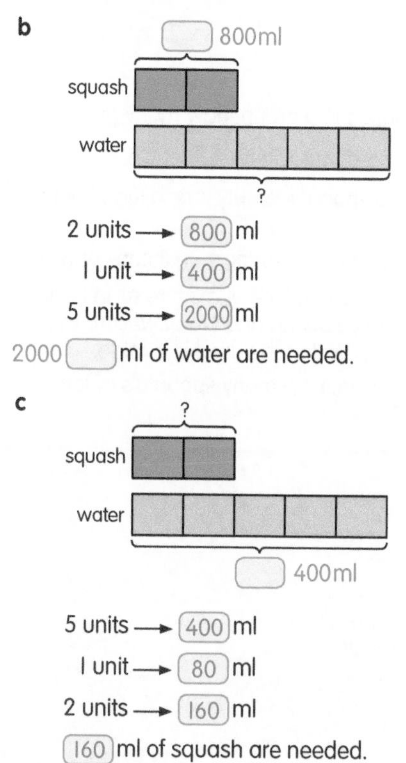

b

2 units → 800 ml

1 unit → 400 ml

5 units → 2000 ml

2000 ml of water are needed.

c

5 units → 400 ml

1 unit → 80 ml

2 units → 160 ml

160 ml of squash are needed.

Teaching sequence

- Ask pupils to work on these questions as practice.
- When using the unitary method, the number representing 1 unit needs to be found and stated. In part **b**, 1 unit is 400 ml and in part **c**, 1 unit is 80 ml.

What you will need

- Green counters and red counters
- Table (see Photocopy master 10 on p 281)
- Cups
- Spoons
- 4 empty jars
- Jug of water
- Food colouring

Thinking skill

Comparing

Teaching sequence

- Ask pupils to work in groups of four and give each group a copy of the table provided on Photocopy master 10. Work with them to carry out the task, reinforcing the concept of equivalent ratios and how it can be used to solve ratio problems.

Activity

6 Work in groups of four.

a You will need some green and red counters.

i Make different groups of counters so that the ratio of the number of green counters to the number of red counters in each group is 3 : 2. Record your results in a table.

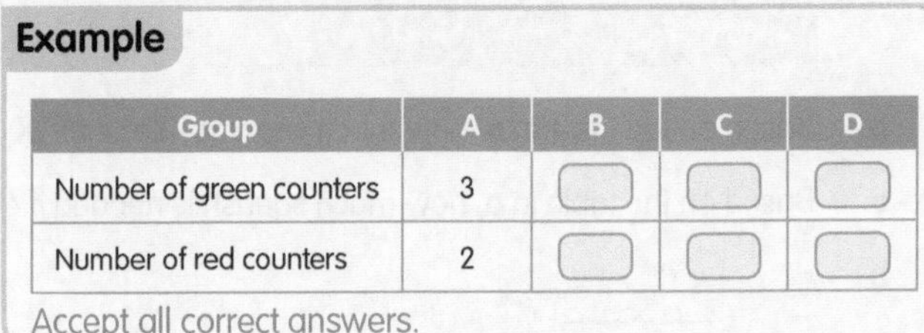

Example

Group	A	B	C	D
Number of green counters	3			
Number of red counters	2			

Accept all correct answers.

ii If there are 72 red counters in a group, how many green counters are there? 108

b Each group will need a cup, a spoon, 4 empty jars, a jug of water and a bottle of food colouring.

i In a jar, mix 1 spoonful of food colouring with 3 cups of water.

ii Prepare 3 more jars of the same type of mixture as in **i** using different amounts of food colouring and water. Record the amounts of water and food colouring used in a table.

iii If 75 cups of water are used, how many spoonfuls of food colouring are needed? 25

Look at some recipes with your child. Together, find the ratios between some of the ingredients.

Independent work

Let's Practise!

Let's Practise!

7 Mr Bell uses 90 g of flour for every 20 g of sugar to make a loaf of bread.

- **a** Find the ratio of the mass of flour to the mass of sugar used. 9 : 2
- **b** To make the loaf of bread, how many grams of sugar does Mr Bell need if he uses 270 g of flour? 60 g
- **c** If he makes 5 loaves of the same type, how many grams of flour and how many grams of sugar will he use? 1350 g of flour, 300 g of sugar

8 Beth uses 3 teaspoons of lemon juice for every 8 oranges to make a drink.

- **a** Find the ratio of the number of oranges used to the number of teaspoons of lemon juice used. 8 : 3
- **b** To make the same type of drink, how many teaspoons of lemon juice does Beth need if she uses 24 oranges? 9 teaspoons
- **c** To make the same type of drink, how many oranges does Beth use if she uses 24 teaspoons of lemon juice? 64 oranges

9 In a science experiment, Mark mixed water and vinegar in the ratio 3 : 1.

- **a** If he used 745·2 ml of water, how many millilitres of vinegar did he use? 248·4 ml
- **b** If 0·28 ℓ of vinegar was used, how many litres of water did Mark use? 0·84 ℓ

What you will need

Scientific calculator

Independent work

Practice 3 in Practice Book 6A, pp 109 to 112.

Unit 5 Ratio

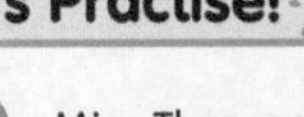

Let's Practise!

10 Miss Thompson mixes blue paint and yellow paint to make green paint. When 4 buckets of blue paint and 5 buckets of yellow paint are mixed, a container of green paint is obtained.

a Find the ratio of the number of buckets of yellow paint used to the number of buckets of blue paint used. 5 : 4

b If Miss Thompson uses a total of 63 buckets of blue and yellow paint, how many buckets of blue paint does she use? 28 buckets

c How many containers of green paint can Miss Thompson get if she uses 12 buckets of blue paint and 15 buckets of yellow paint? 3 containers

d How many buckets of yellow paint does Miss Thompson use if she makes 5 containers of green paint? 25 buckets

11 Mr Sharp used 125 g of butter, 200 g of chocolate chips and 125 g of flour to make a batch of biscuits. Mr Sharp makes 75 batches of the biscuits to sell at a charity sale. Find the:

a ratio of the mass of butter used to that of chocolate chips used to that of flour used 5 : 8 : 5

b mass of flour used, in kilograms 9·375 kg

c total mass of butter, chocolate chips and flour used, in kilograms. 33·75 kg

Practice Book 6A, p.109

Learning objective: Word problems (2)

Pupils will be able to solve higher-order word problems involving ratios using model drawing, the 'before-after' concept and the strategy of working backwards.

Key concept

When quantities are increased or decreased in relation to each other, the ratios of the quantities are also changed.

Thinking skill

Analysing parts and wholes

Let's Learn!

Word problems (2)

1 Michael and Tim had some money in the ratio 6 : 1. Michael gave half of his money to Tim. Find the ratio of the amount of money Michael had left to the amount of money Tim had in the end.

Before

Michael

Tim

After

gave away

Michael

Tim

The ratio of the amount of money Michael had left to the amount of money Tim had in the end is 3 : 4.

2 Mrs Lee pours some cereal into two bowls. The ratio of the mass of cereal in Bowl A to the mass of cereal in Bowl B is 9 : 5. She transfers half of the cereal from Bowl A to Bowl B. What is the new ratio of the mass of cereal in Bowl A to the mass of cereal in Bowl B?

Before

Bowl A

Bowl B

After

[ ] transferred

Bowl A

Bowl B

The new ratio of the mass of cereal in Bowl A to the mass of cereal in Bowl B is [9] : [19].

Teaching sequence

1 and 2

- Work through 1 with pupils and demonstrate how to use the model method and the 'before-after' concept to solve the problem.
- Guide pupils to recognise that the problem can be solved by drawing a model and acting it out; that is, by moving some of the parts in the model to illustrate the 'after' situation.
- Ask pupils to work on 2 as practice.
- You could provide the following details to explain what needs to be done to answer this question: 9 : 5 is equal to 18 : 10. After transferring half A to B the ratio becomes 9 : 19.

Teaching sequence

- Highlight to pupils that the 'before-after' concept is used to solve this problem.
- Explain to pupils that increasing or decreasing the amounts will affect the ratios.
- You could provide the following explanation for this question: 2 : 1 is equal to 4 : 2. Comparing 4 : 2 to 4 : 5, there are 3 more units added to the blue cubes.

3 Miss Phillips puts some green and blue cubes in a box. The ratio of the number of green cubes to the number of blue cubes is 2 : 1. She adds 12 more blue cubes in the box and the ratio becomes 4 : 5.

a How many green cubes are there in the box?

b How many blue cubes does Miss Phillips have in the end?

Before

green

blue

After

green

blue

12

The model above shows that:

a 3 units → 12 cubes

1 unit → $\frac{12}{3}$ = 4 cubes

4 units → 4 × 4 = 16 cubes

There are 16 green cubes in the box.

b 5 units → 5 × 4 = 20 cubes

Miss Phillips has 20 blue cubes in the end.

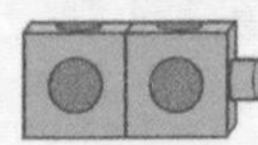

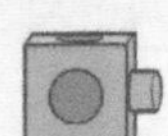

4 Saleem had some photographs of animals and plants. The ratio of the number of photographs of animals to the number of photographs of plants was 3 : 4. He took 21 more photographs of animals and the ratio became 9 : 8.

a How many photographs of plants did Saleem have?

b How many photographs of animals did Saleem have in the end?

Before

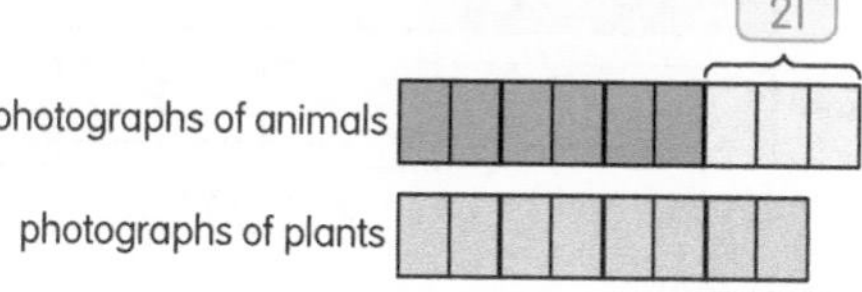

After

21

photographs of animals

photographs of plants

The model above shows that:

a 3 units → 21 photographs

1 unit → 7 photographs

8 units → 56 photographs

Saleem had 56 photographs of plants.

b 9 units → 63 photographs

Saleem had 63 photographs of animals in the end.

Teaching sequence

- Ask pupils to work on these questions as practice.
- Encourage them to recognise that this is a similar problem to 3 and the 'before-after' concept can be applied here.
- The ratios are affected when one of the amounts is increased.
- You could provide the following explanation for this question: 3 : 4 is equal to 6 : 8. Comparing 6 : 8 to 9 : 8, there are 3 more units added to the photographs of animals.
- When using the unitary method, the number representing 1 unit needs to be found and stated. 1 unit is 7 photographs.

Teaching sequence

- Encourage pupils to notice that in this question both amounts are increased. In the 'after' situation the two amounts are equal.
- Guide pupils to interpret the model so they can write a mathematical statement. Then use the unitary method to solve the problem.

5 Miss Cook and Mrs Thompson had some money in the ratio 3 : 7. After Miss Cook received £92 and Mrs Thompson received £40, both women had an equal amou[nt] of money. How much money did each woman have at first?

Before

Miss Cook

Mrs Thompson

After

£92

Miss Cook

Mrs Thompson

£92 – £40 £40

The model above shows that:

4 units ⟶ £92 – £40
= £52

1 unit ⟶ £$\frac{52}{4}$
= £13

3 units ⟶ 3 × £13
= £39

7 units ⟶ 7 × £13
= £91

Miss Cook had £39 and Mrs Thompson had £91 at first.

6 At the start of a game, Jack, Miya and Ruby had the same number of stars. During the game, Jack lost 12 stars to Ruby and Miya lost 20 stars to Ruby. The ratio of Jack's stars to Miya's stars became 4 : 3. How many stars did each child have at first?

Before

Jack

Miya

Ruby

After

20 – 12 = 8   12

Jack

Miya

Ruby

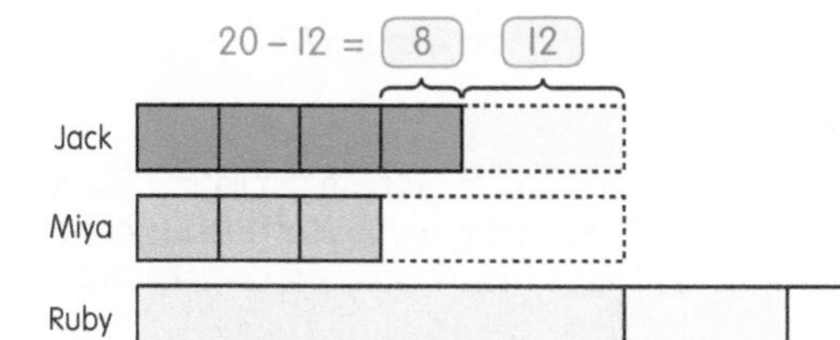

The model above shows that:

1 unit ⟶ 8 stars

4 units ⟶ 4 × 8

= 32 stars

In the end, Jack had 32 stars.

32 + 12 = 44

Each child had 44 stars at first.

Teaching sequence

6

- Ask pupils to work on this question as practice.
- Highlight to pupils that this problem is the reverse of : the amounts are the same in the 'before' situation and different in the 'after' situation.

Independent work

- *Let's Practise!*
- Practice 4 in Practice Book 6A, pp 113 to 118.

Unit 5 Ratio

Let's Practise!

7 The ratio of the volume of water in Jug A to the volume of water in Jug B is 2 : 5. Use this ratio to answer each of the following questions.

a If half of the water in Jug A is poured into Jug B, what is the new ratio of the volumes of water in Jug A to Jug B? 1 : 6

b If half of the water in Jug B is poured into Jug A, what is the new ratio of the volumes of water in Jug A to Jug B? 9 : 5

c If $\frac{1}{3}$ of the water in Jug A is poured into Jug B, what is the new ratio of the volumes of water in Jug A to Jug B? 4 : 17

8 A builder used cement and sand to prepare a mixture. The ratio of the number of buckets of cement to the number of buckets of sand was 1 : 2. The builder then added 8 more buckets of cement and the ratio became 5 : 2.

a How many buckets of cement did he use at first? 2 buckets

b How many buckets of sand did he use at first? 4 buckets

9 The ratio of the amount of money Mr Lake had to the amount of money Mr Harper had was 2 : 5. After Mr Harper's sister gave him £75 the ratio became 4 : 15. How much money did each person have at first?
Mr Lake: £60, Mr Harper: £150

10 The ratio of the number of coins Amos had to the number of coins Ethan had was 3 : 7. Ethan gave 42 coins to Amos and they ended up having the same number of coins. How many coins did each person have at first?
Amos: 63 coins, Ethan: 147 coins

11 Ruby and Ella had some stickers in the ratio 2 : 3. Ella gave half of her stickers away and the ratio became 4 : 3. If Ella had given away 21 stickers, how many stickers did each child have at first?
Ruby: 28 stickers, Ella: 42 stickers

108

Objective of activity

Pupils will be able to use the concept of equivalent ratios to solve the problems.

Let's Practise!

12 There were 3 glasses containing the same volume of liquid. Mr Lee poured 210 ml of the liquid from Glass A into Glass C, and 150 ml of the liquid from Glass B into Glass C. In the end, the ratio of the volume of liquid in Glass A to the volume of liquid in Glass B was 3 : 8.

- **a** What was the final volume of liquid in Glass A? 36 ml
- **b** What was the volume of liquid in each glass at first? 246 ml

Practice Book 6A, p.113

Let's Explore!

13 The ratio of the number of beads collected by Meena to the number of beads collected by Harry is 9 : 4. Meena gave some beads to Harry.

- **a** Find all the possible ratios of the number of beads Meena had to the number of beads Harry had, so that Meena will still have more beads than Harry after she gave Harry some beads. Any ratio $a : b$ is possible where a and b are whole numbers and $1 < \frac{a}{b} < \frac{9}{4}$. E.g. 8 : 5 and 7 : 6
- **b** Is it possible for both Meena and Harry to have the same number of beads after Meena gave Harry some beads? Explain why. Accept all possible answers. Example: Yes. Assume that Meena has 18 beads. Then Harry would have 8 beads. If Meena gives 5 beads to Harry, then they would both have 13 beads.

Let's Wrap It Up!

You have learnt to:

- express one value as a fraction of another given their ratio, and vice versa
- find how many times one value is as large as another given their ratio, and vice versa
- solve word problems which involve:
  - **a** finding one part when the ratio and the whole are given
  - **b** finding one part or the whole when the ratio and the difference are given
  - **c** two pairs of ratios
  - **d** ratios in real-life situations
- use the unitary method and models to solve word problems about ratio.

Teaching sequence

13 *Let's Explore!*

- Ensure that pupils have a clear understanding of the basic concepts of ratio. They should be able to generate a list of equivalent ratios to answer this question.

Let's Wrap It Up!

- Emphasise the key concepts, skills and processes that have been taught in the unit.

Teaching sequence

14 to 18

- Discuss the worked examples with pupils to assess whether they have mastered these concepts, skills and processes.

15 to 18

- Encourage pupils to find the value of 1 unit in each case.

Let's Wrap It Up!

Let's Revise!

14 Find the ratio of red beads to yellow beads.

red beads

yellow beads

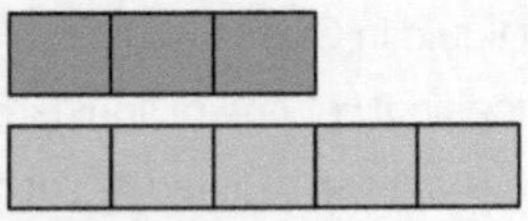

The ratio of red beads to yellow beads is 3 : 5.

15 The ratio of Sita's age to Tom's age is 4 : 7. Express Sita's age as a fraction of Tom's age.

Sita's age is $\frac{4}{7}$ of Tom's age.

16 Tank A's volume is $\frac{5}{2}$ of Tank B's volume. Find the ratio of Tank A's volume to Tank B's volume.

The ratio of Tank A's volume to Tank B's volume is 5 : 2.

17 The mass of a bag of rice is 3 times the mass of a bag of fruit. If the mass of the bag of rice is 15 kg, what is the mass of the bag of fruit?

The mass of the bag of fruit is 5 kg.

Let's Wrap It Up!

18 Mrs Ali had 3 times as much money as Miss Murray. Mrs Ali and Miss Murray had £96 altogether.

a Find the ratio of Mrs Ali's money to Miss Murray's money.

The ratio of Mrs Ali's money to Miss Murray's money was 3 : 1.

b What fraction of the total amount of money was Mrs Ali's money?

Total amount of money = 3 + 1
= 4 units

Mrs Ali's money was $\frac{3}{4}$ of the total amount of money.

c How much money did each person have?

4 units ⟶ £96

1 unit ⟶ £96 ÷ 4
= £24

3 units ⟶ £24 × 3
= £72

Mrs Ali had £72 and Miss Murray had £24.

d How much money must Mrs Ali give to Miss Murray so that Miss Murray will have 3 times as much money as Mrs Ali?

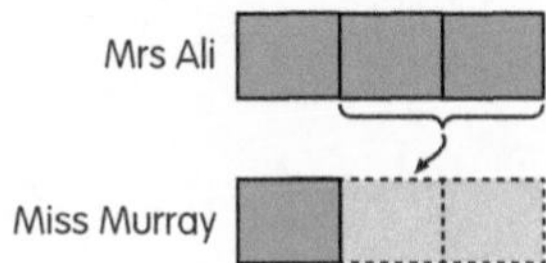

2 units ⟶ £24 × 2 = £48

Mrs Ali must give Miss Murray £48 so that Miss Murray will have 3 times as much money as Mrs Ali.

Objective of activity

Pupils will be able to use the heuristics and hints provided in the question to solve the problem.

Thinking skill

Sequencing

Heuristics for problem solving

- Make a systematic list
- Before-after concept
- Guess and check

Independent work

- *Challenging Practice* and *Problem Solving* in Practice Book 6A, pp 119 to 120.

Teaching sequence

19 *Put On Your Thinking Caps!*

- Ask pupils to use the information provided to complete the table, which will help them solve the problem.

Put On Your Thinking Caps!

19 Mrs Kim had a total of 33 watches and necklaces in her shop. After selling some watches and necklaces, she had 12 of them left. The ratio of the number of watches sold to the number of watches left was 1 : 2. The ratio of the number of necklaces sold to the number of necklaces that were left was 3 : 1. How many necklaces were there at first? Copy the table below and fill it in to solve the problem. (Hint: Make a list and solve the problem using guess and check.)

Number of Watches Sold (W1)	Number of Watches Left (W2)	W1 : W2 (1 : 2)	Number of Necklaces Sold (N1)	Number of Necklaces Left (N2)	N1 : N2 (3 : 1)	Total Number of Watches and Necklaces Left	Total Number of Watches and Necklaces at First
1	2	1 : 2	30	10	3 : 1	12	1 + 2 + 30 + 10 = 43
2	4	1 : 2	24	8	3 : 1	12	2 + 4 + 24 + 8 = 38
3	6	1 : 2	18	6	3 : 1	12	3 + 6 + 18 + 6 = 33 ✓

18 + 6 = 24
There were 24 necklaces at first.

Heuristics: Make a systematic list, use before-after concept, use guess and check
Thinking skills: Sequencing

Practice Book 6A, p.119 Practice Book 6A, p.120

Unit 5 Ratio

Date: ____________

Practice 1 Ratio and fraction

1 Which of the following correctly shows that 'A is $\frac{7}{4}$ of B'?
Write your answer in the box provided.

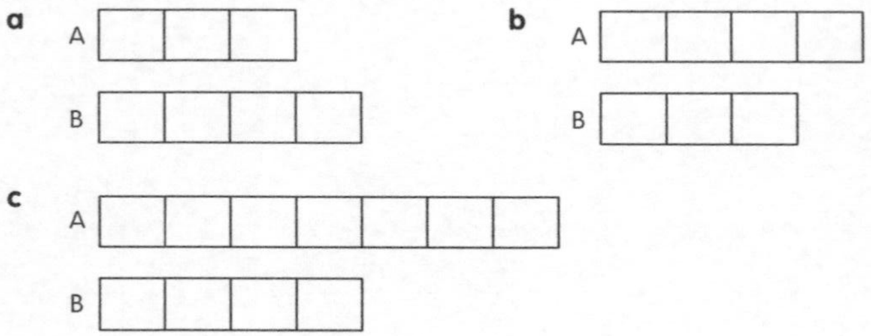

a A B

b A B

c A B

Answer: c

2 The lengths of Stick A and Stick B are represented below.

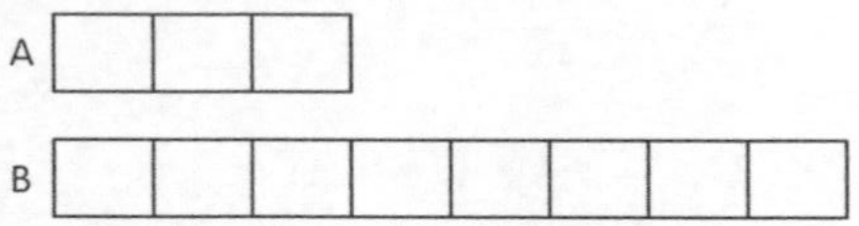

A

B

a The ratio of the length of Stick A to the length of Stick B is 3 : 8.

b The length of Stick A is $\frac{3}{8}$ of the length of Stick B.

c The length of Stick B is $\frac{8}{3}$ of the length of Stick A.

3 The picture below shows the masses of two bags of rice, X and Y.

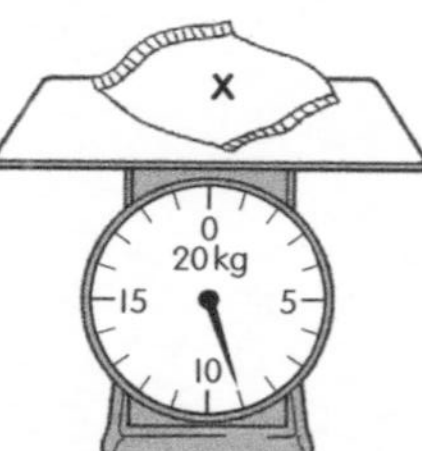

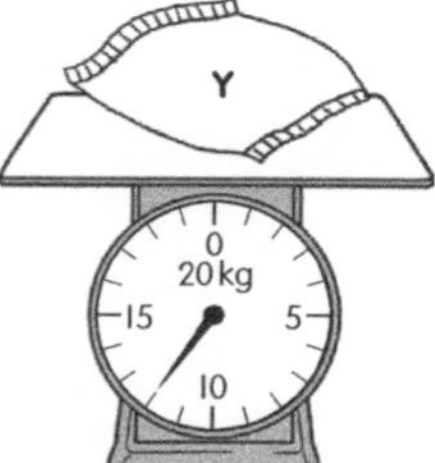

a The ratio of the mass of X to the total mass of X and Y is

3 : 7.

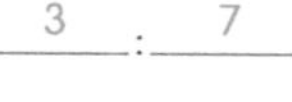

b The mass of Y is $\frac{4}{3}$ of the mass of X.

c The mass of X is $\frac{3}{4}$ of the mass of Y.

d The mass of X is $\frac{3}{7}$ of the total mass of X and Y.

e The mass of Y is $\frac{4}{7}$ of the total mass of X and Y.

4 Farha played 18 tennis matches in a week. Jack played 6 fewer matches than Farha.

a How many tennis matches did Jack play in a week?

18 – 6 = 12

Jack played 12 tennis matches in a week.

b Find the ratio of the number of matches Farha played to the total number of matches both children played.

Total number of matches played = 18 + 12
= 30

Number of matches Farha played : Total number of matches
= 18 : 30
= 3 : 5

The ratio of the number of matches Farha played to the total number of matches both children played is 3 : 5.

c Express the number of matches Jack played as a fraction of the number of matches Farha played.

$$\frac{\text{Number of matches Jack played}}{\text{Number of matches Farha played}} = \frac{12}{18}$$
$$= \frac{2}{3}$$

The number of matches Jack played is $\frac{2}{3}$ of the number of matches Farha played.

d What fraction of the total number of matches played by both children is the number of matches Jack played?

$$\frac{\text{Number of matches Jack played}}{\text{Total number of matches played}} = \frac{12}{30}$$
$$= \frac{2}{5}$$

The number of matches Jack played is $\frac{2}{5}$ of the total number of matches played by both children.

5 Tai, Hardeep and Omar went blackberry picking. They shared out the blackberries among themselves in the ratio 3 : 4 : 5.

a Express Tai's share as a fraction of Omar's share.

$$\frac{\text{Tai's share}}{\text{Omar's share}} = \frac{3}{5}$$

Tai's share was $\frac{3}{5}$ of Omar's share.

b What fraction of the total number of blackberries picked was Hardeep's share?

Total units = 3 + 4 + 5
= 12

$$\frac{\text{Hardeep's share}}{\text{Total number of blackberries picked}} = \frac{4}{12}$$
$$= \frac{1}{3}$$

Hardeep's share was $\frac{1}{3}$ of the total number of blackberries picked.

c Express Omar's share as a fraction of their total share.

$$\frac{\text{Omar's share}}{\text{Total share}} = \frac{5}{12}$$

Omar's share was $\frac{5}{12}$ of the total share.

6 Millie picked $\frac{2}{7}$ of the mass of strawberries Omar picked.

a Express the mass of strawberries Omar picked as a fraction of the mass of strawberries that Millie picked.

$\frac{\text{Mass of strawberries Omar picked}}{\text{Mass of strawberries Millie picked}} = \frac{7}{2}$

The mass of strawberries Omar picked is $\frac{7}{2}$ of the mass of the strawberries Millie picked.

b What is the ratio of the mass of strawberries Millie picked to the mass of strawberries Omar picked?

Millie's strawberries : Omar's strawberries
= 2 : 7

The ratio of the mass of strawberries Millie picked to the mass of strawberries Omar picked is 2 : 7.

c What is the ratio of the mass of strawberries Omar picked to the total mass of the strawberries Omar and Millie picked altogether?

Total units = 2 + 7 = 9

Mass of Omar's strawberries : Total mass of strawberries altogether
= 7 : 9

The ratio of the mass of the strawberries Omar picked to the total mass of the strawberries Omar and Millie picked altogether is 7 : 9.

d Express the mass of strawberries Millie picked as a fraction of the total mass of the strawberries Omar and Millie picked altogether.

$\frac{\text{Mass of Millie's strawberries}}{\text{Total mass of strawberries altogether}} = \frac{2}{9}$

The mass of strawberries Millie picked is $\frac{2}{9}$ of the total mass of the strawberries Omar and Millie picked altogether.

7 Hannah is 3 times as old as Sian.

a Find the ratio of Hannah's age to Sian's age.

Hannah's age : Sian's age
= 3 : 1

The ratio of Hannah's age to Sian's age is 3 : 1.

b Find the ratio of Sian's age to their total age.

Total age = 3 + 1
= 4 units

Sian's age : Total age
= 1 : 4

The ratio of Sian's age to their total age is 1 : 4.

c What fraction of Hannah's age is Sian's age?

Sian's age is $\frac{1}{3}$ of Hannah's age.

8 Miss Green earned 4 times as much money as Mr Ali. Mr O'Brien earned $\frac{3}{4}$ of what Miss Green earned.

a Find the ratio of Miss Green's salary to Mr Ali's salary.

Miss Green's salary : Mr Ali's salary
= 4 : 1

The ratio of Miss Green's salary to Mr Ali's salary was 4 : 1.

b What fraction of Miss Green's salary was Mr Ali's salary?

Mr Ali's salary was $\frac{1}{4}$ of Miss Green's salary.

c What fraction of Mr O'Brien's salary was Mr Ali's salary?

Mr Ali's salary was $\frac{1}{3}$ of Mr O'Brien's salary.

Date: ____________

Practice 2 Word problems (1)

Solve these word problems. Show your workings clearly.

1 The amount of money Ella spent is $\frac{9}{4}$ of the amount of money Ruby spent.

a What fraction of the total amount of money spent is the amount of money Ella spent?

b What fraction of the total amount of money spent is the amount of money Ruby spent?

a Total units = 9 + 4
= 13

$$\frac{\text{Amount of money Ella spent}}{\text{Total amount of money spent}} = \frac{9}{13}$$

The amount of money Ella spent is $\frac{9}{13}$ of the total amount of money spent.

b

$$\frac{\text{Amount of money Ruby spent}}{\text{Total amount of money spent}} = \frac{4}{13}$$

The amount of money Ruby spent is $\frac{4}{13}$ of the total amount of money spent.

2 By the end of a year, Hardeep's savings are $\frac{9}{2}$ of Millie's savings.

a What is the ratio of Hardeep's savings to Millie's savings to their total savings?
b What fraction of the total amount of money saved is Hardeep's?
c What fraction of the total amount of money saved is Millie's?
d Millie saves £28 less than Hardeep. How much do both children save altogether?

a Total units = 9 + 2
= 11

Hardeep's savings : Millie's savings : Total savings
= 9 : 2 : 11

The ratio of Hardeep's savings to Millie's savings to the total savings is 9 : 2 : 11.

b $\frac{\text{Hardeep's savings}}{\text{Total savings}} = \frac{9}{11}$

Hardeep's savings is $\frac{9}{11}$ of the total amount of money saved.

c $\frac{\text{Millie's savings}}{\text{Total savings}} = \frac{2}{11}$

Millie's savings is $\frac{2}{11}$ of the total amount of money saved.

d 9 − 2 = 7

7 units → £28

1 unit → $£\left(\frac{28}{7}\right) = £4$

11 units → £4 × 11 = £44

Both of them save £44 altogether.

3 Jack cut a piece of material into 2 pieces. The length of the shorter piece is $\frac{5}{9}$ of the length of the longer piece.

a Find the ratio of the length of the longer piece to the length of the shorter piece to the total length.
b If the longer piece is 148·6 cm longer than the shorter piece, find the total length of the original piece of material.

a Total length = 5 + 9
= 14 units

The ratio of the length of the longer piece to the length of the shorter piece to the total length is 9 : 5 : 14.

b Difference in length = 9 − 5
= 4 units

4 units → 148·6 cm
1 unit → 148·6 ÷ 4
= 37·15 cm
14 units → 37·15 × 14
= 520·1 cm

The total length of the original piece of material was 520·1 cm.

4 Ruby, Tai and Farha decided to have a typing competition. Ruby typed 2 times as fast as Tai. The ratio of the number of words Tai typed to the number of words Farha typed was 4 : 1. If Farha typed 48 words, how many words did Ruby type?

Number of words Ruby typed : Number of words Tai typed
= 2 : 1
= 8 : 4

Number of words Ruby typed : Number of words Farha typed
= 8 : 1

1 unit → 48 words
8 units → 48 × 8 = 384 words

Ruby typed 384 words.

5 The length of a rectangle is 6 times as long as its width.

a What fraction of the perimeter of the rectangle is the length of the rectangle?
b Find the ratio of the length of the rectangle to its width and to its perimeter.
c If the perimeter of the rectangle is 342·44 cm, find the length and width of the rectangle.

a Perimeter of the rectangle = (6 + 1) × 2
= 14 units

$\frac{6}{14} = \frac{3}{7}$

The length of the rectangle is $\frac{3}{7}$ of the perimeter of the rectangle.

b The ratio of the length of the rectangle to its width and to its perimeter is 6 : 1 : 14.

c 14 units → 342·44 cm
1 unit → 342·44 ÷ 14
= 24·46 cm
6 units → 24·46 × 6
= 146·76 cm

The length is 146·76 cm and the width is 24·46 cm.

Date: ______

Maths Journal

1 Use the words and numbers below to write your own word problem on ratio. Then solve the word problem.

ratio Daniel Matt cakes 5 3 fraction 24 more than make altogether

Answers vary
Example:
The ratio of the number of cakes baked by Daniel to that of Matt was 5 : 3. What fraction of Daniel's cake was Matt's? Daniel made 24 more cakes than Matt. How many cakes did they make altogether?

2 Peter and Hardeep wrote their answers to two questions below. Circle the incorrect answers. Explain their mistakes. If necessary, provide the correct answer(s).

a Miss Barker earned 6 times as much money as Mr Hunt. What fraction of the total salary earned by both Miss Barker and Mr Hunt was Miss Barker's salary?

Peter's Answer
$\frac{1}{7}$ (circled)
Hardeep's Answer
$\frac{6}{7}$

Peter worked out Mr Hunt's salary as a fraction of their total salary instead.

b Isabel's mark was $\frac{5}{9}$ of Amit's mark in their test. Find the ratio of Amit's mark to their total mark.

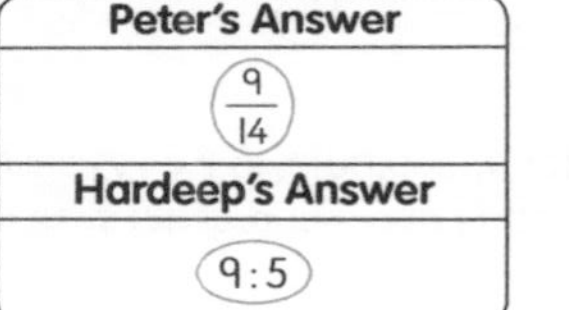

Peter's Answer
$\frac{9}{14}$ (circled)
Hardeep's Answer
9 : 5 (circled)

Peter wrote his answer as a fraction instead of a ratio.
Hardeep worked out the ratio of Amit's mark to Isabel's mark instead.
Correct answer: 9 : 14

Date: ______

Practice 3 Comparing ratios

1 a The table below shows the number of boys and girls in different groups. The number of boys and the number of girls are in a fixed ratio. Complete the table.

Number of boys	2	4	6	8	10	12
Number of girls	5	10	15	20	25	30

b The table below shows the number of sheep and cows in different fields on a farm. The number of sheep and cows are in a fixed ratio. Complete the table.

Number of sheep	9	18	27	36	45	54
Number of cows	4	8	12	16	20	24

c Miya uses the following table to help her make jelly. The number of cups of water and the number of cubes of jelly are in a fixed ratio. Complete the table.

Number of cups of water	7	14	21	28	35	42
Number of cubes of jelly	3	6	9	12	15	18

2 Farha uses 2 eggs for every 240 g of flour to make a cake.

a The ratio of the number of eggs to the amount of grams of flour used is 1 : 120.

b If Farha uses 5 eggs, she needs to use 600 g of flour.

c If Farha uses 720 g of flour, she needs to use 6 eggs.

Solve these word problems. Show your workings clearly.

3 A chef uses mushrooms and tomatoes in the ratio 2 : 7 to make a sauce. If the chef uses 129·5 g of tomatoes, what amount of mushrooms does he use?

7 units → 129·5 g

1 unit → $\frac{129 \cdot 5}{7}$ = 18·5 g

2 units → 18·5 × 2 = 37 g

He uses 37 g of mushrooms.

4 A builder mixes cement and sand to make a mixture. She uses 2 buckets of cement for every 5 buckets of sand.

a Find the ratio of the number of buckets of cement to the number of buckets of sand.
b If she uses 24 buckets of cement, how many buckets of sand does she use?
c If she uses 35 buckets of sand, how many buckets of cement does she use?

a The ratio of the number of buckets of cement to the number of buckets of sand is 2 : 5.

b $\frac{\text{Number of buckets of cement}}{\text{Number of buckets of sand}} = 2:5 = 24:60$

She uses 60 buckets of sand.

c $\frac{\text{Number of buckets of sand}}{\text{Number of buckets of cement}} = 5:2 = 35:14$

She uses 14 buckets of cement.

5 Mr Hall uses 0·4 ℓ of orange juice for every 0·9 ℓ of pineapple juice to make a jug of mixed fruit juice.

a Find the ratio of the amount of orange juice to the amount of pineapple juice.
b For 225 ml of pineapple juice, how much orange juice should Mr Hall use?
c If Mr Hall uses 80 ml of orange juice, how much pineapple juice does he need?

a 0·4 ℓ = 400 ml
0·9 ℓ = 900 ml

The ratio of the amount of orange juice to the amount of pineapple juice is 4 : 9.

b $\frac{\text{Amount of pineapple juice}}{\text{Amount of orange juice}} = \frac{9}{4} = \frac{225}{100}$

Mr Hall should use 100 ml of orange juice.

c $\frac{\text{Amount of orange juice}}{\text{Amount of pineapple juice}} = \frac{4}{9} = \frac{80}{180}$

He needs 180 ml of pineapple juice.

6 A sum of money is shared between Miss Hall, Mrs Webb and Miss Lim in the ratio 3 : 2 : 4. If Mrs Webb receives £4287·50, how much money do Miss Hall and Miss Lim receive altogether?

2 units → £4287·50

1 unit → £$\left(\frac{4287 \cdot 50}{2}\right)$ = £2143·75

3 units → £2143·75 × 3 = £6431·75
4 units → £2143·75 × 4 = £8575

£6431·25 + £8575 = £15 006·25

or 3 + 4 = 7
7 units → £2143·75 × 7
= £15 006·25

Miss Hall and Miss Lim receive £15 006·25 altogether.

7 Mrs Randall bought some tuna and sardines from a market. The ratio of the mass of tuna to the mass of sardines was 1 : 2. If she bought a total of 12 kg of fish, find the mass of each type of fish that she bought.

Total units = 1 + 2
= 3

3 units → 12 kg

1 unit → $\frac{12}{3}$ = 4 kg

2 units → 4 × 2 = 8 kg

She bought 4 kg of tuna and 8 kg of sardines.

8 A piece of wire is bent into a rectangle. The ratio of the length of the rectangle to its width is 9 : 5. If the total length of the wire is 84 cm, find the area of the rectangle made by the wire.

Perimeter of rectangle = 9 + 5 + 9 + 5
= 28 units

28 units → 84 cm

1 unit → $\frac{84}{28}$ = 3 cm

9 units → 3 × 9 = 27 cm

5 units → 3 × 5 = 15 cm

Area of rectangle = 27 × 15
= 405 cm²

Date: ______________

Practice 4 Word problems (2)

1 The ratio of the number of strawberries Hardeep had to the number of strawberries Peter had was 3 : 4. Peter gave half of his strawberries to Hardeep. What was the new ratio of the number of strawberries Hardeep had to the number of strawberries Peter had?

Before Hardeep

Peter

After Hardeep

Peter

The new ratio of the number of strawberries Hardeep had to the number of strawberries Peter had was 5 : 2.

2 The ratio of the mass of flour in Packet A to the mass of flour in Packet B is 1 : 2. Millie uses $\frac{1}{3}$ of the flour in Packet A. What is the new ratio of the mass of flour in Packet A to the mass of flour in Packet B?

Before A B

After A B

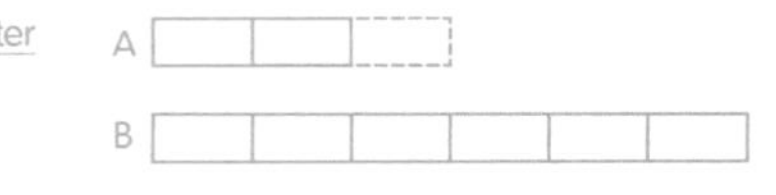

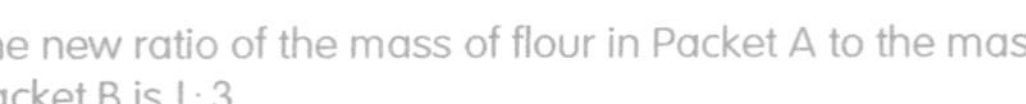

The new ratio of the mass of flour in Packet A to the mass of flour in Packet B is 1 : 3.

3 The ratio of the volume of orange juice in Glass A to the volume of orange juice in Glass B is 5 : 3. Half of the orange juice in Glass A is poured into Glass B. What is the new ratio of the volume of orange juice in Glass A to the volume of orange juice in Glass B?

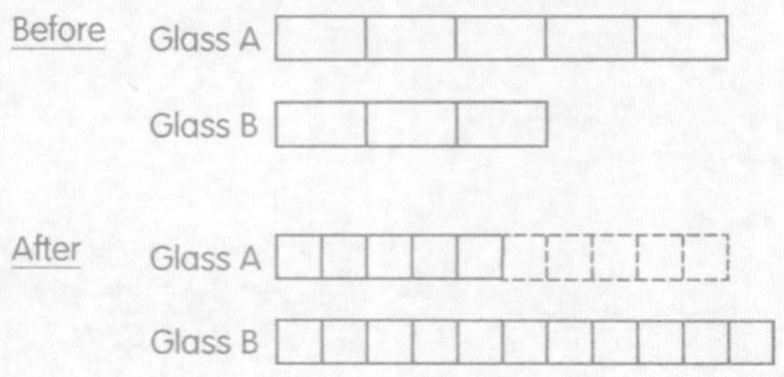

Before Glass A

Glass B

After Glass A

Glass B

The new ratio of the volume of orange juice in Glass A to the volume of orange juice in Glass B is 5 : 11.

4 Mr Lee put some red pens and blue pens into a box. The ratio of the number of red pens to the number of blue pens was 3 : 4. He added 20 red pens into the box and the ratio became 2 : 1.

a Were there more red pens or blue pens in the box in the end?
b How many red pens were there in the end?
c How many blue pens were there?

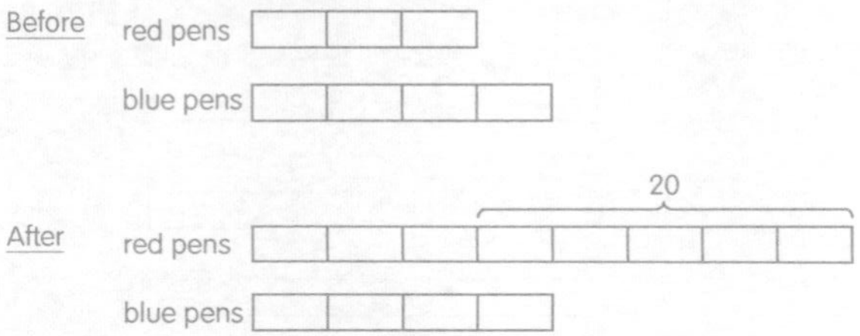

Before red pens

blue pens

20

After red pens

blue pens

a There were more red pens in the end.

b 5 units → 20 pens

1 unit → $\frac{20}{5}$ = 4 pens

8 units → 4 × 8 = 32 pens

There were 32 red pens in the end.

c 4 units → 4 × 4 = 16 pens

There were 16 blue pens.

5 The ratio of the number of cakes Ella had to the number of cakes Farha had was 5 : 2. After Ella sold 28 cakes, the ratio became 3 : 4. How many cakes did each child have at first?

Before Ella
Farha

28

After Ella
Farha

7 units → 28 cakes

1 unit → $\frac{28}{7}$ = 4 cakes

4 units → 4 × 4 = 16 cakes
10 units → 4 × 10 = 40 cakes

Ella had 40 cakes and Farha had 16 cakes at first.

6 The ratio of the number of cows on Farm X to the number of cows on Farm Y was 9 : 4. After 35 cows were moved from Farm X to Farm Y, there was an equal number of cows on each farm. How many cows were there on each farm at first?

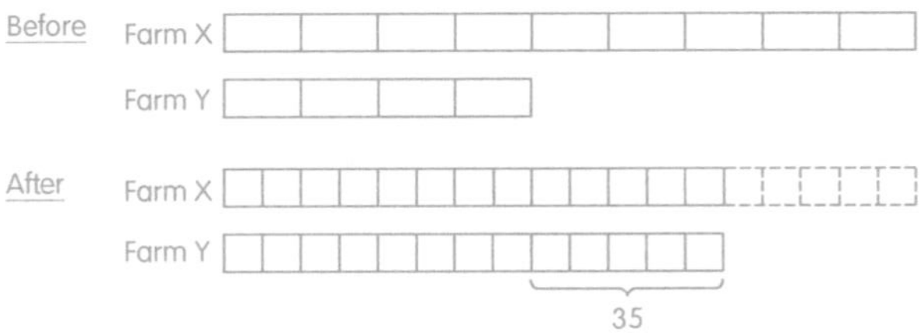

Before Farm X
Farm Y

After Farm X
Farm Y

35

5 units → 35 cows

1 unit → $\frac{35}{5}$ = 7 cows

8 units → 7 × 8 = 56 cows

18 units → 7 × 18 = 126 cows

There were 126 cows on Farm X and 56 cows on Farm Y at first.

7 Jack's mum had the same amount of money in her three bank accounts at first. She put £44 into Account B and £80 into Account C. In the end, the ratio of the amount of money in Account A to the amount of money in Account C was 2 : 7. How much money was there in Account B in the end?

Before: A, B, C

After: A, B (£44), C (£80)

5 units → £80

1 unit → £$\left(\frac{80}{5}\right)$ = £16

2 units → £16 × 2 = £32

£32 + £44 = £76

There was £76 in Account B in the end.

Date: ____________

Challenging Practice

1 The diagram below is made up of two rectangles, P and Q. The area of the shaded part is $\frac{2}{5}$ of the area of rectangle P. The ratio of the area of the shaded part to the area of rectangle Q is 1 : 4. What fraction of the diagram is shaded?

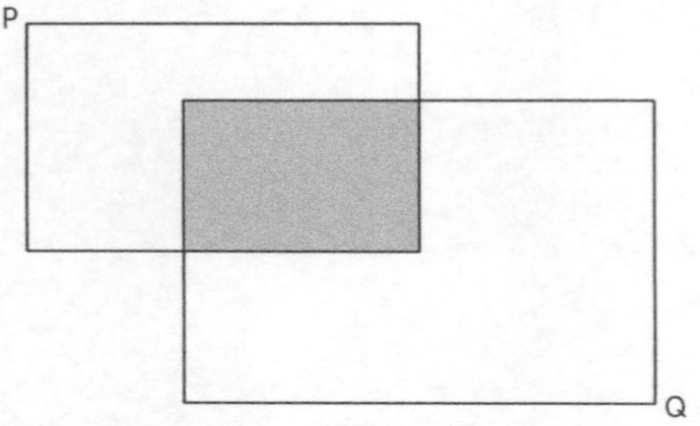

For rectangle P:
Area of shaded part : Area of unshaded part
= 2 : 3

For rectangle Q:
Area of shaded part : Area of unshaded part
= 1 : 3
= 2 : 6

Total area = 2 + 3 + 6
= 11 units

$\frac{\text{Area of shaded part}}{\text{Total area of diagram}} = \frac{2}{11}$

$\frac{2}{11}$ of the diagram is shaded.

Problem Solving

Date: ____________

1 A farmer had a total of 40 sheep and cows on her farm. After selling 29 of them, the ratio of the number of sheep sold to the number of sheep left was 4 : 1. If the ratio of the number of cows sold to the number of cows left was 3 : 2, what was the ratio of the number of sheep left to the number of cows left? Complete the table below to solve the problem.
(Hint: Make a list and solve the problem using guess and check.)

Number of Sheep			Number of Cows		
Sold	Left	Total	Sold	Left	Total
4	1	5	3	2	5
8	2	10	6	4	10
12	3	15	(9)	6	(15)
16	4	20	12	8	20
(20)	5	(25)	15	10	25
24	6	30	18	12	30

Check:
Total number of sheep and cows = 25 + 15
= 40

Total number of sheep and cows sold = 20 + 9
= 29

Number of sheep left : Number of cows left
= 5 : 6

The ratio of the number of sheep left to the number of cows left is 5 : 6.

Heuristics: Use guess and check, make a systematic list
Thinking skills: Sequencing

Unit 6: Percentage

Medium-term plan

Week	Learning Objectives	Thinking Skills	Resources
1	**(1) Finding percentages** Pupils will be able to: • express a fraction or a decimal as a percentage and vice versa • find the whole given a part and the percentage • find a part given the whole and the percentage of the other part	• Analysing parts and wholes	• Pupil Textbook 6A, pp 113 to 119 • Practice Book 6A, pp 121 to 126 • Teacher's Guide 6A, pp 197 to 203
1	**(2) Word problems (1)** Pupils will be able to: • solve word problems using model drawing and the unitary method • find the percentage change (percentage increase or decrease) using the unitary or fractional methods • find the original or final value given the percentage change • solve word problems involving percentage and discount	• Analysing parts and wholes	• Pupil Textbook 6A, pp 120 to 126 • Practice Book 6A, pp 127 to 132 • Teacher's Guide 6A, pp 204 to 210

Week	Learning Objectives	Thinking Skills	Resources
2	**(3) Word problems (2)** Pupils will be able to solve higher-order word problems using model drawing, the 'before-after' concept, the strategy of working backwards and the unitary method. *Maths Journal* Pupils will be able to understand and describe the steps in solving a word problem involving percentage decrease.	• Analysing parts and wholes	• Pupil Textbook 6A, pp 127 to 136 • Practice Book 6A, pp 133 to 140 • Teacher's Guide 6A, pp 211 to 220

Unit 6: Percentage

Medium-term plan

Week	Learning Objectives	Thinking Skills	Resources
2	*Let's Wrap It Up!* Emphasise the key concepts, skills and processes that have been taught in the unit. Discuss the worked examples with pupils to assess whether they have mastered these concepts, skills and processes. *Put On Your Thinking Caps!* Pupils will be able to solve the problem by applying the concept of equal quantities by recognising that the same quantity can represent different percentages.	• Analysing parts and whole Heuristic for problem solving: • Simplify the problem	• Pupil Textbook 6A, pp 137 to 139 • Practice Book 6A, pp 141 to 144 • Teacher's Guide 6A, pp 221 to 223
3	Review 2		• Practice Book 6A, pp 145 to 164 • Teacher's Guide 6A, pp 236 to 246
3	Revision 1		• Practice Book 6A, pp 165 to 186 • Teacher's Guide 6A, pp 246 to 257

Summative assessment opportunities
Assessment Book 6, Test 6, pp 51 to 56 For extension, Assessment Book 6, Challenging Problems 2, pp 57 to 58 Assessment Book 6, Check-up 2, pp 59 to 74

Percentage

Learning objectives: Finding percentages

Pupils will be able to:

- express a fraction or a decimal as a percentage and vice versa
- find the whole given a part and the percentage
- find a part given the whole and the percentage of the other part

Key concepts

- Percentages are similar to decimal fractions.
- A percentage is a special type of decimal fraction, giving the number of parts out of 100 equal parts rather than out of 1.

Thinking skill

Analysing parts and wholes

Unit 6

Percentage

Let's Learn! 

Finding percentages

  Let's recall.

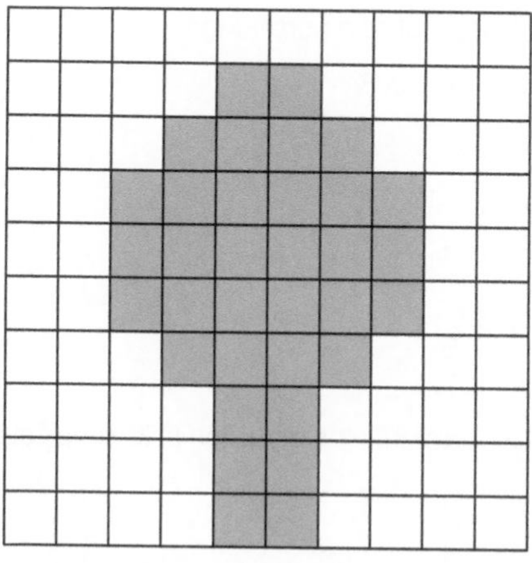

The big square is divided into 100 equal parts.
34 parts are shaded.
The shaded parts can be expressed in the following ways:

As a Fraction	As a Decimal	As a Percentage
$\frac{34}{100}$	0·34	34%

a Express each fraction as a percentage.

i $\frac{13}{20} = \frac{65}{100}$

$= 65\%$

ii $\frac{19}{25} = 76\%$

Teaching sequence

- Help pupils to revise the concepts of fractions, decimals and percentages, and how they can be used to express the same thing in different ways.
- Look at the examples with pupils and revise how to convert a fraction to a percentage by first making the denominator 100.

Teaching sequence

- Use examples to show how to express a decimal as a percentage and vice versa.
- Use examples to show how to express a percentage as a fraction (in its simplest form) and vice versa.

Unit 6 Percentage

iii $\frac{240}{300} = \frac{80}{100}$

$= 80\%$

iv $\frac{300}{500} = 60\%$

v $\frac{3}{4} = 75\%$

vi $\frac{5}{8} = 62{\cdot}5\%$

b Express each decimal as a percentage.

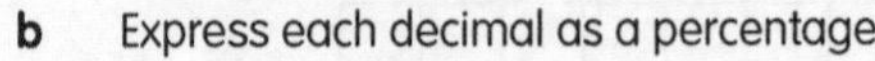

i 0·45 = 0·45 × 100%

= 45 %

ii 0·025 = 2·5 %

iii 0·08 = 8 %

iv 0·105 = 10·5 %

c Express each percentage as a fraction in its simplest form.

i 45% = $\frac{9}{20}$

ii 72% = $\frac{18}{25}$

iii 8% = $\frac{2}{25}$

iv 0·5% = $\frac{1}{200}$

d Express each percentage as a decimal.

i 25% = 0·25

ii 91% = 0·91

iii 4% = 0·04

iv 0·9% = 0·009

What you will need

Scientific calculator

e  Express each fraction as a percentage. Round your answer to the nearest whole number.

i $\frac{79}{120} \approx$ 66 %

ii $\frac{150}{405} \approx$ 37 %

iii $\frac{72}{303} \approx$ 24 %

iv $\frac{429}{579} \approx$ 74 %

2 The table shows the number of boys and girls on a school trip.

Number of boys	22
Number of girls	28
Total number of pupils	50

What percentage of the pupils on the trip are boys?

Method 1

$\frac{\text{Number of boys}}{\text{Total number of pupils}} = \frac{22}{50}$

$\frac{22 \times 2}{50 \times 2} = \frac{44}{100}$

$= 44\%$

44 % of the pupils are boys.

Convert the denominator to 100.

Method 2

$\frac{\text{Number of boys}}{\text{Total number of pupils}} = \frac{22}{50}$

$\frac{22}{50} \times 100\% = 22 \times 2\%$

$= 44\%$

44 % of the pupils are boys.

Multiply by 100%.

Teaching sequence

2

- Explain that the total number of pupils, as a set, is the whole and the number of boys is a part of this whole. If necessary, draw a part-whole model to show this.
- To aid pupils' understanding, it may be helpful to ask them to write a question based on the part-whole model.
- Work through the two methods of expressing a quantity of another quantity as a percentage with pupils:

  Method 1: Convert the denominator to 100.

  Method 2: Multiply by 100%.
- The answer must be expressed to the nearest whole number, so when looking at the numbers involved, you can ask the pupils what the choices are (i.e. the upper and lower bounds) and what would be the better choice.

What you will need

Scientific calculator

Teaching sequence

3 and 4

- Ask pupils to work on these questions as practice.
- If necessary, ask pupils to use the information given in the questions to draw the related part-whole model.

3 George had £28. He bought a book for £15. What percentage of his money did he spend? Give your answer to 1 decimal place.

$\frac{\text{Amount spent}}{\text{Total amount of money}} = \frac{15}{28}$

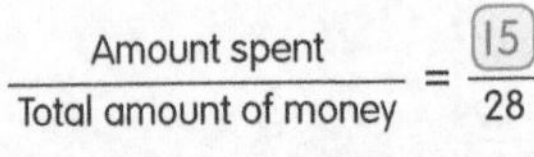

$\frac{15}{28} \times 100\% \approx 53.6\%$

He spent 53·6 % of his money.

4 A cook bought 11 kg of chicken. He used 0·75 kg of the chicken on Monday. What percentage of the chicken was not used? Give your answer to 1 decimal place.

Amount of chicken not used = 11 – 0·75

= ☐ kg 10·25

$\frac{\text{Amount of chicken not used}}{\text{Amount of chicken bought}} = \frac{10.25}{11}$

$\frac{10.25}{11} \times 100\% \approx 93.2\%$

93·2 % of the chicken was not used.

What you will need

Scientific calculator

5 Mr Thompson had £400. He bought a jacket for £78 and spent £48 on a pair of shoes. What percentage of his money was left?

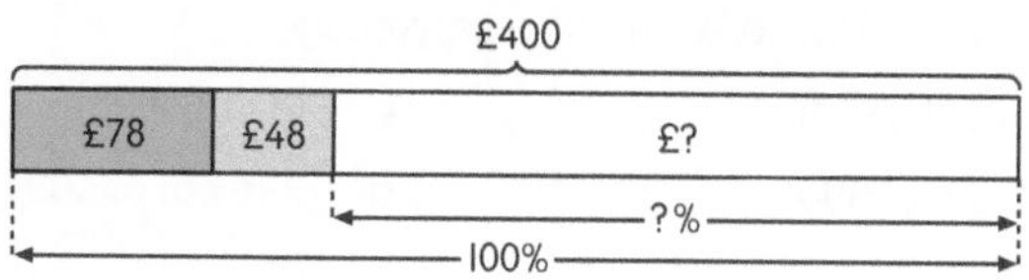

Amount of money left = £400 – £78 – £48
= £274

Percentage of money left = $\frac{274}{400} \times 100\%$
= 68·5%

68·5% of his money was left.

6 The usual price of a piano was £4750. Mr Smith bought the piano at a 10% discount. He had to pay a £49·50 delivery charge on top of the sale price. What percentage of the sale price was the delivery charge? Give your answer to the nearest whole number.

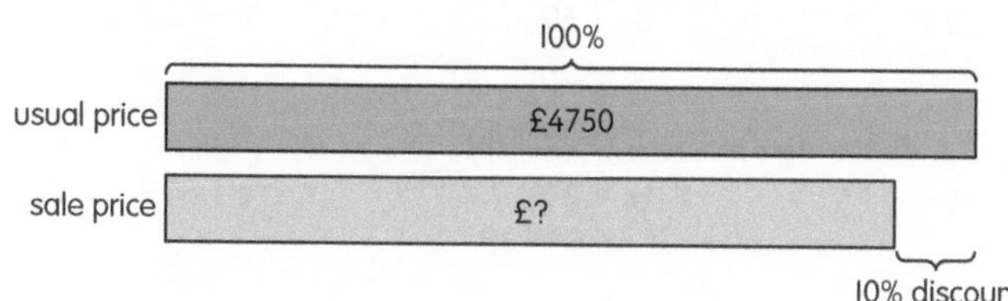

Discount = £475

Sale price = £4750 – £475 = £4275

$\frac{49.50}{4275} \times 100\% \approx 1\%$

The delivery charge was 1% of the sale price.

Teaching sequence

5

- Ask pupils to work on this question as practice.
- Check that pupils understand the three-part model shown in the question.

6

- Ask pupils to work on this question as practice.
- Highlight to pupils that the usual price is 100%, and the discount and sale price are both parts of this whole (100%).

Independent work

Let's Practise!

What you will need

Scientific calculator

Teaching sequence

10 *Let's Practise!*

- You could allow pupils who are confident in performing calculations without a calculator to do so for this particular question. All the denominators of the fractions are powers of 2, so the percentages can be worked out by halving the numerators and denominators an appropriate number of times. For example for part **b**:

$\frac{7}{16} = \frac{700}{16}\% = \frac{350}{8}\% = \frac{175}{4}\%$

$= \frac{87{\cdot}5}{2}\% = 43{\cdot}75\%$

For part **c**, the fraction can be simplified first and then seen to be double the fraction in part **b**.

Let's Practise!

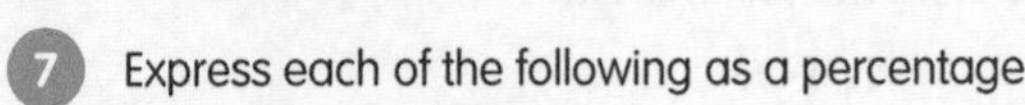

7 Express each of the following as a percentage.

a 9 out of 100 9%
b 18 out of 200 9%
c 165 out of 300 55%
d 296 out of 400 74%

8 Express each fraction as a percentage.

a $\frac{1}{2}$ 50%
b $\frac{3}{5}$ 60%
c $\frac{7}{10}$ 70%
d $\frac{32}{50}$ 64%
e $\frac{24}{25}$ 96%
f $\frac{3}{4}$ 75%

9 Express each decimal as a percentage.

a 0·9 90%
b 0·17 17%
c 0·03 3%
d 0·028 2·8%
e 0·005 0·5%
f 0·104 10·4%

10 Express each fraction as a percentage.

a $\frac{3}{8}$ 37·5%
b $\frac{7}{16}$ 43·75%
c $\frac{28}{32}$ 87·5%

11 Express each percentage as a fraction.

a 32% $\frac{8}{25}$
b 5% $\frac{1}{20}$
c 0·8% $\frac{1}{125}$

12 Express each percentage as a decimal.

a 55% 0·55
b 87% 0·87
c 7% 0·07

13 Express each fraction as a percentage. Round your answer to the nearest whole number.

a $\frac{47}{86}$ 55%
b $\frac{190}{345}$ 55%
c $\frac{84}{505}$ 17%
d $\frac{467}{975}$ 48%

What you will need

Scientific calculator

Independent work

Practice 1 in Practice Book 6A, pp 121 to 126.

Let's Practise!

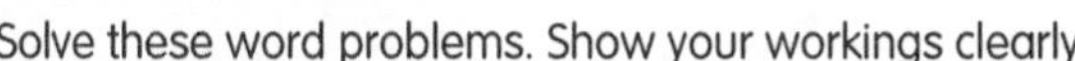

Solve these word problems. Show your workings clearly.

14. Ruby has a ribbon 420 cm long. She uses 216 cm to decorate a present. What percentage of the ribbon is left? Give your answer to 1 decimal place. 48·6%

15. A jug contained 780 ml of milk. Mrs Lee poured 221 ml of the milk into a glass and 130 ml into a cup. What percentage of milk was left in the jug? 55%

16. The price of a poster was £4. Carl bought the poster and paid £4·80 including the delivery charge. What percentage of the original price was the delivery charge? 20%

17. Mr Shaw puts £55 000 in a savings account. The interest rate is 3·3% per year. How much money will he have in the account after 1 year? £56 815

18. Ella spent 2 h 25 mins in a park. She spent 30 mins of the time playing football. What percentage of her time in the park was spent playing football? Round your answer to the nearest whole number. 21%

Practice Book 6A, p.121

Learning objectives: Word problems (1)

Pupils will be able to:

- solve word problems using model drawing and the unitary method
- find the percentage change (percentage increase or decrease) using the unitary or fractional methods
- find the original or final value given the percentage change
- solve word problems involving percentage and discount

Thinking skill

Analysing parts and wholes

What you will need

Scientific calculator

Teaching sequence

- This problem involves using the part-whole concept. We equate the whole to 100%.
- There are two parts in this context. One part is the set of children wearing football kits and the other is the set of children not wearing football kits. The entire group of children is therefore equated to 100%.
- You could allow pupils who are confident in performing the calculations for this question without a calculator to do so.

- Ask pupils to work on this question as practice. Highlight to pupils that the total number of marks is equated to 100%, but explain that this may not always be the case.

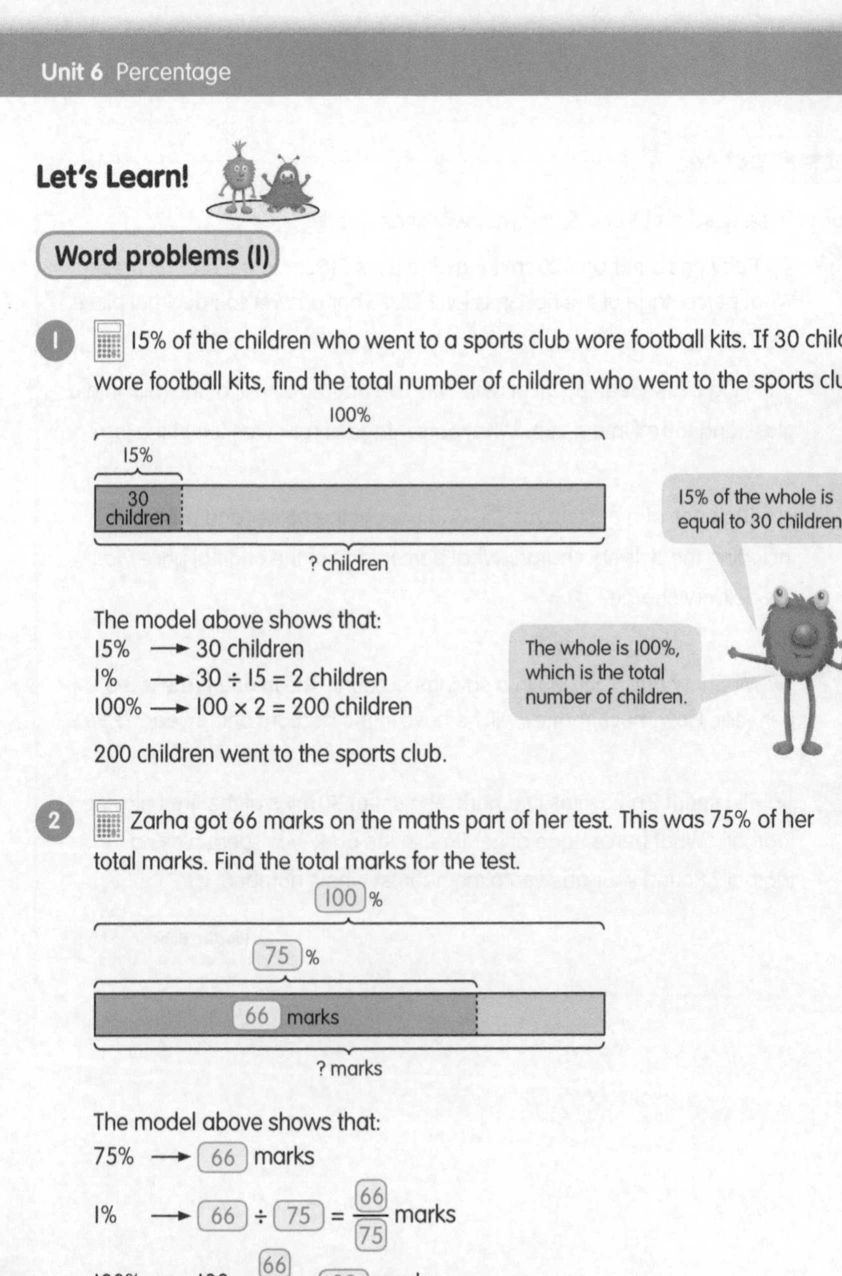

Unit 6 Percentage

Let's Learn!

Word problems (1)

1 15% of the children who went to a sports club wore football kits. If 30 children wore football kits, find the total number of children who went to the sports club.

The model above shows that:

15% ⟶ 30 children

1% ⟶ 30 ÷ 15 = 2 children

100% ⟶ 100 × 2 = 200 children

200 children went to the sports club.

2 Zarha got 66 marks on the maths part of her test. This was 75% of her total marks. Find the total marks for the test.

The model above shows that:

75% ⟶ 66 marks

1% ⟶ 66 ÷ 75 = $\frac{66}{75}$ marks

100% ⟶ 100 × $\frac{66}{75}$ = 88 marks

Her total mark for the test was 88.

120

What you will need

Scientific calculator

Teaching sequence

3 to 5

- Ask pupils to work on these questions as practice.
- Highlight to pupils that questions 4 and 5 are examples of percentages being used in the real world.

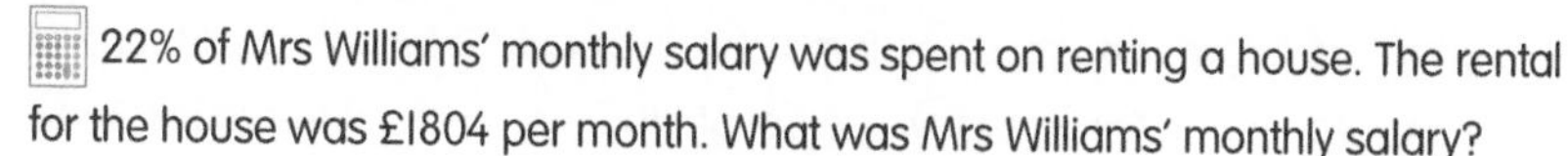

3 22% of Mrs Williams' monthly salary was spent on renting a house. The rental for the house was £1804 per month. What was Mrs Williams' monthly salary?

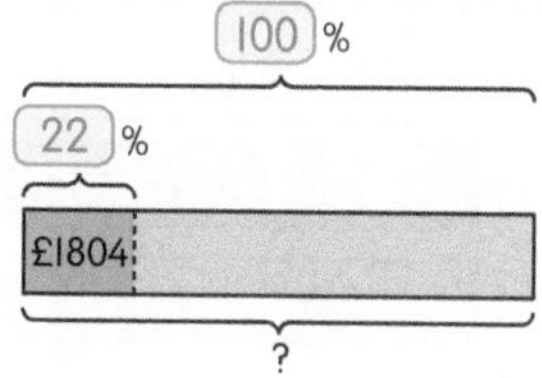

The model above shows that:

22 % → £ 1804

1% → £ 1804 ÷ 22 = £ 82

100% → 100 × £ 82 = £ ___ 8200

Mrs Williams' monthly salary was £ ___. 8200

4 Miss Knight bought a watch in a sale and she paid £40. The sale price was 20% of the original price. How much did the watch cost originally?

20 % → £ 40

1% → £ 40 ÷ 20 = £ 2

100% → 100 × £ 2 = £ 200

The watch cost £ 200 originally.

5 Mrs Sharma put some money in a savings account. The interest was 5% of the amount of money she put in. At the end of the year, Mrs Sharma received £72·25 as interest. How much did Mrs Sharma put into the account?

5 % → £ 72·25

1% → £ 72·25 ÷ 5 = £ 14·45

100% → 100 × £ 14·45 = £ 1445

Mrs Sharma put £ 1445 in the savings account.

What you will need

Scientific calculator

Teaching sequence

- Highlight to pupils that this question involves a percentage increase.
- Encourage pupils to notice that, when a quantity is increased by a certain amount, the original quantity is equated to 100%. Here, the final quantity is more than the original quantity.
- Ensure that pupils are able to work out the solutions using both of the methods described.

6 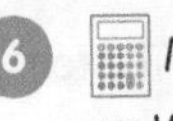 Mrs Adams bought some tomatoes and paid £2·50 per kg at a market on Wednesday. On Saturday, she bought the same type of tomatoes. The price had increased by 20%. What was the price of the tomatoes per kg on Saturday?

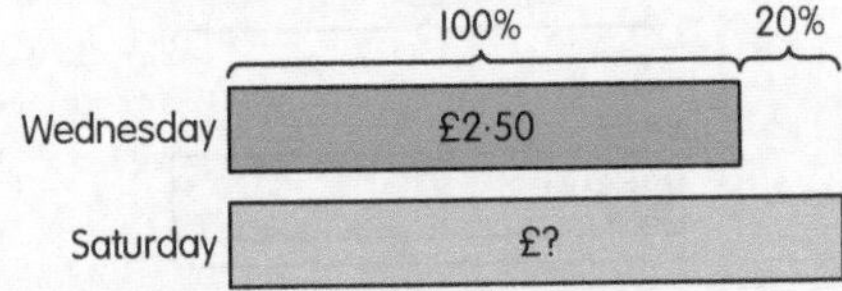

Method 1

100% ⟶ £2·50

1% ⟶ $£2{\cdot}50 \div 100 = £\left(\frac{2{\cdot}50}{100}\right)$

120% ⟶ $120 \times £\left(\frac{2{\cdot}50}{100}\right)$

$= £3$

The price of the tomatoes on Saturday was £3 per kg.

On Saturday the price of the tomatoes was 120% of the price of the tomatoes on Wednesday.

Method 2

20% of £2·50 $= \frac{20}{100} \times £2{\cdot}50$

$= £0{\cdot}50$

$£2{\cdot}50 + £0{\cdot}50 = £3$

The price of the tomatoes on Saturday was £3 per kg.

First find the increase in price. The increase was 20% of the price on Wednesday.

122

What you will need

Scientific calculator

 When Jack was 9 years old, his mass was 28 kg. Two years later, his mass had increased by 30%. Find Jack's mass now he is 11 years old.

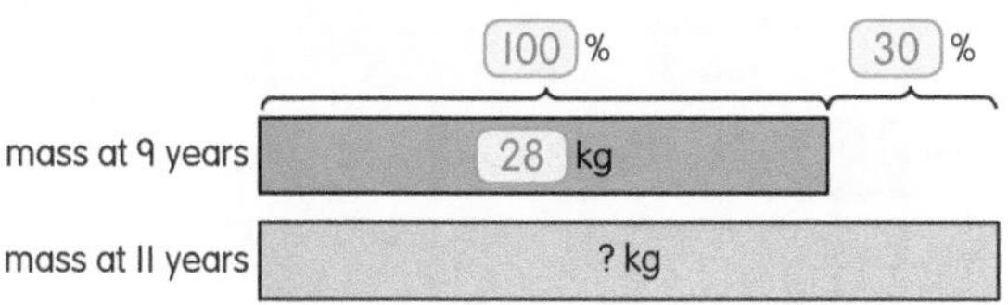

Method 1

Jack's mass when he is 11 years old is [130] % of his mass when he was 9 years old.

100% ⟶ 28 kg

1% ⟶ 28 ÷ 100 = [0·28] kg

[130] % ⟶ [130] × [0·28] = [36·4] kg

Jack's mass when he is 11 years old is [36·4] kg.

Method 2

100% ⟶ 28 kg

1% ⟶ 28 ÷ 100 = [0·28] kg

30% ⟶ 30 × [0·28] = [8·4] kg

28 kg + [8·4] kg = [36·4] kg

Jack's mass when he is 11 years old is [36·4] kg.

Teaching sequence

- Ask pupils to work on this question as practice.

What you will need

Scientific calculator

Teaching sequence

- Highlight to pupils that this question involves a percentage decrease.
- Again encourage pupils to notice that, when a quantity is decreased by a certain amount, the original quantity is equated to 100%. Here, the final quantity is less than the original quantity.

- This is also a percentage decrease question, but this time pupils are asked to find out the percentage change, rather than the final value. Stress that the percentage discount is expressed as the percentage of the usual price.

8 The price of a new boat was £43 750 in April. However, the price of the boat was reduced by 5% in May. Find the price of the boat in May.

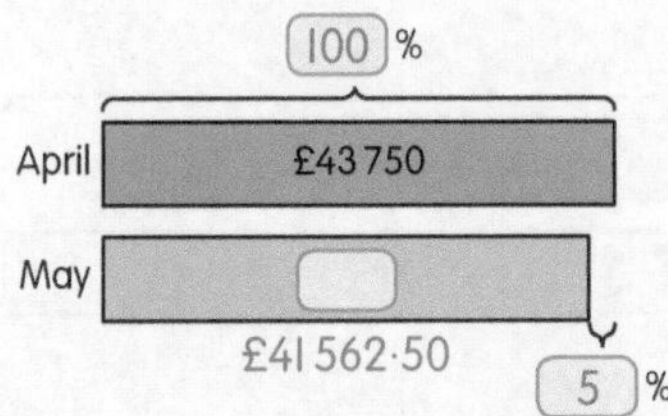

In May, the price of the boat was 95 % compared to the price of the boat in April.

100% → £ 43 750

1% → £ 43 750 ÷ 100 = £ 437·50

95 % → £ 95 × 437·50 = £ 41 562·50

The price of the boat in May was £ 41 562·50.

9 The usual price of a pair of trainers was £32. A shop sold the trainers for £24. Find the percentage discount.

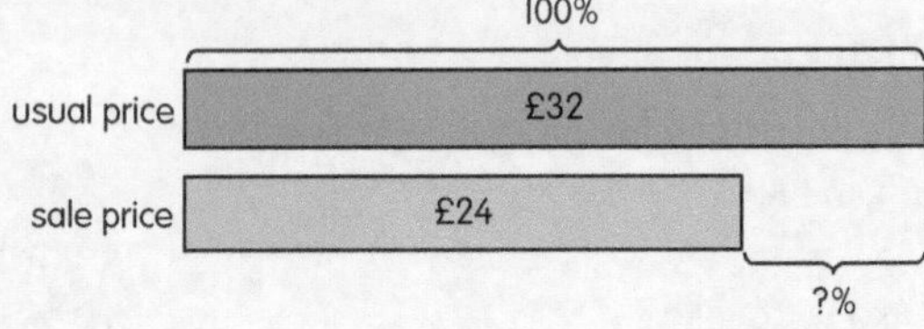

£32 – £24 = £8

The discount was £8.

£32 → 100%

£1 → $\frac{100}{32}$ %

£8 → $8 \times \frac{100}{32}$ % = 25%

The percentage discount was 25%.

What you will need

Scientific calculator

Independent work

Let's Practise!

10 The usual price of a model aeroplane is £64. However, one shop sells the model aeroplane for £72. Find the percentage increase in price.

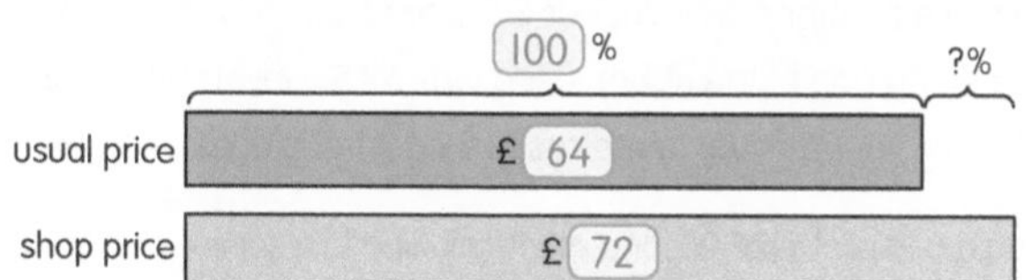

We are comparing the shop price with the usual price. We take the usual price as 100 %.

The increase in price was £ 8.

£ 64 → 100%

£ 8 → $8 \times \frac{100}{64}\% = 12{\cdot}5\%$

The percentage increase in price was 12·5 %.

11 The temperature in a town was 16°C in the morning. In the afternoon, the temperature was 20°C. Find the percentage increase in temperature.

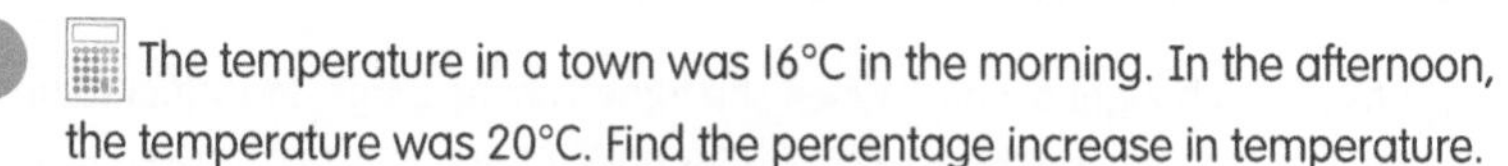

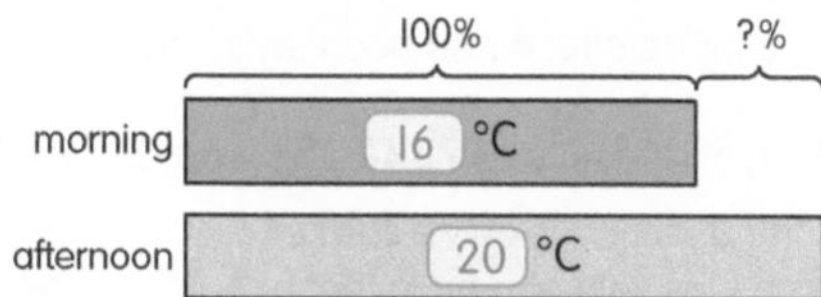

The increase in temperature was 4 °C.

$\frac{4}{16} \times 100\% = 25\%$

The percentage increase in temperature was 25 %.

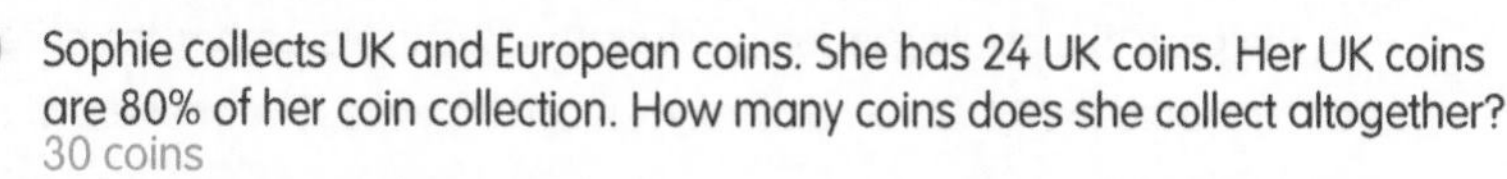

Let's Practise!

Solve these word problems. Show your workings clearly.

12 Sophie collects UK and European coins. She has 24 UK coins. Her UK coins are 80% of her coin collection. How many coins does she collect altogether?
30 coins

Teaching sequence

10 and 11

- Ask pupils to work on these questions as practice.

What you will need

Scientific calculator

Independent work

Practice 2 and *Maths Journal* in Practice Book 6A, pp 127 to 132.

Let's Practise!

13 Alisha had a piece of ribbon. She cut out 4·5 m from the ribbon to make decorations. The percentage of the ribbon used was 62%. How much ribbon did she have left? Give your answer in metres to 2 decimal places. 2·76 m

14 Miss Palmer paid a total of £124·20 for a meal including 15% service charge on the cost of the meal. How much was the cost of the meal without the service charge? £108

15 During a sale, Mr Davies bought a digital camera for £810. This was 90% of the usual price. How much was the discount? £90

16 The room temperature was 24°C in the morning. Five hours later, the room temperature had increased by 12%.

- **a** What was the increase in the temperature of the room to the nearest degree? 3°C
- **b** What was the room temperature five hours later to the nearest degree? 27°C

17 Mrs Patel bought a fridge. When she turned on the fridge, the temperature in it was 16·2°C. After 10 hours, the temperature dropped by 75%. What was the temperature of the fridge after it had been switched on for 10 hours? 4·05°C

18 The sale price of 1 kg of chicken was £5·40. This was 10% less than the usual price.

- **a** What was the usual price of the chicken? £6·00
- **b** If the chicken was sold at a price that was 8% more than the usual price, what would be the price of the chicken? £6·48

19 The price of an entertainment system was £8999. After a year, the price of the same entertainment system was £4200. Find the percentage decrease in price. Round your answer to the nearest whole number. 53%

20 In January, the price of a kilogram of tangerines in the supermarket was £3·20. In May, a kilogram of the same type of tangerines cost £2·99. Find the percentage decrease in price. Give your answer to 1 decimal place. 6·6%

21 The price of a painting in January was £16 525. In November, the price had increased to £24 725. Find the percentage increase. Give your answer to 1 decimal place. 49·6%

Practice Book 6A, p.127

Learning objective: Word problems (2)

Pupils will be able to solve higher-order word problems using model drawing, the 'before-after' concept, the strategy of working backwards and the unitary method.

Thinking skill

Analysing parts and wholes

Note

1 to 4 involve discounts where you are given $(100 - x)\%$ of the original price.

Let's Learn! 

Word problems (2)

1 Mr Clark paid £240 for a new suit. He had been given a 20% discount on the usual price. What was the usual price of the suit?

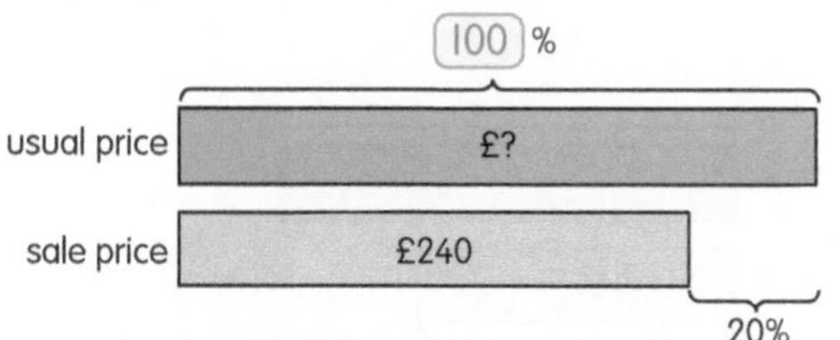

100% – 20% = 80%
The sale price was 80% of the usual price.

80% ⟶ £240

1% ⟶ $£\left(\frac{240}{80}\right) = £3$

100% ⟶ 100 × £3 = £300

The usual price of the suit was £300.

2 A supermarket sold 75 bags of apples on Thursday. This was 40% less than the number of bags of apples that it sold on Wednesday. How many bags of apples did the supermarket sell on Wednesday?

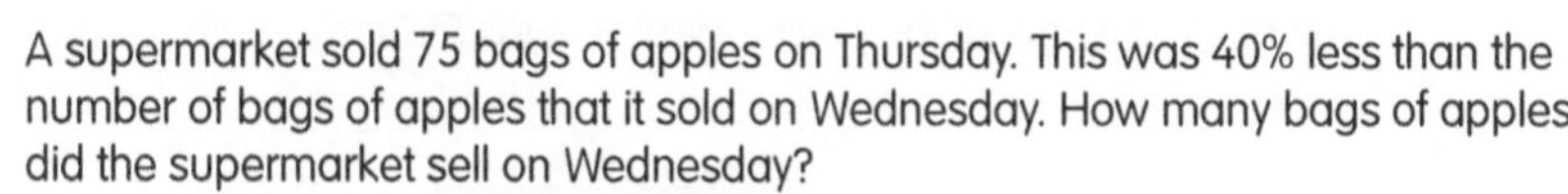

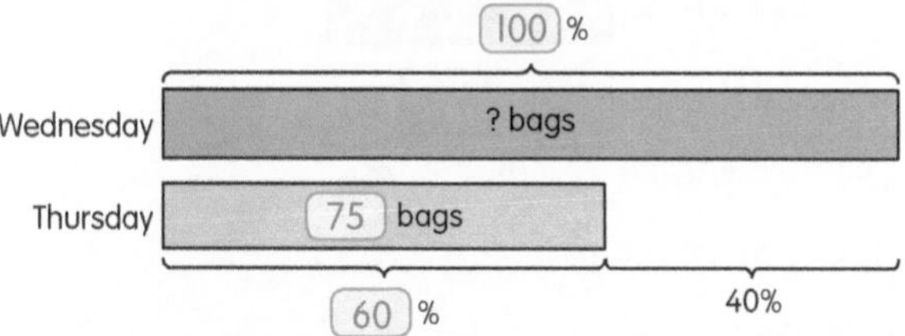

The number of bags of apples the supermarket sold on Thursday is 60 % of the number of bags that it sold on Wednesday.

60 % ⟶ 75 bags

1% ⟶ $\frac{75}{60}$ = 1·25 bags

100% ⟶ 100 × 1·25 = 125 bags

The supermarket sold 125 bags of apples on Wednesday.

Teaching sequence

1 and 2

- In 1, we take the usual price as 100%. Explain to pupils that if there was no discount, then the sale price would be the same as the usual price. As there is a discount, then the sale price is less than 100%.
- Ask pupils to work on 2 as practice.

What you will need

Scientific calculator

Teaching sequence

- In the first part of this question, pupils are given the value of a part and the percentage of the other part, and asked to find the whole.
- In the second part, pupils will need to draw a second part-whole model. Emphasise that the value equated to 100% will be different from that in the first model.

3  Mr Ward had a piece of leather. He cut off 30% of the piece of leather to make a belt. The remaining length of the piece of leather was 385 cm long. He then cut off 25% of the remaining piece of leather to make a necklace.

a What was the original length of the piece of leather?

b What was the remaining length of the piece of leather after he made the necklace?

a

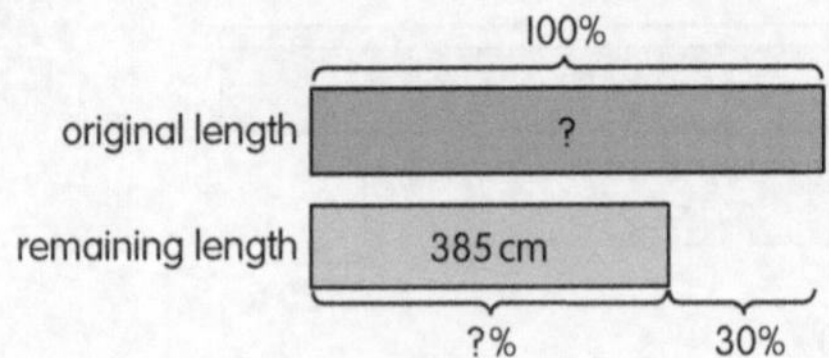

100% – 30% = 70%

70% ⟶ 385 cm

1% ⟶ 385 ÷ 70 = 5·5 cm

100% ⟶ 100 × 5·5 = 550 cm

The original length of the piece of leather was 550 cm.

b

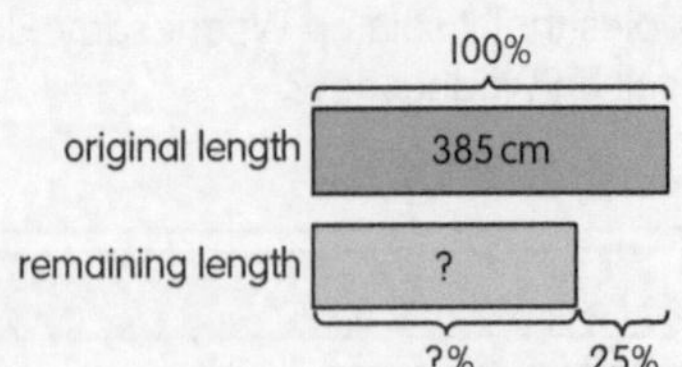

100% – 25% = 75%

75% × 385 = 288·75

The remaining length of the piece of leather after he made the necklace was 288·75 cm.

4 A flask of hot water was left to cool. After 10 minutes, the temperature had decreased by 24% to 76°C. After another 5 minutes, the temperature of the water decreased by another 20%.

a What was the original temperature of the water in the flask?

b What was the final temperature after 15 minutes?

a

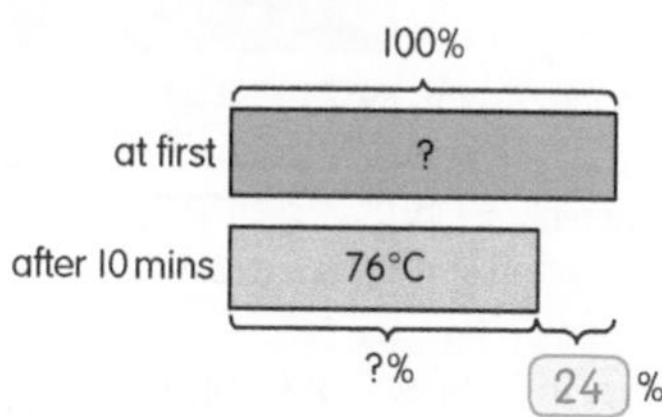

100% – 24 % = 76 %

76 % ⟶ 76 °C

1% ⟶ 76 ÷ 76 = 1 °C

100% ⟶ 100 × 1 = 100 °C

The original temperature was 100 °C.

b

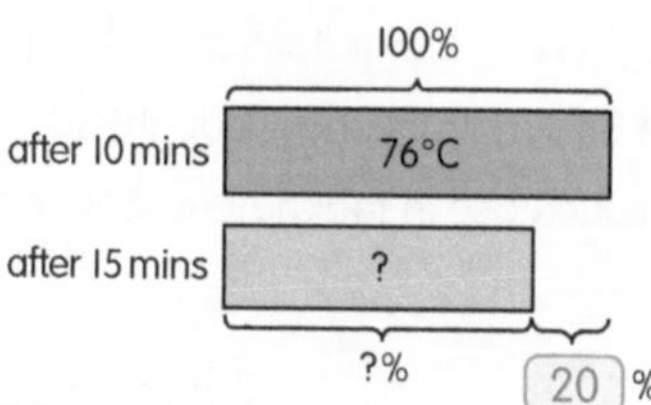

100% – 20 % = 80 %

80 % × 76°C = 60·8 °C

The final temperature after 15 minutes was 60·8 °C.

Teaching sequence

4

- Ask pupils to work on these questions as practice.
- Ensure that pupils are able to answer **a** without assistance before asking them to move on to **b**.
- If necessary, remind pupils that the value equated to 100% will be different for the second model.

Teaching sequence

- Explain to pupils that this question involves a three-part model, but is essentially a basic percentage increase question with one additional calculation step to be carried out at the beginning.
- Ensure that pupils equate the correct portion of the model to 100%.

- Ask pupils to work on this question as practice.
- Ask pupils to identify which part of the model should be equated to 100%, and why.

5 In 2014, Mr Hall's monthly salary was £2000. Mr Brook's monthly salary was $\frac{4}{5}$ of Mr Hall's monthly salary. In 2015, Mr Brook's monthly salary was increased by 20%. Find the increase in Mr Brook's monthly salary.

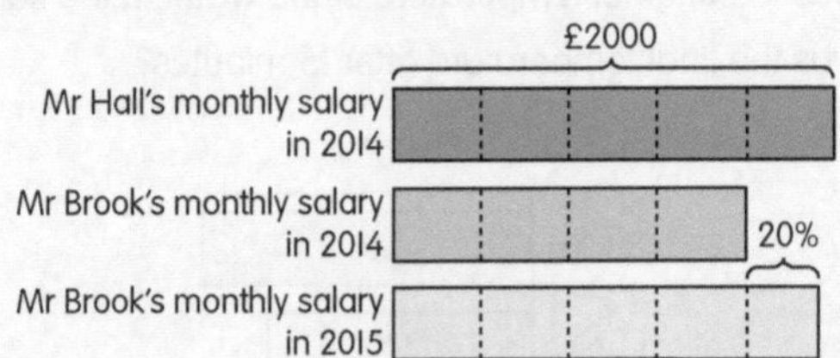

Mr Brook's monthly salary in 2014 $= \frac{4}{5} \times$ £2000

= £1600

100% ⟶ £1600

1% ⟶ £1600 ÷ 100 = £16

20% ⟶ 20 × £16 = £320

The increase in Mr Brook's monthly salary was £320.

We are comparing Mr Brook's monthly salary in 2014 with his monthly salary in 2015. So we take his monthly salary in 2014 as 100%.

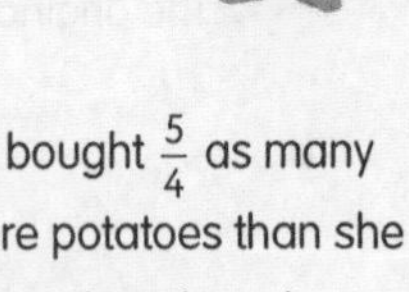

6 In May Mr Phillips bought 12 kg of potatoes and Mrs Shaw bought $\frac{5}{4}$ as many potatoes as Mr Phillips. In June Mrs Shaw bought 30% more potatoes than she bought in May. Find the increase in the mass of potatoes Mrs Shaw bought in June.

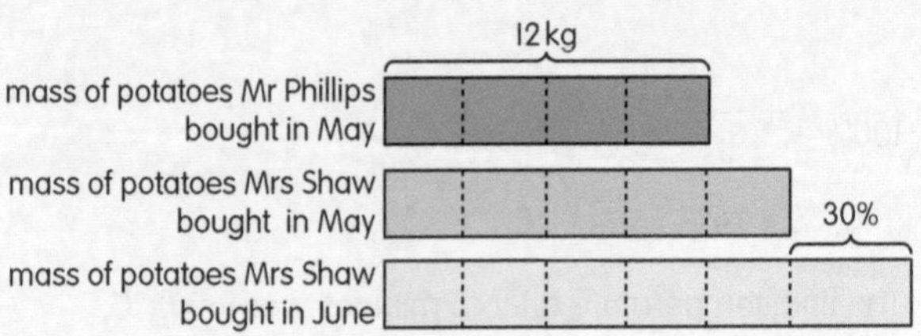

What you will need

Scientific calculator

Mass of potatoes Mrs Shaw bought in May = $\frac{5}{4} \times 12$

= 15 kg

100% → 15 kg

1% → $\frac{15}{100}$ kg

30% → $30 \times \frac{15}{100} = 4\frac{1}{2}$ kg

We take the mass of potatoes Mrs Shaw bought in May as 100%.

The increase in the mass of potatoes Mrs Shaw bought in June was $4\frac{1}{2}$ kg.

7  Matt had an orange ribbon and a blue ribbon. The orange ribbon was 2 m long. The blue ribbon was $\frac{4}{5}$ as long as the orange ribbon. Matt cut 25% off the blue ribbon.

a What was the length of the blue ribbon before it was cut?

b Find the length of blue ribbon that Matt cut off.

a

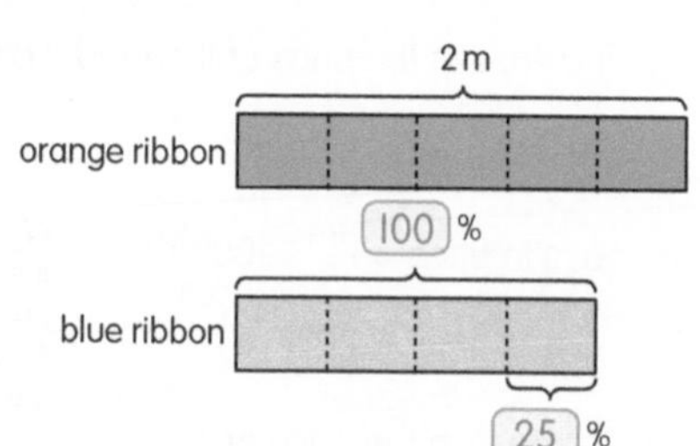

$\frac{4}{5} \times 2 = 1{\cdot}6$

The blue ribbon was 1·6 m long before it was cut.

b 25% × 1·6 = 0·4

Matt cut 0·4 m of the blue ribbon.

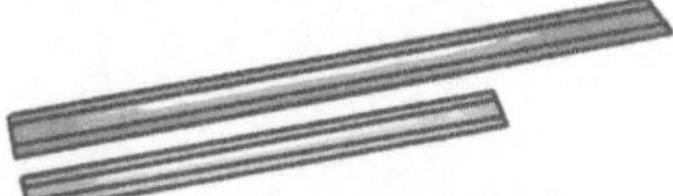

131

Teaching sequence

7

- Ask pupils to work on these questions as practice.

What you will need

Scientific calculator

Teaching sequence

- Encourage pupils to look at the model and identify the question as a two-step percentage increase problem.
- In the first part of the question, take the 2011 price as 100% and calculate the percentage increase based on £12.
- In the second part of the question, take the 2013 price as 100% and calculate the percentage increase based on £15.
- You can decide which quantity is the 100% from the wording of the question.

8  The usual price of a model car in 2011 was £12. In 2013, the price of the model car increased to £15. In 2015, the price of the model car was £3 more than the price of the model car in 2013.

a Find the percentage increase in the price of the model car from 2011 to 2013.

b Find the percentage increase in the price of the model car from 2013 to 2015.

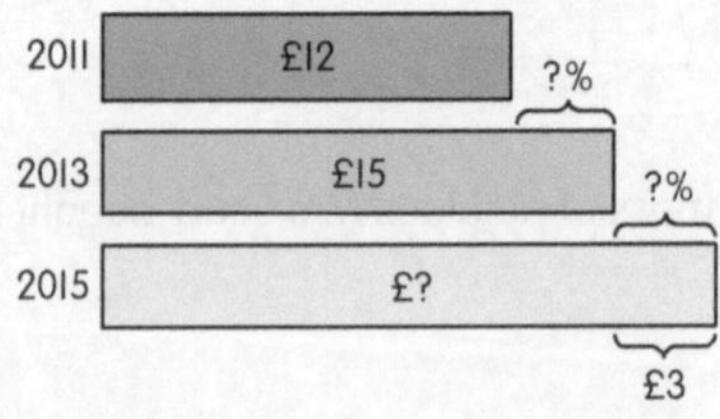

a Increase in price of model car from 2011 to 2013 = £15 – £12
= £3

Percentage increase = $\frac{3}{12} \times 100\%$
= 25%

The percentage increase in the price of the model car from 2011 to 2013 was 25%.

b Percentage increase in price = $\frac{3}{15} \times 100\%$
= 20%

The percentage increase in the price of the model car from 2013 to 2015 was 20%.

We are comparing the price of the model car in 2013 with the price of the model car in 2015. So we take the price of the model car in 2013 as 100%.

What you will need

Scientific calculator

9 The temperature of the water in a mug was 50°C at first. After 10 minutes, it dropped to 45°C. Another 15 minutes later, the temperature had dropped to 40°C.

a Find the percentage decrease in temperature after the first 10 minutes.

b What was the percentage decrease in temperature from 45°C to 40°C? Give your answer to 1 decimal place.

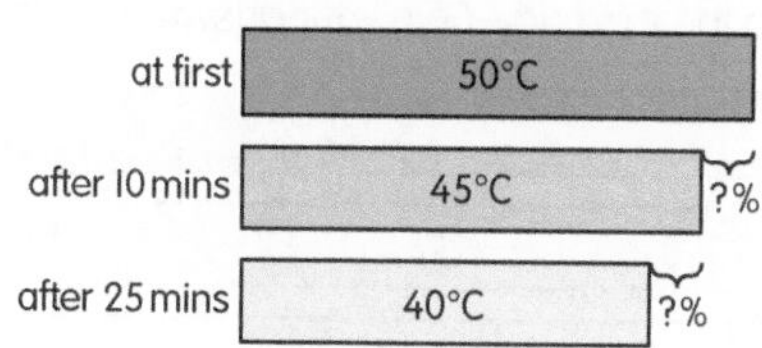

a Decrease in temperature = 50°C − 45°C

= 5 °C

$\frac{5}{50} \times 100\% = 10\%$

The percentage decrease in temperature after the first 10 minutes was 10 %.

b Decrease in temperature = 45°C − 40°C

= 5 °C

$\frac{5}{45} \times 100\% \approx 11{\cdot}1\%$

The percentage decrease in temperature from 45°C to 40°C was 11·1 %.

Teaching sequence

9

- Ask pupils to work on these questions as practice.
- This question is similar to  8, but involves percentage decrease.
- For each part of the question, ask pupils to identify which value should be equated to 100%.

What you will need

Scientific calculator

Teaching sequence

- This question involves both percentage increase and percentage decrease. Ensure pupils read the question carefully and identify £2538 as the total amount raised over three days, and not the amount raised on the third day.

a

- Pupils should be able to identify the first-day amount as equivalent to 100%.

b

- Emphasise to pupils that the illustration provided in the model does not necessarily mean that the answer is a 'percentage increase'.
- Agree that, in this case, they should identify the second-day amount as the new 100%.

Unit 6 Percentage

10 Mr Smith raised money for charity by walking for three days across the countryside. He raised £925 on the first day. On the second day, he raised £728. By the third day he had raised a total of £2538.

a What was the percentage decrease in the amount of money raised from the first day to the second day? Give your answer to 1 decimal place.

b Find the percentage increase or decrease in the amount raised from the second day to the third day. Give your answer to 1 decimal place.

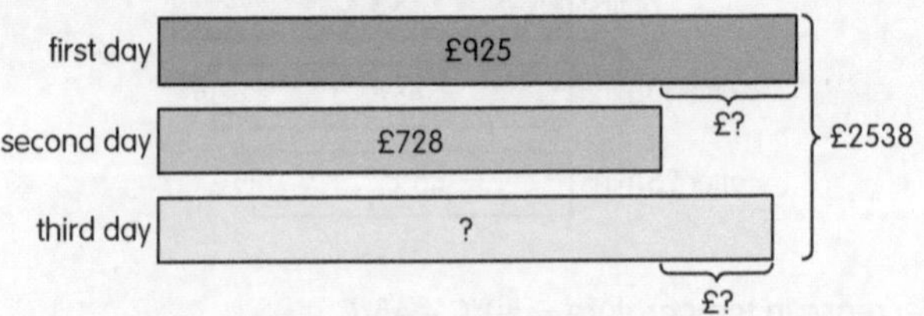

a Decrease in amount of money raised = £925 – £728

= £ 197

Percentage decrease = $\frac{197}{925}$ × 100%

≈ 21·3 %

The percentage decrease in the amount of money raised from the first day to the second day was 21·3 %.

b Amount raised on the third day = £2538 – £925 – £728

= £ 885

Increase in amount of money raised = £ 885 – £ 728

= £ 157

Percentage increase = $\frac{157}{728}$ × 100%

≈ 21·6 %

The percentage increase in the amount of money raised from the second day to the third day was 21·6 %.

Objective of activity

Pupils will be able to understand and describe the steps in solving a word problem involving percentage decrease.

Maths Journal

 Miya and Hardeep worked out the following:

In an experiment, a scientist had to record the temperature change of some liquid in a flask. The temperature of the liquid in the flask was 50°C at first. After 10 minutes, the temperature of the liquid dropped to 40°C. Another 20 minutes later, the temperature of the liquid had dropped to 30°C.

Find the percentage decrease in temperature from 40°C to 30°C.

Miya's answer:
40°C − 30°C = 10°C
$\frac{10}{50} \times 100\% = 20\%$
The percentage decrease in temperature was 20%.

Hardeep's answer:
40°C − 30°C = 10°C
$\frac{10}{40} \times 100\% = 25\%$
The percentage decrease in temperature was 25%.

a Whose answer is incorrect? Miya

b Explain why. Miya should take the temperature of the liquid at 40°C as 100% instead of the original 50°C.

Teaching sequence

11 *Maths Journal*

- Use this question to stress the importance of identifying the 100% value correctly.
- If necessary, encourage pupils to sketch the model for easier identification of the 100% value.

Independent work

- *Let's Practise!*
- Practice 3 and *Maths Journal* in Practice Book 6A, pp 133 to 140.

What you will need

Scientific calculator

Teaching sequence

16 *Let's Practise!*

- You could allow pupils who are confident in performing the calculations for part **a** of this question without a calculator to do so.
  For example:

$$\% \text{ increase} = \frac{450}{10\,000} \times 100\%$$
$$= \frac{450}{100}\%$$
$$= 4{\cdot}5\%$$

Let's Practise!

12 Mrs Baker paid £120 for a suitcase. She had been given a discount of 20% on the usual price. What was the usual price of the suitcase? £150

13 In 2014, the number of subscribers for Magazine A was 475 and the number of subscribers for Magazine B was $\frac{4}{5}$ of the number of subscribers for Magazine A. In 2015, the number of subscribers for Magazine B increased by 35%. Find the total number of subscribers for Magazine B in 2015. 513

14 Ishani had 20 cards. Emma had $\frac{7}{2}$ of the number of cards Ishani had. Emma gave 25 cards to her friends. Find the percentage decrease in the number of cards Emma had. Give your answer to 2 decimal places. 35·71%

15 The temperature at noon in Delhi was 32°C. In the evening, it had dropped to 28°C. At midnight, the temperature was 24°C.

a Find the percentage decrease in temperature from noon to evening. 12·5%

b Find the percentage decrease in temperature from evening to midnight. Give your answer to 2 decimal places. 14·29%

16 Mr Bell put £10 000 into a savings account. At the end of the first year, the amount of money in the account had increased to £10 450. At the end of the second year, he had £10 900 in the savings account.

a Find the percentage increase in his money at the end of the first year. 4·5%

b Find the percentage increase in his money from the end of the first year to the end of the second year. Give your answer to 1 decimal place. 4·3%

Practice Book 6A, p.133

What you will need

Scientific calculator

Let's Wrap It Up!

You have learnt to:

- find the whole given a part and the percentage
- find a part given the whole and the percentage of the other part
- solve word problems by finding percentage increase and percentage decrease
- solve word problems involving percentage and discount.

Let's Revise!

17 During a sale, Mrs Green paid £176 for an oven at a discount of 12%. What was the usual price of the oven?

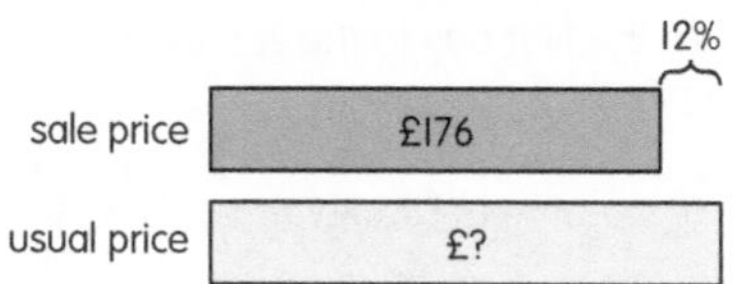

100% – 12% = 88%

The sale price was 88% of the usual price.

88% → £176
1% → £2
100% → £200

The usual price of the oven was £200.

Teaching sequence

Let's Wrap It Up!

- Emphasise the key concepts, skills and processes that have been taught in the unit.

17

- Discuss the worked example with pupils to assess whether they have mastered these concepts, skills and processes.

What you will need

Scientific calculator

Teaching sequence

Let's Wrap It Up!

- Discuss the worked example with pupils to assess whether they have mastered these concepts, skills and processes.

Let's Wrap It Up!

18 A charity raised money by selling raffle tickets. It raised £450 on the first day. On the second day it raised £600. On the third day, the charity raised £950.

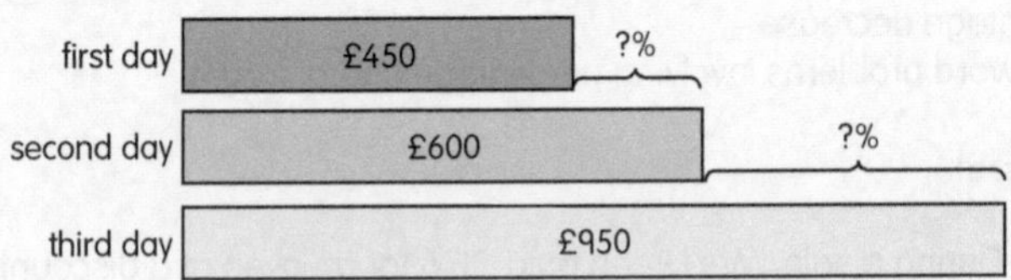

a What was the percentage increase in the amount of money raised from the first day to the second day? Give your answer to 1 decimal place.

Increase in amount of money raised = £600 – £450
= £150

Percentage increase $= \frac{150}{450} \times 100\%$
$\approx 33{\cdot}3\%$

The percentage increase in the amount of money raised from the first day to the second day was 33·3%.

b Find the percentage increase in the amount raised from the second day to the third day. Give your answer to 1 decimal place.

Increase in amount of money raised = £950 – £600
= £350

Percentage increase $= \frac{350}{600} \times 100\%$
$\approx 58{\cdot}3\%$

The percentage increase in the amount of money raised from the second day to the third day was 58·3%.

Objective of activity

Pupils will be able to solve the problem by applying the concept of equal quantities by recognising that the same quantity can represent different percentages.

What you will need

Scientific calculator

Thinking skill

Analysing parts and wholes

Heuristic for problem solving

Simplify the problem

Independent work

- *Challenging Practice, Problem Solving,* Review 2 and Revision 1 in Practice Book 6A, pp 141 to 186.

Put On Your Thinking Caps!

19 In the diagram below, the area of the shaded part is 30% of the area of Circle P. It is also 20% of the area of Circle Q. What percentage of the diagram is shaded? Give your answer to 2 decimal places. (Hint: Find the ratio of the area of the shaded part to the unshaded part of each circle.)

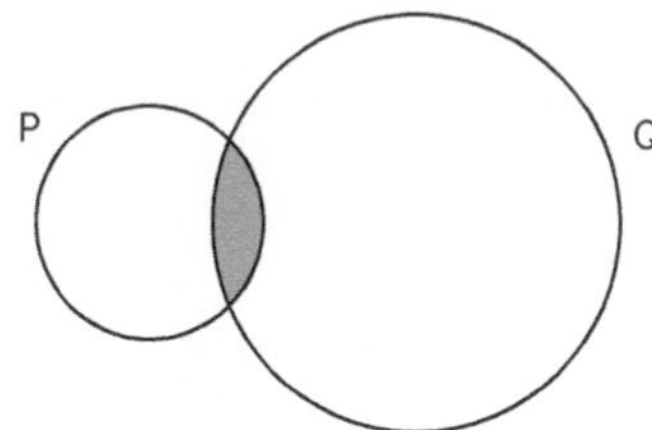

For Circle P:
Shaded area : unshaded area
= 30 : 70
= 3 : 7
= 6 : 14

For Circle Q:
Shaded area : unshaded area
= 20 : 80
= 2 : 8
= 1 : 4
= 6 : 24

$6 + 14 + 24 = 44$

$\frac{6}{44} \times 100\% = \frac{600}{44}\%$
$\approx 13{\cdot}64\%$

Heuristic: Simplify the problem
Thinking skill: Analysing parts and whole

Practice Book 6A, p.141 Practice Book 6A, p.144

Teaching sequence

19 *Put On Your Thinking Caps!*

- Guide pupils to see that the shaded area is common to both circles, then to approach the problem by expressing the percentages shaded and unshaded in each circle as ratios, using the same number for the shaded part in each ratio.
- Next find the percentage of the unshaded part. Then apply the part-whole concept to find the percentage of the diagram that is shaded.

Unit 6 Percentage

Date: ____________

Practice 1 Finding percentages

1 Express each of the following as a percentage.

a 13 out of 100 = 13 %

b 46 out of 200 = 23 %

c 207 out of 300 = 69 %

d 316 out of 400 = 79 %

2 Express each of the following as a percentage, fraction and/or decimal.

As a Percentage	As a Fraction (in its Simplest Form)	As a Decimal
70%	$\frac{7}{10}$	0·7
40%	$\frac{2}{5}$	0·4
25%	$\frac{1}{4}$	0·25
5%	$\frac{5}{100} = \frac{1}{20}$	0·05
28%	$\frac{28}{100} = \frac{7}{25}$	0·28
3·2%	$\frac{32}{1000} = \frac{8}{250} = \frac{4}{125}$	0·032
87·5%	$\frac{7}{8}$	0·875
4%	$\frac{4}{100} = \frac{1}{25}$	0·04
33%	$\frac{3}{100}$	0·33
68%	$\frac{68}{100} = \frac{17}{25}$	0·68
22·5%	$\frac{22 \cdot 5}{100} = \frac{225}{1000} = \frac{9}{40}$	0·225

3 Express each fraction as a percentage to 2 decimal places.

a $\frac{79}{148} \approx$ 53·38%

b $\frac{58}{379} \approx$ 15·30%

c $\frac{15}{52} \approx$ 28·85%

d $\frac{43}{95} \approx$ 45·26%

Solve these word problems. Show your workings clearly.

4 Aisha was asked to paint some walls with a total area of 84 m². In three hours, she had painted 21 m².

a What percentage of the walls were painted?

b What percentage of the walls were left unpainted?

a $\frac{21}{84} \times 100\% = 25\%$

25% of the walls were painted.

b $100\% - 25\% = 75\%$

75% of the walls were left unpainted.

5 Ben is cycling from his house to his cousin's house. The houses are 15 km apart. If Ben has cycled a distance of 9·5 km, what percentage of the total distance does he have left? Give your answer to 1 decimal place.

Distance left to cycle = 15 – 9·5
= 5·5 km

$\frac{5 \cdot 5}{15} \times 100\% = 36 \cdot 7\%$

He has 36·7% of the total distance left.

6 Selina had £80. She spent £24 on a pair of shoes and £18 on a T-shirt. What percentage of her money was left?

£24 + £18 = £42
£80 – £42 = £38

Selina had £38 left.

$\frac{38}{80} \times 100\% = 47 \cdot 5\%$

47·5% of her money was left.

7 John bought 3 kg of beef. He used 0·75 kg of the beef to cook dinner with and another 0·13 kg to make a stew for the next day. What percentage of the beef was not used? Give your answer to 1 decimal place.

Amount of beef used = 0·75 + 0·13 kg
= 0·88 kg

$$\frac{\text{Amount of beef not used}}{\text{Total amount of beef}} = \frac{3 - 0{\cdot}88}{3} = \frac{2{\cdot}12}{3}$$

$$\frac{2{\cdot}12}{3} \times 100\% \approx 70{\cdot}7\%$$

70·7% of the beef was not used.

8 Amit bought a pair of trousers online for £45. He had to pay 7% postage.

a How much postage did Amit pay?
b How much did Amit pay for the pair of trousers, including postage?

a $\frac{7}{100} \times £45 = £3{\cdot}15$
Amit paid £3·15 postage.

b £45 + £3·15 = £48·15
Amit paid £48·15 for the pair of trousers, including postage.

9 The usual price of a suitcase was £100. During an online sale, a 13% discount was given. Mr Lee bought the suitcase but had to pay an additional amount of 7% of the sale price for postage and packaging.

a What was the sale price of the suitcase?
b How much did Mr Lee pay altogether for the suitcase and the postage and packing?

a 100% − 13% = 87%
The sale price was 87% of the usual price.

$\frac{87}{100} \times £100 = £87$
The sale price of the suitcase was £87.

b $\frac{7}{100} \times £87 = £6{\cdot}09$
The postage and packaging was £6·09.

£87 + £6·09 = £93·09
Mr Lee paid £93·09 altogether for the suitcase and the postage and packing.

10 Karen took 1 h 45 mins to drive from Town A to Town B. She took another 25 mins to drive from Town B to Town C. After that, she drove back to Town A. The journey from Town A to Town C and then back to Town A took 3 h 35 mins. Find the percentage of the total journey time she spent driving back to Town A from Town C. Give your answer to 1 decimal place.

3 h 35 mins = 215 mins

Time taken from Town A to Town C = 1 h 45 mins + 25 mins
= 105 mins + 25 mins
= 130 mins

Time taken from Town C to Town A = 215 mins – 130 mins
= 85 mins

$\frac{\text{Time take from Town C to Town A}}{\text{Total time taken}} = \frac{3 - 0{\cdot}88}{3}$

$\frac{\text{Time take from Town C to Town A}}{\text{Total time taken}} = \frac{85}{215}$

$\frac{85}{215} \times 100\% \approx 39{\cdot}5\%$

The percentage of the time she spent driving back to Town A from Town C was 39·5%.

Date: ______________

Practice 2 Word problems (1)

Solve these word problems. Show your workings clearly.

1 John had £5 in his wallet. This was 10% of the amount that he received from his sister. Find the total amount of money that John received from his sister.

$10\% \rightarrow £5$

$1\% \rightarrow £\left(\frac{5}{10}\right) = £0{\cdot}50$

$100\% \rightarrow £0{\cdot}50 \times 100 = £50$

The total amount of money that John received from his sister was £50.

2 35% of the books Peter owns are fiction books. If Peter has 70 fiction books, find:

a the total number of books he owns

b the number of non-fiction books he owns.

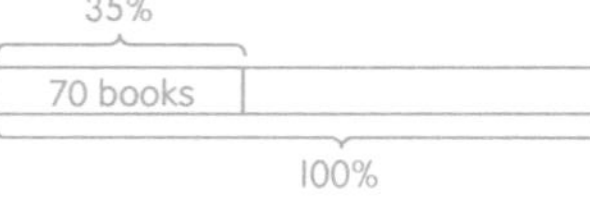

a $35\% \rightarrow 70$ books

$1\% \rightarrow \frac{70}{35} = 2$ books

$100\% \rightarrow 2 \times 100 = 200$ books

The total number of books he owns is 200.

b $100\% - 35\% = 65\%$

$65\% \rightarrow 65 \times 2 = 130$

He owns 130 non-fiction books.

3 Simon used wholewheat flour and plain flour to bake some bread. 19% of the flour used was wholewheat flour. If he used 475 g of wholewheat flour, find:

a the total mass of flour he used for the bread

b the mass of plain flour he used.

19%
wholewheat flour 475 g
plain flour ?
81%
?

a 100% – 19% = 81% (plain flour)

19% → 475 g
1% → 25 g
100% → 2500 g

The total mass of flour he used for the bread was 2500 g.

b 81% → 2025 g

He used 2025 g of plain flour.

4 On Tuesday, the price of 8 kg of fish at a market was £88. This was an increase of 10% in the price of the same amount of fish on Monday. Find the price of 8 kg of fish on Monday.

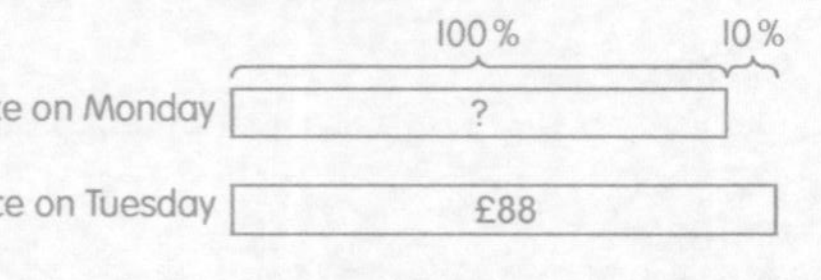

100% + 10% = 110% (Tuesday)

110% → £88
1% → £0·80
100% → £80

The price of 8 kg of fish on Monday was £80.

5 The usual price of a television was £392. Mr Adams bought a television after the price was increased by 8·5%. How much did Mr Adams pay?

100% 8·5%
usual price £392
increased price ?

Method 1

100% + 8·5% = 108·5%

£392 × 108·5% = £425·32

Mr Adams paid £425·32.

Method 2

£392 × 8·5% = £33·32

£392 + £33·32 = £425·32

6 The temperature of a piece of metal was 32°C. It was then lowered into a container of hot water and the temperature of the piece of metal increased to 36°C. Find the percentage increase in temperature of the piece of metal.

36°C – 32°C = 4°C (increase in temperature)

$\frac{4}{32} \times 100\% = 12{\cdot}5\%$

The percentage increase in temperature of the piece of metal was 12·5%.

7 The midday temperature in Dubai in June was 41°C. At midnight, the temperature had decreased to 31·5°C. Find the percentage decrease in temperature. Give your answer to 1 decimal place.

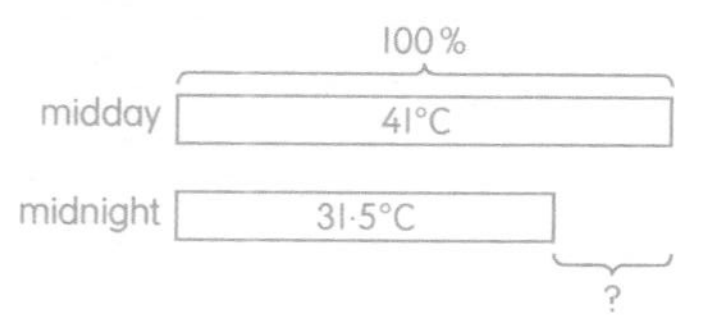

41°C – 31·5°C = 9·5°C

$\frac{9.5}{41} \times 100\% \approx 23.2\%$

The percentage decrease in temperature was 23·2%.

8 The usual price of a bag of oranges was £4. During a sale, 2 bags of oranges were sold for £5·99. Find the discount given for the 2 bags of oranges. Give your answer to 1 decimal place.

£4 × 2 = £8 (2 bags of oranges)

£8 – £5·99 = £2·01 (decrease in price)

$\frac{2.01}{8} \times 100\% \approx 25.1\%$

The percentage decrease in the price of 2 bags of oranges is 25·1%.

Date: __________

Maths Journal

1 Use the words, numbers and percentages below to write your own percentage word problem. Then solve the word problem.

a price | box of fruit | £72 | 15% | increase | morning | evening

Answers vary

Example:
In the morning, the price of a box of fruit was £72. This was an increase of 15% in the price of a box of fruit in the evening. Find the price of a box of fruit in the evening. Give your answer to 2 decimal places.

100% + 15% = 115%

115% → £72

1% → $£\left(\frac{72}{115}\right)$

100% → $£\left(\frac{72}{115}\right) \times 100 = £62.61$

The price of a box of fruit in the evening was £62·61.

b

sugar	salt	45%	2·4 g	total	mass

Answers vary

Example:
Kerry had some sugar and salt. The percentage of sugar was 45%. The mass of the salt was 2·4 g.

i Find the mass of the sugar and give your answer to 2 decimal places.

ii Find the total mass of the sugar and salt Kerry had.

i $100\% - 45\% = 55\%$

$55\% \rightarrow 2{\cdot}4\,g$

$1\% \rightarrow \left(\frac{2{\cdot}4}{55}\right) g$

$45\% \rightarrow \left(\frac{2{\cdot}4}{55}\right) \times 45 \approx 1{\cdot}96\,g$

The mass of the sugar was 1·96 g.

ii $2{\cdot}4\,g + 1{\cdot}96\,g = 4{\cdot}36\,g$

The total mass of the sugar and salt Kerry had was 4·36 g.

Date: ____________

Practice 3 Word problems (2)

Solve these word problems. Show your workings clearly.

1 The sale price of a piece of silk is 12% less than its usual price. If the sale price is £44, find the usual price of the piece of silk.

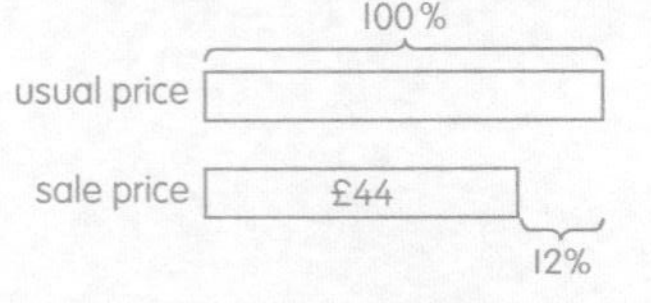

$100\% - 12\% = 88\%$

$88\% \rightarrow £44$

$1\% \rightarrow £\left(\frac{44}{88}\right) = £0{\cdot}50$

$100\% \rightarrow £0{\cdot}50 \times 100 = £50$

The usual price of the piece of silk is £50.

2 Sophie's mum paid £117 for a guitar. She had been given a 35% discount on the usual price. What was the usual price of the guitar?

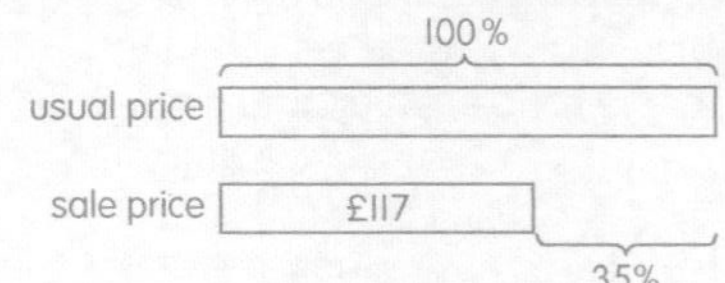

$100\% - 35\% = 65\%$

$65\% \rightarrow £117$

$1\% \rightarrow £\left(\frac{117}{65}\right) = £1{\cdot}80$

$100\% \rightarrow £1{\cdot}80 \times 100 = £180$

The usual price of the guitar was £180.

3 Mrs Brown's income was £2500 in June. This was 20% less than her income in April. What was Mrs Brown's income in April?

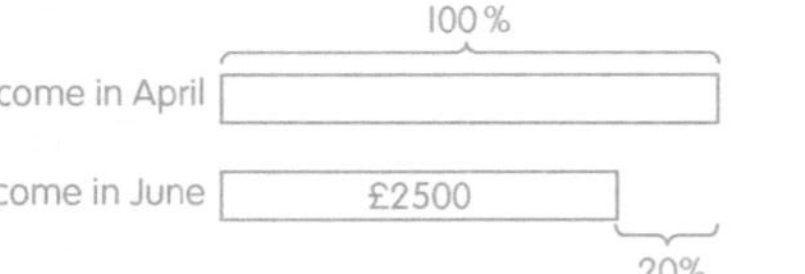

100% – 20% = 80%

80% → £2500

1% → £$\left(\frac{2500}{80}\right)$ = £31·25

100% → £3125

Mrs Brown's income in April was £3125.

4 Mrs Lim bought a painting for £1760. This was 20% less than the original price. Later Mrs Lim sold the same painting for 5% more than the original price. How much did Mrs Lim sell the painting for?

100% – 20% = 80%

80% → £1760

1% → £$\left(\frac{1760}{80}\right)$ = £22

100% → £22 × 100 = £2200

The original price was £2200.

100% + 5% = 105%

100% → £2200

105% → £22 × 105 = £2310

Mrs Lim sold the same painting for £2310.

5 The usual price of a skateboard was £35. The usual price of a bike was $\frac{5}{2}$ of the usual price of the skateboard. During a sale, Marek bought the bike at a discount of 10%. Find the discount given on the bike.

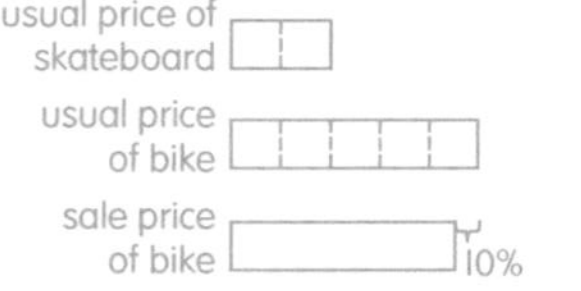

£35 × $\frac{5}{2}$ = £87·50

10% × £87·50 = £8·75

The discount given on the bike was £8·75.

6 Mrs Payne's monthly rent for her flat was £1270. Mr Wright's monthly rent was $\frac{9}{10}$ of Mrs Payne's monthly rent. Mr Wright's landlady increased his monthly rent by 35%. Find the increase in Mr Wright's monthly rent.

Mrs Payne's monthly rent
Mr Wright's monthly rent 35%
Mr Wright's increased monthly rent

$£1270 \times \frac{9}{10} = £1143$

$£1143 \times 35\% = £400{\cdot}05$

The increase in Mr Wright's monthly rent was £400·05.

7 Hardeep collected 24 football cards in January. In February, he collected another 30 football cards. In March, the number of football cards Hardeep collected increased to 36.

a Find the percentage increase in the number of football cards collected between January and February.

b Find the percentage increase in the number of football cards collected between February and March.

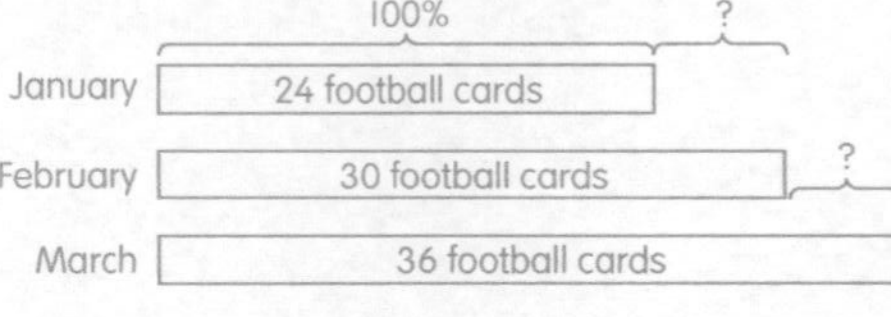

a $30 - 24 = 6$

$\frac{6}{24} \times 100\% = 25\%$

The percentage increase in the number of football cards collected between January and February was 25%.

b $36 - 30 = 6$

$\frac{6}{30} \times 100\% = 20\%$

The percentage increase in the number of football cards collected between February and March was 20%.

8 On Sunday, the water level of a reservoir was 11 m. After some heavy rain, the water level of the reservoir rose to 13 m on Monday. The water level decreased to 11·25 m on Tuesday.

a Find the percentage increase in water level between Sunday and Monday. Give your answer to 2 decimal places.

b Find the percentage decrease in water level between Monday and Tuesday. Give your answer to 2 decimal places.

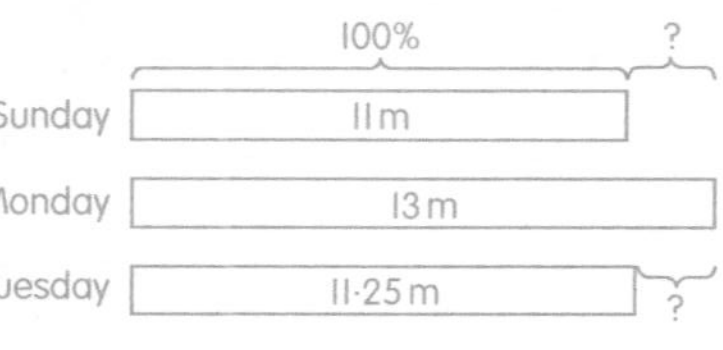

a $13 - 11 = 2$ m (increase in water level)

$\frac{2}{11} \times 100\% \approx 18{\cdot}18\%$

The percentage increase in water level between Sunday and Monday was 18·18%.

b $13 - 11{\cdot}25 = 1{\cdot}75$ m (decrease in water level)

$\frac{1{\cdot}75}{13} \times 100\% \approx 13{\cdot}46\%$

The percentage decrease in water level between Monday and Tuesday was 13·46%.

Date: ______________

Maths Journal

1 Miya answered the following questions incorrectly. Explain and correct her mistakes.

a 40 pupils took part in a running competition. 12 pupils qualified for the finals. What percentage of pupils qualified for the finals? Give your answer to 1 decimal place.

Miya's workings:

$\frac{40}{12} \times 100\% \approx 333{\cdot}3\%$

The percentage of pupils who qualified for the finals was 333·3%.

Miya used 12 as the denominator instead of 40.

Correct answer:

$\frac{12}{40} \times 100\% = 30\%$

b In the morning, the temperature in a greenhouse was 32°C. At noon, the temperature increased to 34°C. What was the percentage increase in temperature? Give your answer to 2 decimal places.

Miya's workings:

$34°C - 32°C = 2°C$

$\frac{2}{34} \times 100\% \approx 5{\cdot}88\%$

The percentage increase was 5·88%.

The denominator should be 32 instead of 34.

Correct answer:

$\frac{2}{32} \times 100\% = 6{\cdot}25\%$

c A kite was sold at £12·60 after a discount of 10%.

i What was the discount?
ii Find the original price of the kite.

Miya's workings:

i £12·60 × 10% = £1·26
The discount was £1·26.

ii £12·60 + £1·26 = £13·86
The original price was £13·86.

Miya misunderstood by thinking that £12·60 was the original price of the kite.

Correct answer:
100% – 10% = 90%
90% → £12·60

$1\% \rightarrow £\left(\frac{12 \cdot 60}{90}\right) = £0 \cdot 14$

10% → 10 × £0·14 = £1·40

The discount was £1·40.

100% → 100 × £0·14 = £14

Date: ________

Challenging Practice

1 Mrs Attah's salary was £720 per month. This month, her salary increased by 10%. Mr Attah's monthly salary is $\frac{2}{3}$ of Mrs Attah's new salary. How much money do they earn altogether this month?

100% → £720

$1\% \rightarrow £\left(\frac{720}{100}\right) = £7 \cdot 20$

110% → £7·20 × 110 = £792

Mrs Attah's new salary is £792.

$\frac{2}{3} \times £792 = £528$

£792 + £528 = £1320

They earn £1320 altogether this month.

2 The current temperature in a room is 20°C. This is 20% lower than the normal temperature. What will the temperature be if it increases by 30% of the normal temperature?

100% – 20% = 80%
80% → 20°C

$1\% \rightarrow \frac{20}{80} = 0 \cdot 25°C$

100% → 0·25 × 100 = 25°C

The normal temperature is 25°C.

100% + 30% = 130%
$130\% \rightarrow 0 \cdot 25 \times 130 = 32\frac{1}{2}°C$

The temperature will be $32\frac{1}{2}°C$.

3 Mrs Harrison gave some money to charity. 20% of her money was given to Charity A. $\frac{1}{4}$ of her remaining money was given to Charity B and the rest was given to Charity C. What percentage of her money was given to Charity C?

20%

Charity A Charity B Charity C

60% of her money was given to Charity C.

or

100% – 20% = 80%

$1 - \frac{1}{4} = \frac{3}{4}$

$\frac{3}{4}$ of the remaining money was given to Charity C.

$\frac{3}{4} \times 80\% = 60\%$

60% of her money was given to Charity C.

4 Mr Bell earns £20 an hour. He is paid an additional 50% an hour if he works overtime during the weekdays and an additional 75% an hour if he works over the weekends. How much overtime pay will Mr Bell receive if he works an overtime of 4 hours on Friday and 6 hours on Sunday?

100% + 50% = 150%

100% → £20

1% → $£\left(\frac{20}{100}\right)$ = £0·20

150% → £0·20 × 150 = £30

Mr Bell will receive £30 an hour if he works overtime on weekdays.

100% + 75% = 175%
175% → 175 × £0·20 = £35

Mr Bell will receive £35 an hour if he works overtime over weekends.

£30 × 4 = £120
£35 × 6 = £210
£210 + £120 = £330

Mr Bell will receive £330 of overtime pay.

Date: ____________

Problem Solving

1 Mrs Bennett sold some cakes to Shops A, B and C. Shop A bought 20% of the cakes. Shop B bought 4 times as many cakes as Shop C. Shop B bought 88 more cakes than Shop A. How many cakes did Mrs Bennett sell altogether?

100% – 20% = 80%

Shop B
Shop C
80% of cakes

5 units → 80%
1 unit → 16%
4 units → 16 × 4 = 64%

64% of the cakes were sold to Shop B.

64% – 20% = 44%

44% → 88 cakes

1% → $\frac{88}{44}$ = 2 cakes

100% → 2 × 100 = 200 cakes

Mrs Bennett sold 200 cakes altogether.

Heuristic: Use a model
Thinking skill: Analysing parts and whole

Review 2

Date: ____________

Section A

Choose the correct answer for each question.
Write its letter in the box.

1 7 ones 2 tenths and 3 thousandths is:

a 0·723 **b** 7·023
c 7·203 **d** 7·230

[c]

2 What is the value of $\frac{3}{5} \div \frac{3}{7}$?

a $\frac{9}{35}$ **b** $\frac{1}{2}$
c $1\frac{2}{5}$ **d** $2\frac{1}{5}$

[c]

3 40 cm 50 cm 60 cm

What is the best estimate of the reading shown by the arrow?

a 50·3 cm **b** 50·5 cm
c 51 cm **d** 53 cm

[d]

4 At a birthday party, the ratio of the number of boys to the number of girls was 4 : 9. When 17 girls left, the ratio became 6 : 5. Find the total number of boys and girls at first.

a 13 **b** 26
c 39 **d** 52

[c]

5 Find the value of $\frac{2 + y}{8}$ when $y = 23$.

a $1\frac{1}{2}$ b $1\frac{5}{8}$

c $2\frac{5}{8}$ d $3\frac{1}{8}$

d

6 Look at the number pattern below.

Column A	Column B	Column C	Column D	Column E
1	2	3	4	5
10	9	8	7	6
11	12	13	14	15
20	19	18	17	16
...	...	...	...	...

Which column would you find the number '829' in?

a B b C

c D d E

a

7 ABCD is a rectangle of area $96\,cm^2$. What is the area of the shaded triangle?

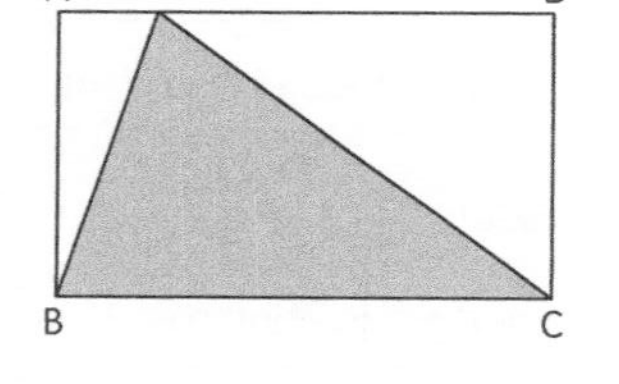

a $24\,cm^2$ b $32\,cm^2$

c $48\,cm^2$ d $192\,cm^2$

c

8 Which of the following is the net of the pyramid shown below?

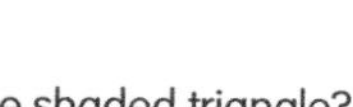

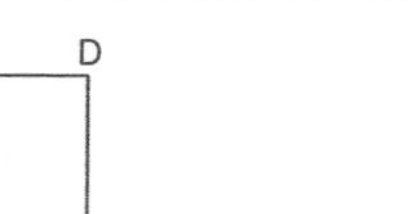

a b

c d

b

9 A box contains some red, yellow and blue counters. The ratio of the number of red counters to that of yellow counters is 2 : 5. The ratio of the number of blue counters to that of red counters is 4 : 7. What fraction of the counters are yellow?

a $\frac{5}{11}$ b $\frac{5}{18}$

c $\frac{35}{43}$ d $\frac{35}{57}$

d

10 1 kg of raspberries costs as much as 3 kg of peaches. Miss Brook paid £56 for 3 kg of raspberries and 5 kg of peaches. What was the cost of 1 kg of raspberries?

a £4 b £7

c £12 d £20

c

11 Machine A can print 3 times as fast as Machine B. If Machine B prints 5 pages of a document in a minute, how long will it take for both machines to print 120 pages of the same document?

a 6 minutes b 24 minutes

c 30 minutes d 40 minutes

a

12 Raj and Luke had the same amount of money. After Raj spent £38 and Luke spent £14, Luke had twice as much money as Raj. How much did Luke have at first?

a £48 **b** £52
c £62 **d** £86

[c]

13 There are 300 adults and children at a concert altogether. There are 60 children at the concert. What is the percentage of children at the concert?

a 20% **b** 60%
c 240% **d** 400%

[a]

14 The table below shows the parking charges at a car park.

First hour	£1·00
Every additional $\frac{1}{2}$ hour or less	£0·60

Mr Inness parked his car at the car park and paid £3·40 in parking charges. How long did he park his car for?

a $1\frac{1}{2}$ hours **b** $2\frac{1}{5}$ hours
c 3 hours **d** 4 hours

[c]

Section B

Read the questions and fill in the answers.

15 Simplify $6x + 10 - 2x + 5$.

$4x + 15$

16 A number is a factor of 96. It is also a multiple of 8. What is the number if it is between 25 and 40?

Multiple of 8: 8, 16, 24, 32, 40, 48…
Factor of 96: 1, 2, 3, 4, 6, 8, 12, 16, 24, 32, 48

32

17 In a class, 5 out of 8 pupils like football. What is the ratio of the number of pupils who like football to the number of pupils who do not like football?

8 – 5 = 3

5 : 3

18 What is the value of Y in the following scale?

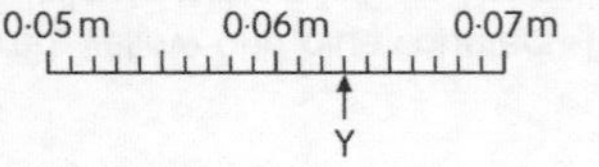

0·063 m

19 The shape below is made up of 4 equilateral triangles, each with a side of 9 cm. Find its perimeter.

9 × 6 = 54

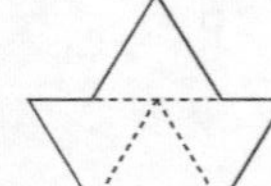

54 cm

20 Express $17\frac{4}{5} - 10\frac{1}{18}$ as a decimal, correct to 1 decimal place.

7·7

21 The table below shows the amount of money donated by parents during a school fundraising event.

Amount Donated	Number of Parents
£1	10
£2	8
£3	9
£4	6
£5	5

How many parents donated at least £4?

11

22 The diagram below, which is not drawn to scale, shows a trapezium and a straight line XY.

From the diagram, $\angle a + \angle b = \angle d +$ [ ].

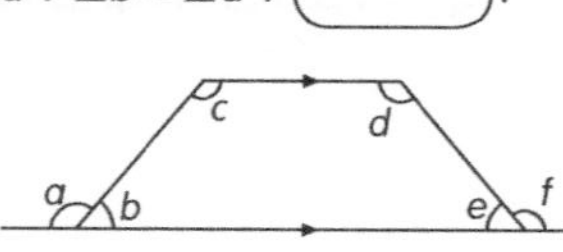

$\angle$ e

23

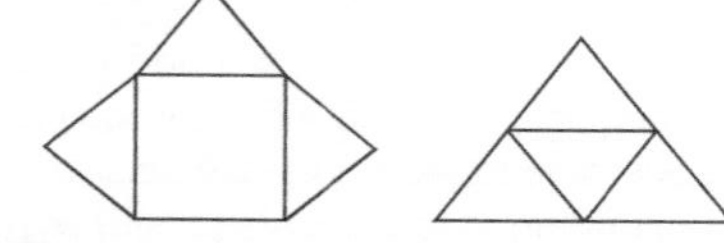

Four diagrams are shown below. Circle the diagram that is the net of the solid shown above.

24 In the rectangle below, find the ratio of the area of the shaded part to the area of the unshaded part.

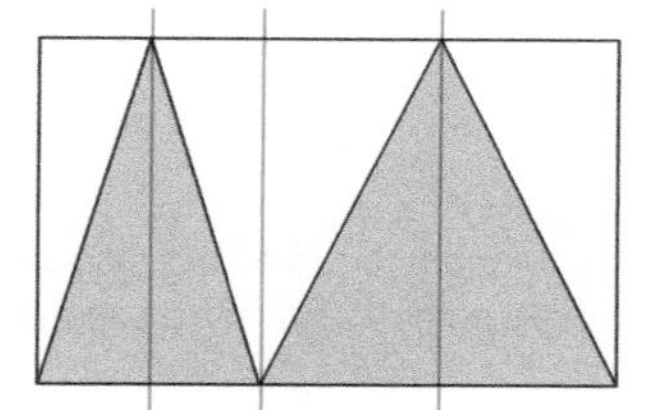

1:1

25 How much does Mr Lee have to pay if he buys 75 oranges and 12 watermelons at the prices shown?

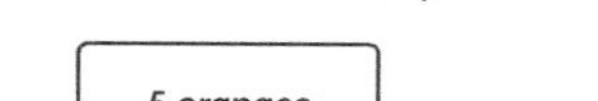

75 ÷ 5 = 15
£1·95 × 15 = £29·25

12 ÷ 3 = 4
£7·40 × 4 = £29·60

£29·25 + £29·60 = £58·85

£ 58·85

26 If some marbles are shared among 18 children, each child will get 76 marbles and there will be 4 marbles left. If the same number of marbles is shared equally among 14 children, how many marbles will each child get?

76 × 18 + 4 = 1372
1372 ÷ 14 = 98

98 marbles

27 The ratio of the number of boys to the number of girls in a swimming club is 2 : 3. The ratio of the number of girls who wear goggles to the number of girls who do not wear goggles is 1 : 3. If there are 12 more girls than boys, how many girls wear goggles?

$3u - 2u = 1u$
1 unit → 12 children
3 units → 12 × 3 = 36 children
4 units → 36 children
1 unit → 36 ÷ 4 = 9

9 girls

28 The attendance at a concert on the first night was 800 people. On the second night, it increased by 20%. How many people attended the concert in the two nights?

100% + 20% = 120%
100% → 800 people
120% → $\frac{800}{100}$ × 120 = 960 people
960 + 800 = 1760

1760 people

29 36 people visit a library on the same day. Each child borrows 8 books and each adult borrows 3 books. The total number of books the children borrow is 46 more than the total number of books the adults borrow. How many children visited the library that day?

Using guess and check:

Number of Children	Number of Adults	Total Number of Books (Children)	Total Number of Books (Adults)	Difference
18	18	144	54	90
17	19	136	57	79
16	20	128	60	68
15	21	120	63	57
14	22	112	66	46 ✓

14 children

30 In the tessellation below, the unit shape is [shape]. Extend the tessellation by adding 4 more unit shapes.

Answers vary

31 The table below shows the postage charges for posting letters from Country A to Country B.

Mass	Cost
First 20 g	60p
Every additional 10 g or less	25p

A person in Country A had a letter to be sent to Country B. The mass of their letter was 135 g. They gave the person at the post office counter £10. How much change did they get?

135 − 20 = 115
115 ÷ 10 = 11·5 ≈ 12
12 × 25p = 300p = £3·00
£3·00 + £0·60 = £3·60
£10·00 − £3·60 = £6·40

£ 6·40

32 The mean height of 3 sunflowers is 150 cm. The heights of two of the sunflowers are 1·6 m and 1·47 m. What is the height of the third sunflower?

150 × 3 = 450
1·6 m = 160 cm
1·47 m = 147 cm
450 − 160 − 147 = 143
143 cm = 1·43 m

1·43 m

33 In the diagram below, ACDH, DEGH and BCDJ are rectangles. Find the area of the triangle EFG. AB : BC = 3 : 1.

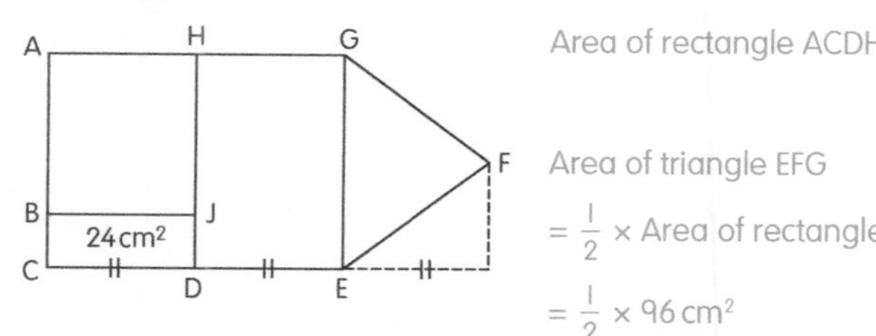

Area of rectangle ACDH = 24 cm² × 4
= 96 cm²

Area of triangle EFG

$= \frac{1}{2} \times$ Area of rectangle ACDH

$= \frac{1}{2} \times 96\ \text{cm}^2$

= 48 cm²

48 cm²

34 The graph below shows the time taken in minutes by 5 artists to each paint 6 pictures.

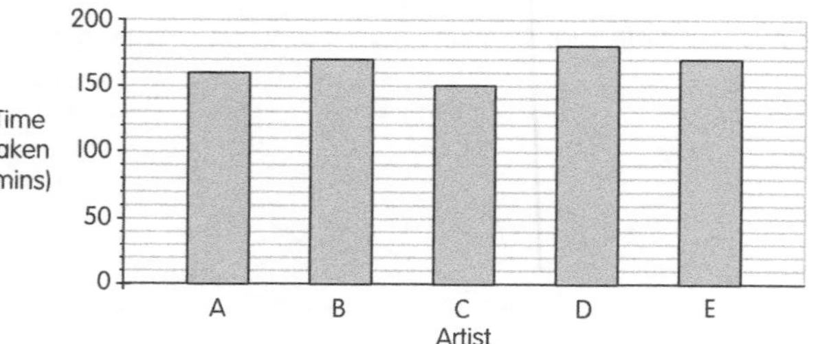

a Which artist was the slowest?

b Find the mean time taken by the fastest artist to paint one picture.

b The fastest artist is Artist C.
150 ÷ 6 = 25

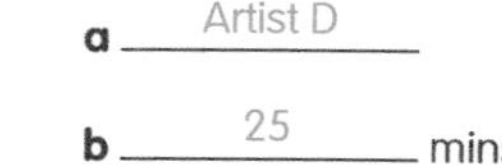

a Artist D

b 25 mins

Section C

Read the questions and write your answers in the spaces. Show your workings clearly.

35 The shape below is not drawn to scale. ABCD is a square and DCE is an equilateral triangle. Find ∠DAE.

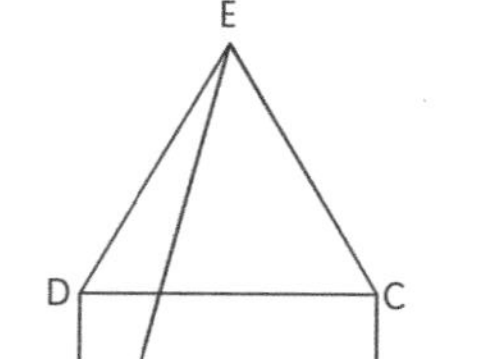

∠EDC = 60°
∠CDA = 90°
∠EDA = 60° + 90°
= 150°

Since ED = AD, ADE is an isosceles triangle.

∠DAE = (180° − 150°) ÷ 2
= 15°

15°

36 The diagram below shows a rectangular field with a 1 m wide concrete path running across it. Find the area of the path.

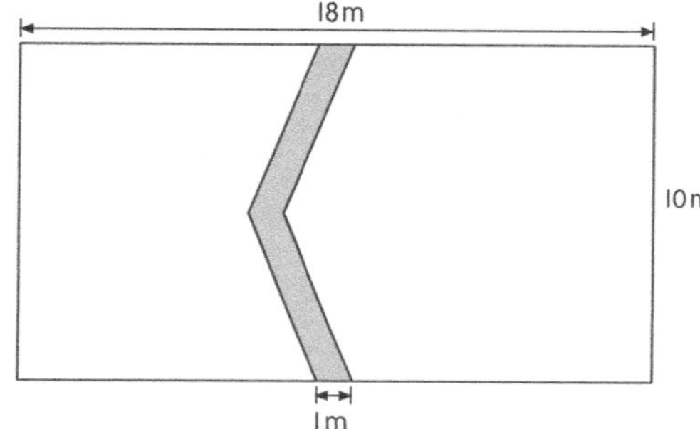

If we lift up the whole path and put the two parts together, they make a rectangle 17 m by 10 m.

Area of diagram = 18 × 10
= 180 m²

18 − 1 = 17
17 × 10 = 170

Area of path = 180 − 170
= 10 m²

10 m²

37 Look at the shape below. AB = BC = 7 cm.

a Measure ∠ABC.
b If AB and BC are the two sides of a rhombus, complete the shape.

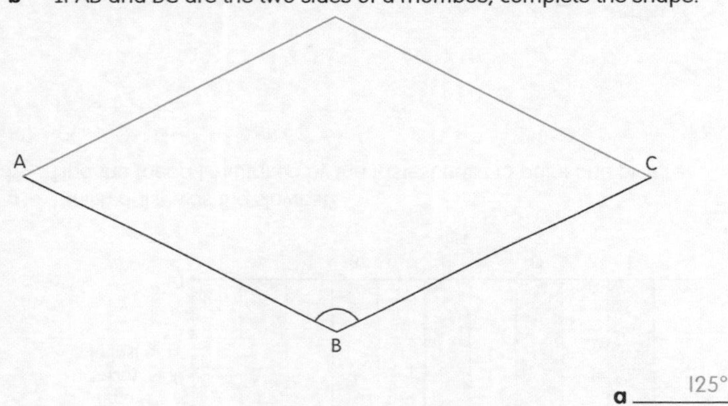

a 125°

38 Tom has £x. Aisha has 3 times as much money as Tom. Emma has £5 more than Aisha.

a How much do they have altogether? Give your answer in terms of x.
b If $x = 7$, how much do they have altogether?

a Aisha has £$3x$.
Emma has £$(3x + 5)$.

$$£x + £3x + £(3x + 5) = £x + £3x + £3x + £5$$
$$= £7x + £5$$
$$= £(7x + 5)$$

They have £$(7x + 5)$ altogether.

b If $x = 7$,

$$£(7x + 5) = £7x + £5$$
$$= £(7 \times 7) + £5$$
$$= £49 + £5$$
$$= £54$$

a £$(7x + 5)$

b £54

39 1080 sweets were given to 42 people. $\frac{5}{7}$ of the people were adults and each of them received the same number of sweets. Each of the children received twice as many sweets as the adults. How many sweets did each adult receive?

$\frac{5}{7} \times 42 = 30$ (adults)

$42 - 30 = 12$ (children)

children [|] × 12 = 24 units

adults [ ] × 30 = 30 units

Total units = 24 + 30 = 54 units

54 units → 1080 sweets

1 unit → $\frac{1080}{54}$ = 20 sweets

Each adult received 20 sweets.

20 sweets

40 Miya has $\frac{1}{2}$ as many cards as Ruby. Ruby has $\frac{1}{2}$ as many cards as Farha.

a What is the ratio of Miya's cards to Ruby's cards to Farha's cards?

b How many more cards does Farha have than Miya if Ruby has 36 cards?

a 1 : 2 : 4

b 2 units → 36 cards

1 unit → $\frac{36}{2}$ = 18 cards

3 units → 18 × 3 = 54 cards

Farha has 54 cards more than Miya.

a 1 : 2 : 4

b 54 cards

41 There were 40 pupils in a choir. 30% of them were girls. Later, some girls left the choir and the percentage of girls dropped to 20%. How many girls left the choir?

$\frac{30}{100} \times 40 = 12$ (girls)

$40 - 12 = 28$ (boys)

$100\% - 20\% = 80\%$

80% of pupils = 28

1% of pupils = $\frac{28}{80}$

20% of pupils = $\frac{28}{80} \times 20$

= 7

There were 7 girls left.

$12 - 7 = 5$

5 girls left the choir.

5 girls

42 A cuboid tank 40 cm by 20 cm by 20 cm is filled with water up to $\frac{2}{5}$ of its height. Water from a tap flows into the tank at 2·5 ℓ a minute. How much water is in the tank in total after 3 minutes? Give your answer in litres. (1 ℓ = 1000 cm^3)

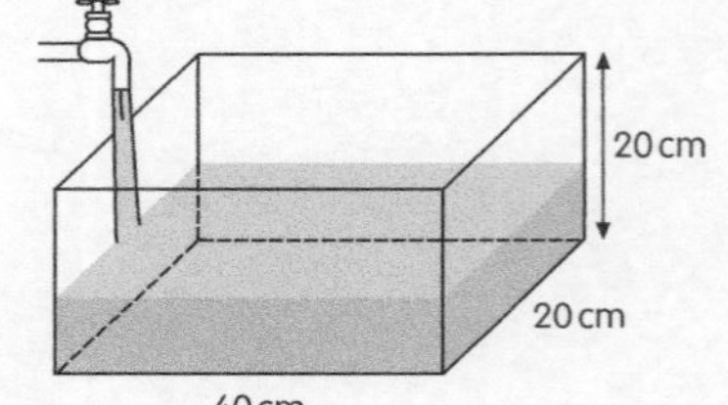

$40 \times 20 \times 20 \times \frac{2}{5}$

$= 6400\ cm^3 = 6{\cdot}4\ \ell$ (volume of water in tank)

$2{\cdot}5 \times 3 = 7{\cdot}5\ \ell$ (volume of water from tap)

$6{\cdot}4 + 7{\cdot}5 = 13{\cdot}9\ \ell$

13·9 ℓ of water is in the tank in total after 3 minutes.

13·9 ℓ

43 In a factory, there were 2115 employees. $\frac{8}{15}$ of them were women. $\frac{1}{2}$ of the women and $\frac{2}{3}$ of the men drove to work.

a What was the total number of employees who drove to work?

b What fraction of the employees in the factory drove to work? Give your answer in its simplest form.

a $\frac{8}{15} \times 2115 = 1128$ (women)

$2115 - 1128 = 987$ (men)

$\frac{1}{2} \times 1128 = 564$ (women who drove to work)

$\frac{2}{3} \times 987 = 658$ (men who drove to work)

$564 + 658 = 1222$

The total number of employees who drove to work was 1222.

b $\frac{1222}{2115} = \frac{26}{45}$

$\frac{26}{45}$ of the employees drove to work.

a 1222

b $\frac{26}{45}$

44 Rectangle MNPQ is divided into 4 parts – A, B, C and D. QN is a straight line. The ratio of the area of A to the area of B is 5 : 13 and the ratio of the area of C to the area of D is 2 : 1. Find the ratio of the area of B to the area of D.

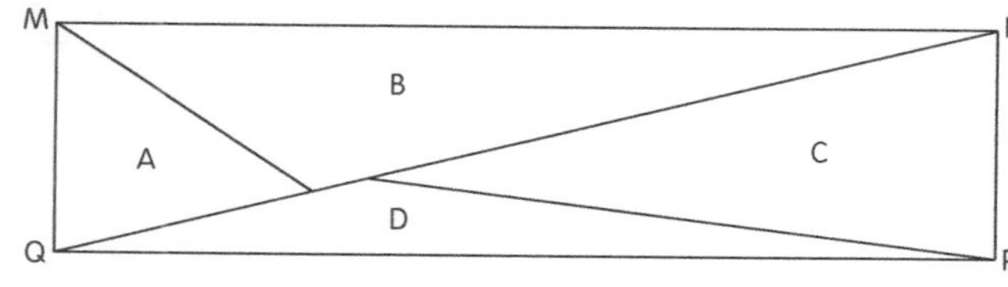

A : B = 5 : 13
C : D = 2 : 1

Total units (A and B) = 5 + 13
= 18

Total units (C and D) = 2 + 1
= 3

A + B = $\frac{1}{2}$ area of rectangle = area of C + D

(A and B) = (C and D)
A : B = 5 : 13
C : D = 2 : 1 = 12 : 6

Check:
12 + 6 = 18
5 + 13 = 18

Area of B : Area of D
= 13 : 6

13 : 6

45 Mr Johnson spent some money on a watch and 60% of the remainder on a surfboard. He had £48 left. The total amount of money spent was $\frac{2}{3}$ of the amount of money he had at first. How much money did he spend on the watch?

$1 - \frac{2}{3} = \frac{1}{3}$

$\frac{1}{3}$ of total amount = £48

$\frac{2}{3}$ of total amount = £48 × 2
= £96

Mr Johnson spent £96.

40% of the remainder = £48

1% of the remainder = £$\left(\frac{48}{40}\right)$
= £1·20

60% of the remainder = £1·20 × 60
= £72

The surfboard cost £72.

£96 – £72 = £24
He spent £24 on the watch.

£24

46 Mrs Taylor has 3 times the number of raffle tickets that Mr Green has. Miss Wallace has $\frac{1}{6}$ as many tickets as Mrs Taylor and 12 fewer raffle tickets than Mr Green.

a How many raffle tickets do they have altogether?

b How many raffle tickets must Mrs Taylor give to Miss Wallace so that the two of them will have the same number of raffle tickets?

Mrs Taylor (before buying)
Mrs Taylor
Mr Green
Miss Wallace
12
?

a 1 unit → 12 raffle tickets
9 units → 12 × 9 = 108 raffle tickets

They have 108 raffle tickets altogether.

b 5 units → 12 × 5 = 60 raffle tickets
60 ÷ 2 = 30

Mrs Taylor must give Miss Wallace 30 raffle tickets.

a 108 raffle tickets

b 30 raffle tickets

Revision 1

Date: __________

Section A

Choose the correct answer for each question.
Write its letter in the box.

1 What is the sum of 1500 and 0·015?

a 151·50 **b** 1515
c 1500·015 **d** 1501·50

[c]

2 Find the value of 36 – 2 × 3 + 6.

a 15 **b** 36
c 48 **d** 56

[b]

3 The shape shown below is not drawn to scale. ABC is an equilateral triangle. DB is a straight line. Find ∠DAB.

a 40°
b 59°
c 124°
d 146°

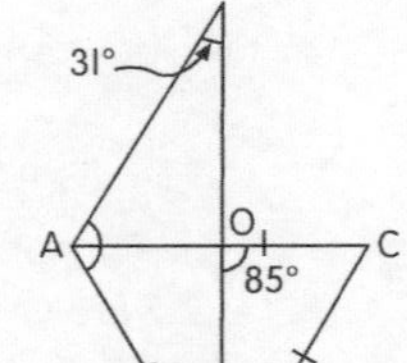

[c]

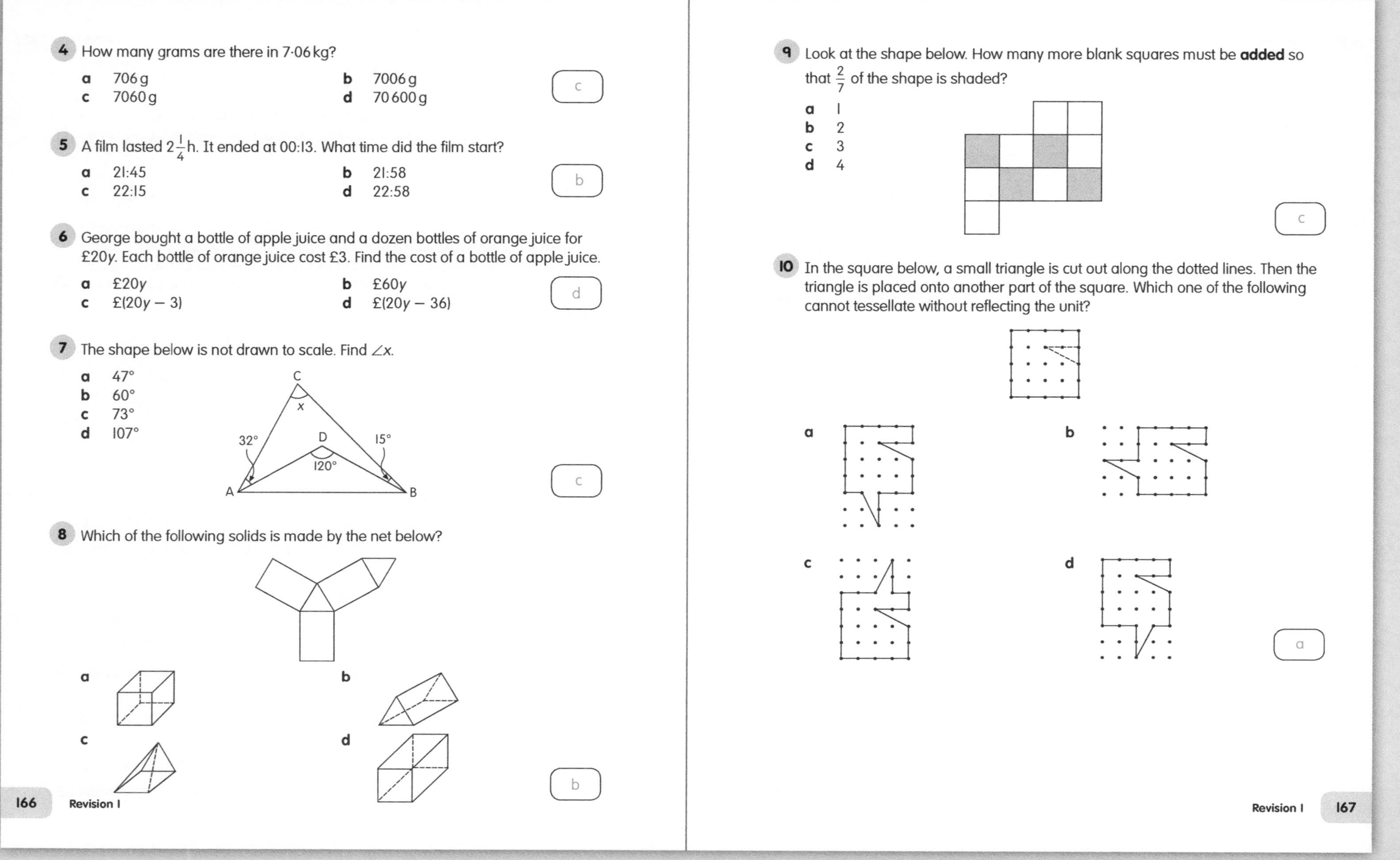

4 How many grams are there in 7·06 kg?

a 706 g b 7006 g
c 7060 g d 70 600 g

c

5 A film lasted $2\frac{1}{4}$ h. It ended at 00:13. What time did the film start?

a 21:45 b 21:58
c 22:15 d 22:58

b

6 George bought a bottle of apple juice and a dozen bottles of orange juice for £20*y*. Each bottle of orange juice cost £3. Find the cost of a bottle of apple juice.

a £20*y* b £60*y*
c £(20*y* − 3) d £(20*y* − 36)

d

7 The shape below is not drawn to scale. Find $\angle x$.

a 47°
b 60°
c 73°
d 107°

c

8 Which of the following solids is made by the net below?

a b
c d

b

9 Look at the shape below. How many more blank squares must be **added** so that $\frac{2}{7}$ of the shape is shaded?

a 1
b 2
c 3
d 4

c

10 In the square below, a small triangle is cut out along the dotted lines. Then the triangle is placed onto another part of the square. Which one of the following cannot tessellate without reflecting the unit?

a b
c d

a

11 Millie has 420 stickers. Ruby has $\frac{3}{5}$ of what Millie has. How many more stickers does Millie have than Ruby?

a 90
b 140
c 152
d 168

d

12 Alisha was $\frac{2}{5}$ of her mum's age in 2015. Her mum was 27 years old in 2007.

When will Alisha's age be $\frac{1}{2}$ of her mum's age?

a 2019
b 2020
c 2021
d 2022

d

13 Which of the following is a net of a triangular pyramid?

a
b
c
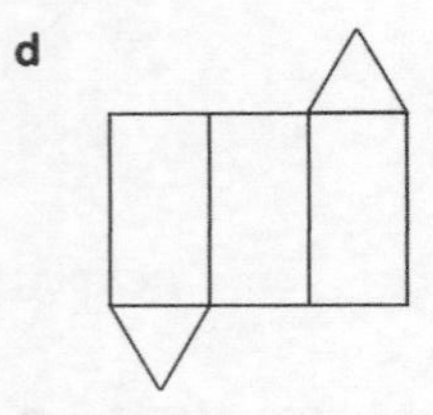
d

b

14 The ratio of the number of men to the number of women at a football match was 4 : 3. The ratio of the number of women to the number of children was 5 : 2. There were 56 more men than children. How many people were there at the football match?

a 164
b 252
c 574
d 2296

a

15 Peter and Miya have £50 altogether. Miya's money is 20% of the total amount of money they have. How much money does Peter have?

a £20
b £30
c £40
d £45

c

Section B

Read the questions and fill in the answers.

16 3 mangoes cost £5r and 8 plums cost £2r. Jason bought 6 mangoes and 4 plums. How much did he pay? Give your answer in terms of r.

£$5r \times 2$ = £$10r$
£$2r \div 2$ = £r
£$10r$ + £r = £$11r$

£ $11r$

17 What is the value of $\frac{2}{5} \times \frac{1}{4}$? Express your answer as a decimal.

$\frac{2}{5} \times \frac{1}{4} = \frac{1}{10}$
$= 0{\cdot}1$

0·1

18 Round 62·098 to the nearest hundredths.

62·10

19 What is the mass of Box B?

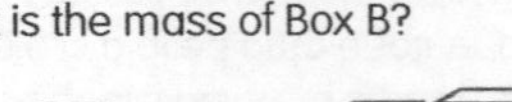
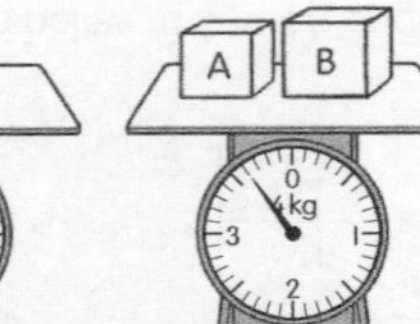
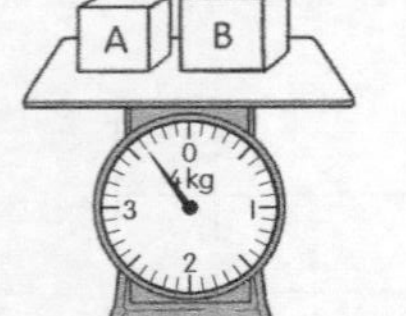

2·2 kg

20 A machine can sew 250 buttons in 15 mins. How many buttons can it sew in 1 hour?

15 mins → 250 buttons
60 mins → 250 × 4 = 1000 buttons

1000 buttons

21 Make the greatest odd number using these digits: 3, 8, 2 and 5.

8523

22 Look at the solid below carefully.

a Count the number of faces on the solid.
b Name the shape(s) of the faces.

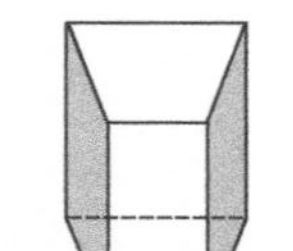

a 6

b rectangle, parallelogram, trapezium

23 Draw all the lines of symmetry for the pattern below. Answers vary

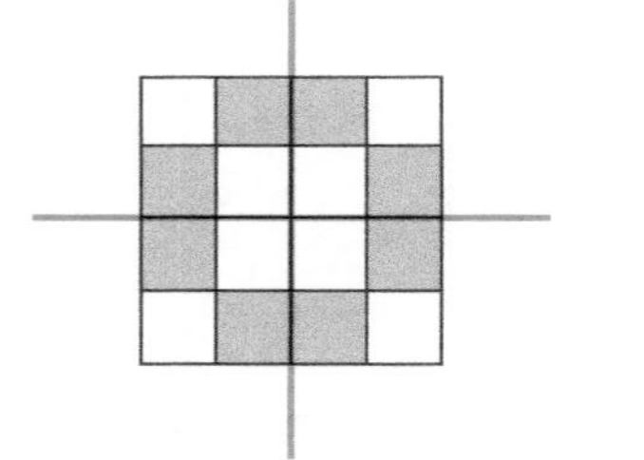

24 PQRS is a trapezium, not drawn to scale, where PS // QR and QR = RS. PQTU is a parallelogram. Find the value of $\angle x$.

124 °

25 The mass of a box of chocolates with 5 equal pieces of chocolate inside was 130 g. After Ella ate 2 pieces of chocolate, the mass of the box of chocolates was 90 g. Find the mass of the empty box.

130 – 90 = 40

2 pieces → 40 g
1 piece → 20 g
5 pieces → 100 g

130 – 100 = 30 g

30 g

26 The diagram below shows 2 sides of an incomplete rhombus. Complete the rhombus and label it ABCD.

a Measure the length of AC and BD.
b How much longer than BD is AC?

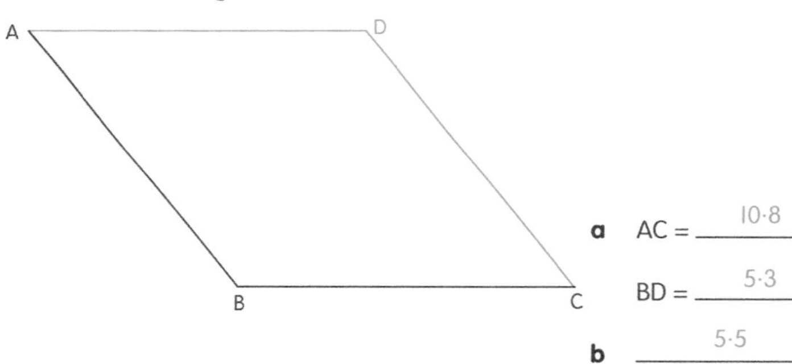

a AC = 10·8 cm

BD = 5·3 cm

b 5·5 cm

27 Draw a parallelogram ABCD where AB = CD = 6 cm, BC = AD = 4·5 cm and ∠ADC = 70°.

Answers vary

D C 70° 110° 4·5 cm 110° 70° A 6 cm B

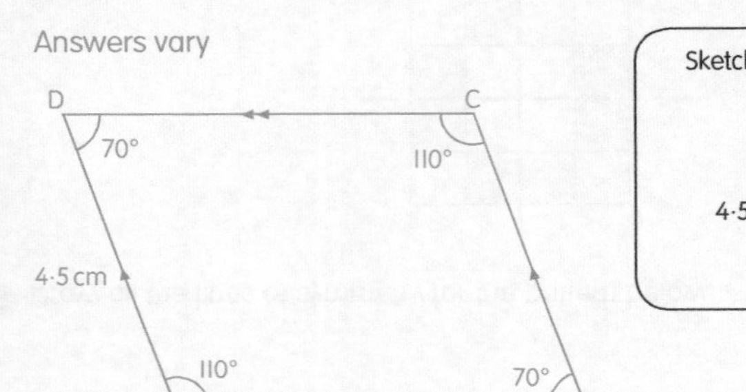

Sketch of Parallelogram ABCD

D C 70° 4·5 cm A 6 cm B

28 Matt bought a cake. He cut off 40% of the cake to give to his friends. He then cut off $\frac{3}{5}$ of the remaining cake to give to his neighbours. Matt had 0·6 kg of cake left. What was the original mass of the cake?

40% | friends | neighbours

2 units → 0·6 kg
1 unit → 0·3 kg
5 units → 1·5 kg

60% → 1·5 kg

$100\% \rightarrow \frac{1 \cdot 5}{60} \times 100$
= 2·5 kg

2·5 kg

29 The ratio of the number of beads in Box A to the number of beads in Box B is 3 : 5. The ratio of the number of beads in Box A to the number of beads in Box B became 1 : 3 when 10 beads were transferred from Box A to Box B. How many beads were there in Box A at first?

Before
Number of beads in Box A : Number of beads in Box B
= 3 : 5 (8 units)

After
Number of beads in Box A : Number of beads in Box B
= 1 : 3
= 2 : 6 (8 units)

3 – 2 = 1 unit
1 unit → 10 beads
3 units → 30 beads

30 beads

30 $\frac{1}{5}$ of Rectangle A and $\frac{2}{7}$ of Rectangle B is shaded. What is the ratio of the shaded area to the area of the whole diagram?

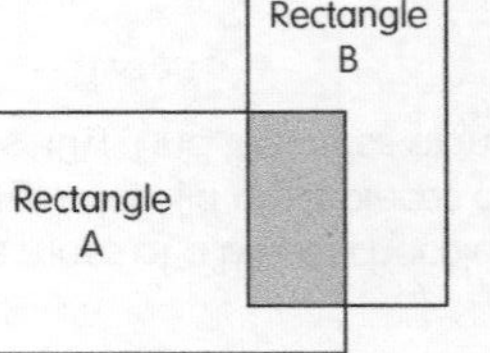

Shaded area : Area of Rectangle A = 1 : 5
= 2 : 10

Shaded area : Area of Rectangle B = 2 : 7

Area of whole diagram = 10 + 7 – 2
= 15 units

2 : 15

Section C

Read the questions and write your answers in the spaces.
Show your workings clearly.

31 Express $8\frac{7}{9}$ as a decimal correct to 2 decimal places.

$8\frac{7}{9} \approx 8{\cdot}78$

32 A shop sells 4 identical hardback books for £165·40 and 5 identical computer games for £170·30. Emily buys 3 books and 3 computer games from the shop.

How much does she have to pay?

£165·40 ÷ 4 = £41·35 (cost of 1 book)
£41·35 × 3 = £124·05 (cost of 3 books)

£170·30 ÷ 5 = £34·06 (cost of 1 computer game)
£34·06 × 3 = £102·18 (cost of 3 computer games)

£124·05 + £102·18 = £226·23
Emily has to pay £226·23.

33 A stadium has 25 460 seats. 25% of them are Category A seats. For a football match, the club requires 40% of the seats to be Category A seats.

Find the increase in the number of Category A seats.

40% − 25% = 15%
15% × 25 460 = 3819

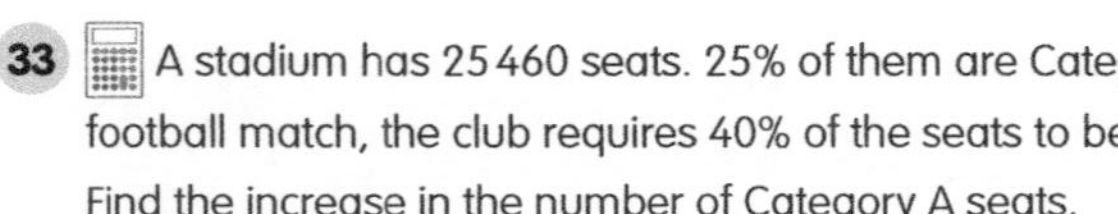

The increase in the number of Category A seats is 3819.

34 The bar graph below shows the number of pets owned by the children in a primary school.

Number of Pets Owned by the Children in a Primary School

Number of children: 0, 20, 40, 60, 80, 100, 120, 140, 160, 180, 200, 220

Number of pets: 0, 1, 2, 3

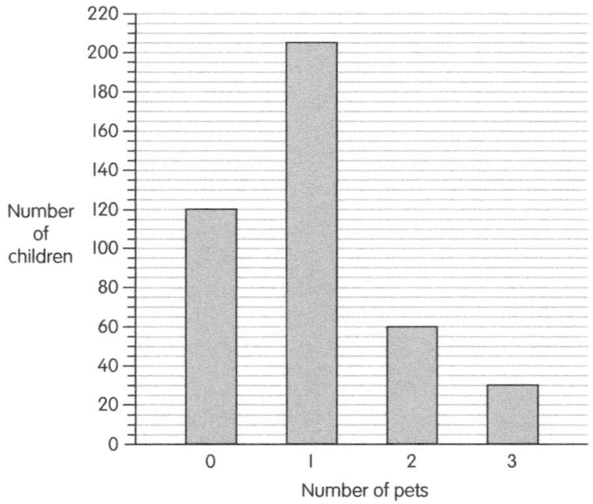

a How many children own a pet?
b How many children own more than 1 pet?

a 205 children own a pet.

b 60 + 30 = 90
90 children own more than 1 pet.

35 The table shows the amount of time Daniel spent on various activities last Saturday. What percentage of Saturday did he spend on other activities?

Activity	Time (h)
Sleep	$7\frac{3}{5}$
Travel	$2\frac{1}{2}$
Watching television	3
Meals	$1\frac{1}{2}$
Exercise	1
Play	$2\frac{2}{5}$
Other activities	?

$7\frac{3}{5} + 2\frac{1}{2} + 3 + 1\frac{1}{2} + 1 + 2\frac{2}{5} = 18$

$24 - 18 = 6$

$\frac{6}{24} \times 100\% = 25\%$

He spent 25% of Saturday on other activities.

36 Mrs Kelly saved a mean amount of £7150 per year from 2011 to 2013. She saved a mean amount of £9646·50 from 2011 to 2014. How much did she save per month in 2014 if she saved the same amount each month?

£7150 × 3 = £21 450
£9646·50 × 4 = £38 586

£38 586 − £21 450 = £17 136
£17 136 ÷ 12 = £1428

She saved £1428 per month in 2014.

37 The table below shows the parking charges at a car park.

For the first hour	£2·05
For every additional 5 mins or less	£0·03

Anna paid £3·10. What is the longest possible time her car was parked in the car park? Give your answer in hours and minutes.

£3·10 − £2·05 = £1·05
£1·05 = 105 pence

105 ÷ 3 = 35

35 × 5 = 175 mins = 2 h 55 mins

2 h 55 mins + 1 h = 3 h 55 mins
The longest possible time that Anna parked her car is 3 h 55 mins.

38 The diagram shows two triangles in a square with a side of 52 cm. Find the area of the shaded part of the diagram.

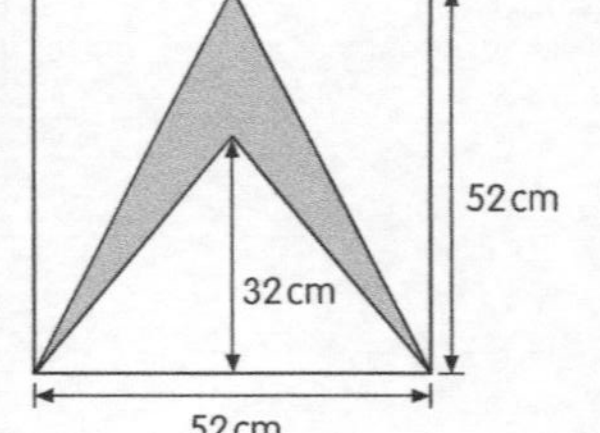

$\frac{1}{2} \times 52 \times 52 = 1352$

$\frac{1}{2} \times 52 \times 32 = 832$

1352 − 832 = 520
The area of the shaded part of the diagram is 520 cm².

39 5 pears and 1 mango cost as much as 2 pears and 2 mangoes. If each mango costs £0·75, find the total cost of 100 pears and 450 mangoes.

5 pears | 1 mango

2 pears | 2 mangoes

The model above shows that:
Cost of 3 pears = Cost of 1 mango
= £0·75

Cost of 1 pear = £0·75 ÷ 3
= £0·25

Cost of 100 pears = £0·25 × 100
= £25

Cost of 450 mangoes = £0·75 × 450
= £337·50

£337·50 + £25 = £362·50

The total cost of 100 pears and 450 mangoes is £362·50.

40 A car showroom had $10y$ cars, $20y$ motorbikes and 18 vans. In a particular month, $4y$ cars, $3y$ motorbikes and 15 vans were sold.

a Find the total number of wheels on the remaining vehicles in terms of y.

b If $y = 21$, how many wheels were there?

a Number of vehicles left
$= (10y - 4y)$ cars, $(20y - 3y)$ motorbikes and $(18 - 15)$ vans
$= 6y$ cars, $17y$ motorbikes and 3 vans

Number of wheels
$= (4 \times 6y) + (2 \times 17y) + (4 \times 3)$
$= 24y + 34y + 12$
$= 58y + 12$

The total number of wheels on the remaining vehicles is $58y + 12$.

b If $y = 21$, $58y + 12 = 58 \times 21 + 12$
$= 1230$

There were 1230 wheels.

41 The table below shows the prices of some items sold at a market.

Fish	Spinach	Carrots	Prawns	Melon
£2·99 per 100 g	£0·11 per 100 g	£0·26 per 100 g	£1·09 per 100 g	£0·32 per 100 g

Mrs Howard bought a fish with a mass of $2\frac{1}{2}$ kg, $\frac{1}{2}$ kg of carrots, $1\frac{1}{2}$ kg of prawns and a melon with a mass of 1·6 kg. How much did she pay for the items altogether?

$2\frac{1}{2}$ kg = 2500 g
£2·99 × 25 = £74·75 (cost of fish)

$\frac{1}{2}$ kg = 500 g
£0·26 × 5 = £1·30 (cost of carrots)

$1\frac{1}{2}$ kg = 1500 g
£1·09 × 15 = £16·35 (cost of prawns)

1·6 kg = 1600 g
£0·32 × 16 = £5·12 (cost of melon)

£74·75 + £1·30 + £16·35 + £5·12 = £97·52
She paid £97·52 for the items altogether.

42 24% of the mass of the vegetables in a box were potatoes and the remaining mass were carrots. The mass of the vegetables in the box were 5400 g. Mr Anderson added more potatoes into the box and the percentage of potatoes in the box increased to 52%. All the potatoes and 60% of the carrots in the box were sold.

a Find the mass of potatoes added into the box in kilograms.
b Find the mass of carrots that were not sold.

a 24% × 5400 g = 1296 g (mass of potatoes at first)
5400 g − 1296 g = 4104 g (mass of carrots at first)

48% → 4104 g
1% → 85·5 g
52% → 4446 g

4446 − 1296 = 3150

3150 g = 3·15 kg
3·15 kg of potatoes was added into the box.

b 40% × 4104 = 1641·6
1641·6 g of carrots were not sold.

43

1st 2nd 3rd

The table below shows the number of sticks required to make the shapes above.

Position	Number of Sticks Used
1st	4
2nd	10
3rd	18
...	...
5th	?
...	...
?	54

a How many sticks are needed to make the 5th shape?
b If 54 sticks are used, what is the position of the shape made?

a 1st → 4
2nd → 4 + 6 = 10
3rd → 4 + 6 + 8 = 18
4th → 4 + 6 + 8 + 10 = 28
5th → 4 + 6 + 8 + 10 + 12 = 40

40 sticks are needed to make the 5th shape.

b If 54 sticks are used, the shape made will be in the 6th position.

44 Miss Clark saved £345 in £5, £10 and £50 notes. There were 35 notes altogether. She had 4 more £10 notes than £50 notes. How many £5 notes did she have?

Using guess and check:

£5	£10	£50	Total Amount
27	6	2	£295
25	7	3	£345 ✓

She had twenty-five £5 notes.

45 Mr Barnes has some raffle tickets. If he sends 4 tickets each to some schools, he will need 20 more tickets. However, if he sends 3 tickets each to the same schools, he will have a remainder of 50 tickets. How many tickets does he have?

If Mr Barnes sends 3 tickets to each school:

total number of tickets

3 3 ... 3 3 50

If Mr Barnes sends 4 tickets to each school:

4 4 ... 4 4

20 tickets short

50 + 20 = 70

The model above shows that:
If Mr Barnes wants to send 1 more ticket to each school, he will require 70 more tickets. Therefore, there are 70 schools.

70 × 3 + 50 = 260
Mr Barnes has 260 tickets.

46 Jack and Miya had some cards. In a game, Jack lost $\frac{1}{10}$ of his cards to Miya. After Jack lost his cards to Miya, the ratio of the number of cards Jack had to the number of cards Miya had was 3 : 1. The next day, after Jack lost more cards to Miya, the ratio became 4 : 7 and Miya had 72 more cards than Jack.

a What was the ratio of the number of cards Jack had to the number of cards Miya had at first?
b How many cards did Miya win from Jack altogether?

a Number of cards Jack had : Number of cards Miya had
= 3 : 1
= 9 : 3 (after)
10 : 2 (before)
= 5 : 1
The ratio was 5 : 1 at first.

b 7 – 4 = 3
3 units → 72 cards
1 unit → 24 cards
7 units → 7 × 24 = 168 cards (number of cards Miya has)
11 units → 11 × 24 = 264 cards (total number of cards)

At first 6 units → 264 cards
1 unit → 44 cards

168 – 44 = 124
Miya won 124 cards altogether.

47 In the trapezium below, not drawn to scale, ACDF is a parallelogram, BD and DF are straight lines, ∠FAC = 68° and ∠ACE = 56°.

a Name an angle equal to ∠DFA.
b Find ∠CEF.
c If ∠ABC is 20° more than ∠BAC, find ∠ABC.

A F 68° E 56° B C D

a ∠ACD is equal to ∠DFA.

b Method 1
∠ACD = 180° – 68°
= 112°

∠ECD = 112° – 56°
= 56°

∠CDE = 68°

∠DEC = 180° – 56° – 68°
= 56°

∠CEF = 180° – 56°
= 124°

Method 2
∠CEF = 180° – 56°
= 124°

c ∠BCA = 180° – 112°
= 68°

∠ABC + ∠CAB = 180° – 68°
= 112°

112° – 20° = 92°
92° ÷ 2 = 46°

∠ABC = 46° + 20°
= 66°

48 Mr Lim, Mr Bell and Mrs Walker paid for a meal. Mr Lim paid $\frac{1}{5}$ of the amount Mr Bell and Mrs Walker paid together. Mr Bell paid $\frac{1}{4}$ of the amount Mr Lim and Mrs Walker paid.

a What fraction of the total cost of the meal did Mrs Walker pay?

b If the meal cost £205·20, how much did Mr Lim pay?

Mr Lim | Mr Bell & Mrs Walker

Mr Bell | Mr Lim & Mrs Walker

a $\frac{1}{6} + \frac{1}{5} = \frac{11}{30}$

$1 - \frac{11}{30} = \frac{19}{30}$

Mrs Walker paid $\frac{19}{30}$ of the meal.

b 30 units → £205·20 or $\frac{1}{6} \times$ £205·20 = £34·20

1 unit → £6·84

5 units → £34·20

Mr Lim paid £34·20.

HEURISTICS-BASED QUESTIONS

Heuristic 1: Draw a model

Example

In a mixture of red and white paint, there is 25% more white paint than red paint. How many litres of each colour of paint are there in 5 ℓ of the mixture?

Solution:

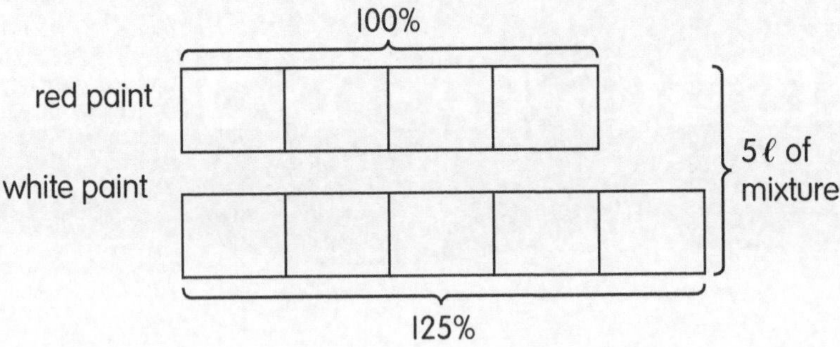

From the model: 9 units → 5 ℓ

1 unit → $\frac{5}{9}$ ℓ

4 units → $4 \times \frac{5}{9} = \frac{20}{9}$ ℓ $= 2\frac{2}{9}$ ℓ and

5 units → $5 \times \frac{5}{9} = \frac{25}{9}$ ℓ $= 2\frac{7}{9}$ ℓ

There are $2\frac{2}{9}$ ℓ of red paint and $2\frac{7}{9}$ ℓ of white paint in 5 ℓ of the mixture.

Heuristic 2: Look for patterns

Example

Diagram 1

Diagram 2

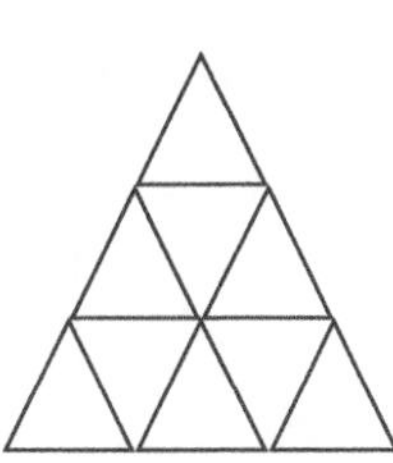

Diagram 3

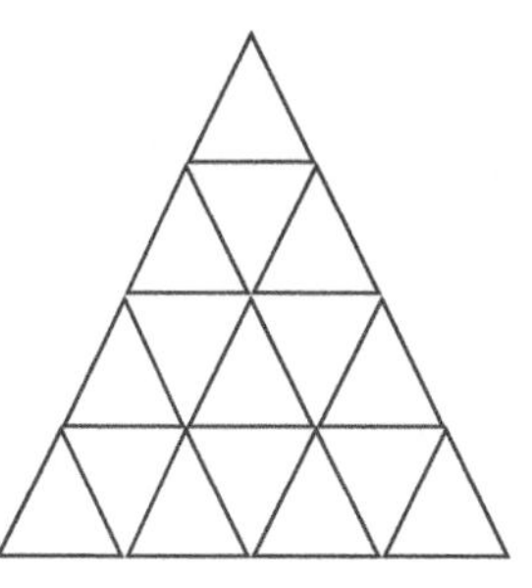

Diagram 4

The number of sticks used to build each diagram is shown in the table below.

Diagram	1	2	3	4
Number of sticks	3 = 1 × 3	9 = 3 × 3	18 = 6 × 3	30 = 10 × 3

Find the number of sticks in

(a) Diagram 5

(b) Diagram 10.

Solution:

From the pattern, the numbers multiplied by 3 in Diagram 1 to Diagram 4 are 1, 3, 6 and 10.

Now, Diagram 1: 1 = 1

Diagram 2: 3 = 1 + 2

Diagram 3: 6 = 1 + 2 + 3

Diagram 4: 10 = 1 + 2 + 3 + 4

so Diagram 5: 1 + 2 + 3 + 4 + 5 = 15

15 × 3 = 45

Diagram 10: 1 + 2 + 3 + 4 + 5 + 6 + 7 + 8 + 9 + 10 = 55

55 × 3 = 165

The number of sticks in Diagram 5 is 45.

The number of sticks in Diagram 10 is 165.

Heuristic 3: Act it out / draw a diagram

Example 1

A tangram is a square made up of 7 pieces, as shown below.

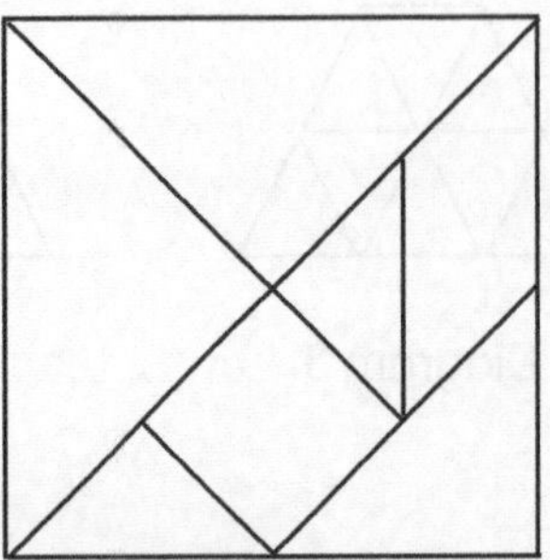

Use all 7 pieces of the tangram to make

(a) a right-angled isosceles triangle

(b) a parallelogram.

Solution:

(a) (b)

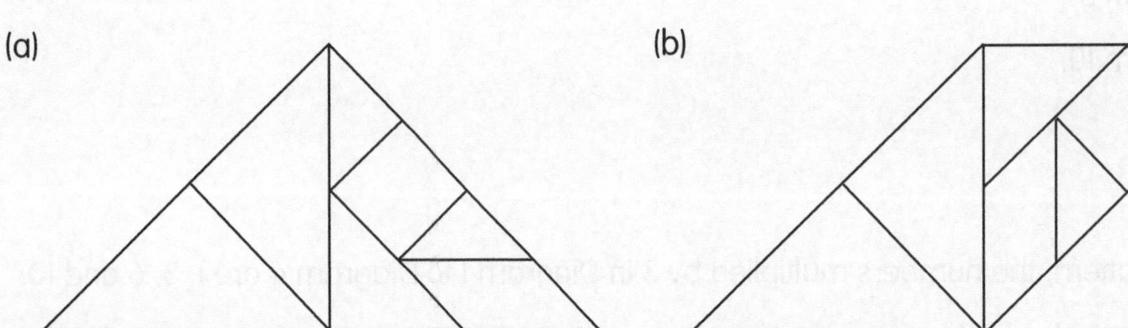

(Note: Different orientations of the above arrangements are possible.)

Example 2

From the rectangle shown, a triangle is cut out and placed in different positions to make two shapes, A and B.

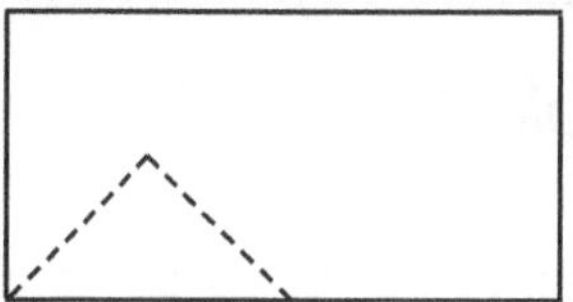

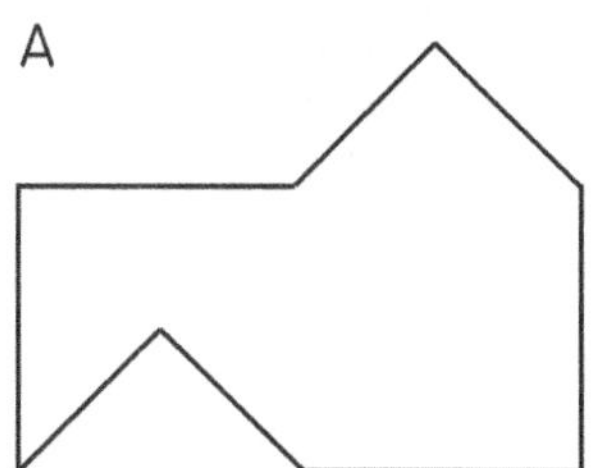

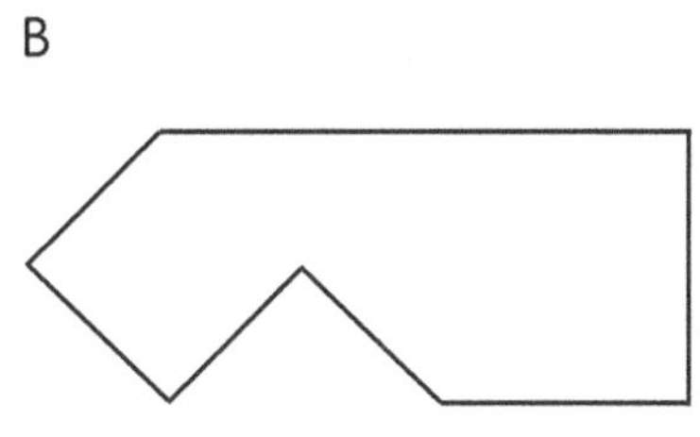

Can the above shapes tessellate?

Solution:

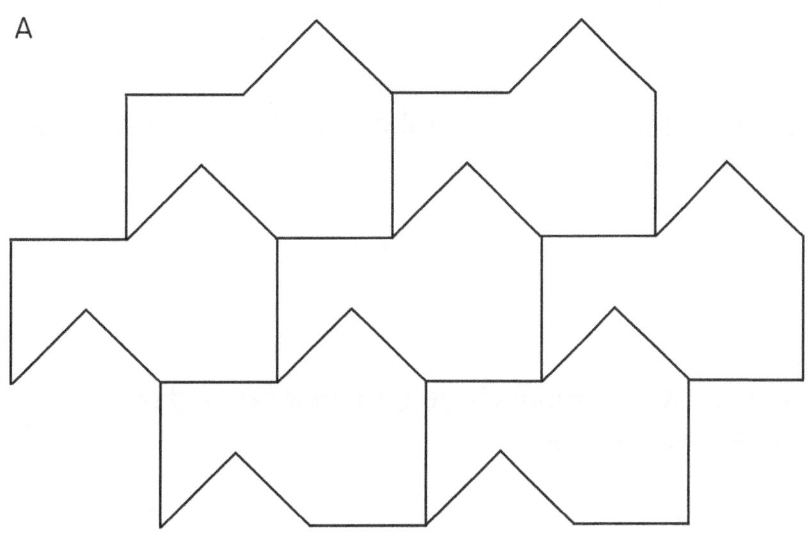

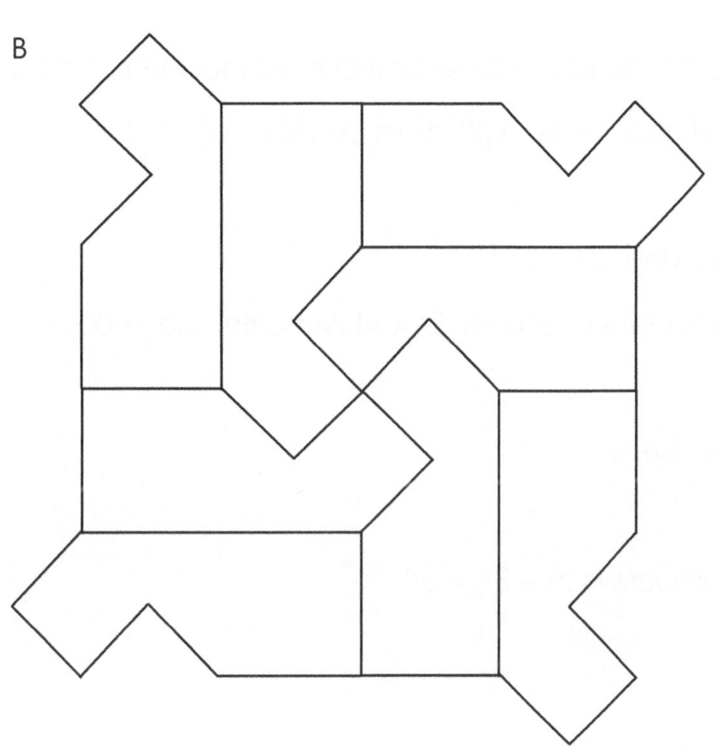

Heuristic 4: Guess and check

Example 1

Jack thinks of a two-digit number. He reverses the order of the digits to get a second number. When he adds these two numbers, he gets 165. What number could Jack be thinking of?

Solution:

Since the last digit of 165 is 5, the two digits in the starting number must add up to 5 or 15.

The possible pairs of numbers with digits reversed are:
14 + 41, 23 + 32, 50 + 5, 69 + 96 or 78 + 87.

On checking, the four possible starting numbers are 69, 78, 87 and 96.

Example 2

The difference between two numbers is 20 and their product is 741.
What is the sum of the two numbers?

Solution:

Since the difference is 20, the two numbers must have the same ones digit.

Since the product is 741, their ones digits must be either 1 or 9.

Try 11 and 31, 19 and 39, and 21 and 41.

We don't need to guess further because 21×41 is greater than 800.

On checking, $19 \times 39 = 741$.

The sum of the two numbers is $19 + 39 = 58$.

Heuristic 5: Simplify the problem

Example

The sum of the angles in a triangle is 180°. What is the sum of the angles in:

(a) a four-sided shape?

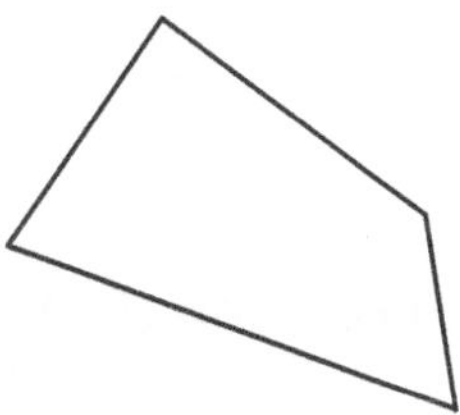

(b) a five-sided shape?

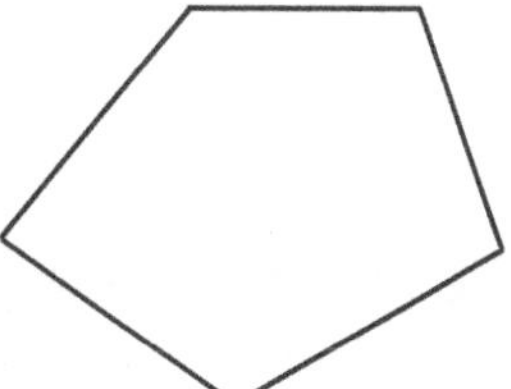

Solution:

(a) Simplify the problem by drawing a line across the shape to make 2 triangles.

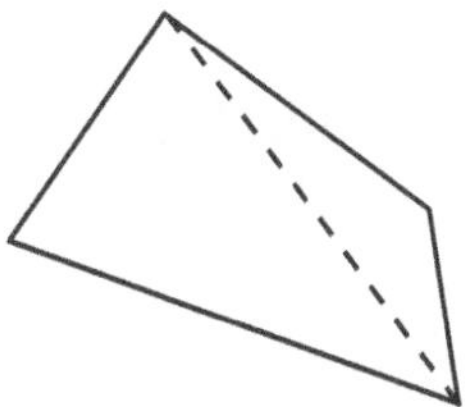

Sum of angles in a four-sided shape = 2 × 180° = 360°

(b) Simplify the problem by drawing two lines across the shape to make 3 triangles.

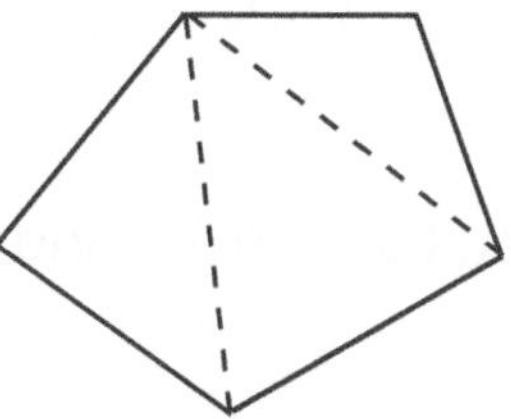

Sum of angles in a five-sided shape = 3 × 180° = 540°

Heuristic 6: Make a systematic list

Example 1

Miya thinks of a three-digit odd number. The digit in the hundreds place is less than 3 but not 0. The digit in the tens place is greater than 7. If the sum of the digits is 18, what number is Miya thinking of? There is more than one possible answer.

Solution:

The digit in the hundreds place is 1 or 2, the digit in the tens place is 8 or 9 and the digit in the ones place is 1, 3, 5, 7 or 9. Make a list of the possible numbers.

181	191	281	291
183	193	283	293
185	195	285	295
187	197	287	***297***
189	199	289	299

The numbers in which the sum of the digits is 18 are 189 and 297.

Example 2

In a right-angled triangle ABC, the sum of the sides AB and BC is 10 cm. If each of these sides is a whole number of centimetres, what is the greatest possible area of the triangle?

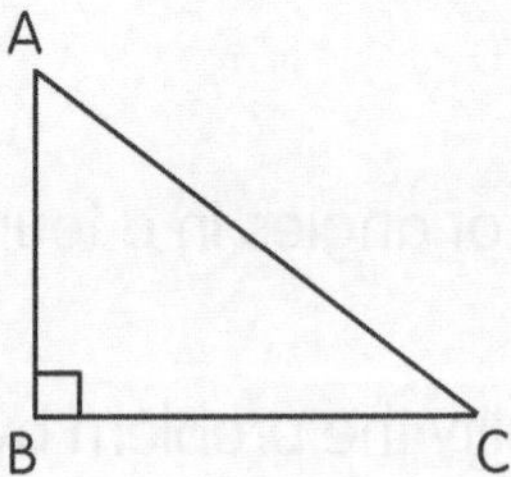

Solution:

Make a list of the possible lengths of AB and BC and the corresponding areas of the triangles.

Length of AB (cm)	Length of BC (cm)	Area of triangle ABC (cm^2)
1	9	4·5
2	8	8
3	7	10·5
4	6	12
5	5	12·5
6	4	12

The greatest possible area of triangle ABC is 12·5 cm^2.

Heuristic 7: Work backwards

Example 1

Chantal had some money. She spent $\frac{1}{6}$ of it on Monday, $\frac{2}{5}$ of the remainder on Tuesday and £16 on Wednesday. If she had £20 left, how much money did she have to begin with?

Solution:

Working backwards, she had £20 + £16 = £36 before Wednesday.

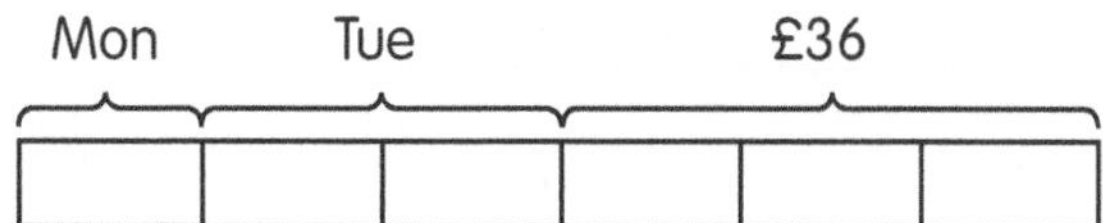

Based on the model: 3 units → £36

1 unit → £12

6 units → £72

Chantal had £72 to begin with.

Example 2

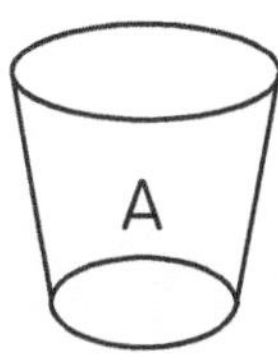

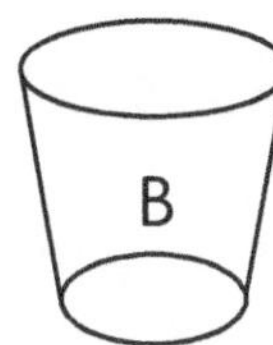

Each of the three buckets, A, B and C, contains some water. When 2 ℓ of water are poured from A to B, 4 ℓ from B to C and 3 ℓ from C to A, each bucket then contains 6 ℓ of water. How much water was in each bucket to begin with?

Solution:

Work backwards from the amount of water now in each bucket.

	A	B	C
	6 ℓ	6 ℓ	6 ℓ
Pour 3 ℓ from A to C:	3 ℓ	6 ℓ	9 ℓ
Pour 4 ℓ from C to B:	3 ℓ	10 ℓ	5 ℓ
Pour 2 ℓ from B to A:	5 ℓ	8 ℓ	5 ℓ

A contained 5 ℓ, B contained 8 ℓ and C contained 5 ℓ of water to begin with.

Heuristic 8: Before and after

Example

A tour group had 35 people in it. 20% of the group were men. Some more men joined the tour and the percentage of men went up to 30%. How many more men joined the tour?

Solution:

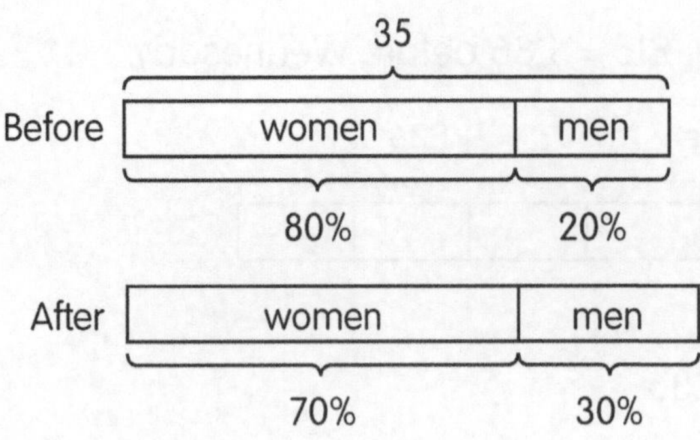

Before: Number of men $= \frac{20}{100} \times 35 = 7$

Number of women $= 35 - 7 = 28$

After: 70% of the group = 28

30% of the group $= \frac{30}{70} \times 28 = 12$

$12 - 7 = 5$

5 more men joined the tour.

Heuristic 9: Solve part of the problem

Example

Sue scored a mean of 64 marks in three maths tests.

(a) If her three test scores were in the ratio 4 : 5 : 7, what was her score in each test?

(b) If she takes another test, how many marks must she get to increase her mean score in the four tests to 68?

Solution:

Solve the problem in steps.

Step 1: Total marks scored in 3 tests = $3 \times 64 = 192$

Step 2: Since her test scores were in the ratio 4 : 5 : 7,

score in first test = $\frac{4}{16} \times 192 = 48$

score in second test = $\frac{5}{16} \times 192 = 60$

score in third test = $192 - 48 - 60 = 84$

Step 3: Total marks scored in 4 tests = $4 \times 68 = 272$

$272 - 192 = 80$ marks

(a) She scored 48 in the first test, 60 in the second and 84 in the third.

(b) She must get 80 marks in a fourth test.

Heuristic 10: Make a supposition

Example 1

There are 128 birds and bees in a wood. There are a total of 360 legs. How many birds and bees are there in the wood?

Solution:

Suppose all the 128 creatures are birds.

The number of legs = 2 × 128 = 256

However, there are 360 − 256 = 104 more legs than this.

Each bee has 4 more legs than a bird.

Therefore the number of bees = 104 ÷ 4
= 26

128 − 26 = 102

There are 26 bees and 102 birds.

Example 2

Abby thinks of a number. She divides it by 2 and adds 15. Then she subtracts half the number she thought of and multiplies the result by 3. Show that, no matter what number Abby is thinking of, she will always get 45 as her final answer.

Solution:

Suppose the number Abby thinks of is x.

x divided by 2: $\frac{x}{2}$

Add 15 to $\frac{x}{2}$: $15 + \frac{x}{2}$

Subtract $\frac{1}{2}$ of x from $15 + \frac{x}{2}$: $15 + \frac{x}{2} - \frac{x}{2}$

$= 15$

Multiply 15 by 3: 3 × 15 = 45

Her final answer will always be 45.

PHOTOCOPY MASTERS

Unit 1: Algebra

Activity (Pupil Textbook 6A, p 10)

a	b	x	y
z	3	5	8
	12	30	

Unit 2: Angles in Shapes and Diagrams

Maths Journal (Pupil Textbook 6A, p32)

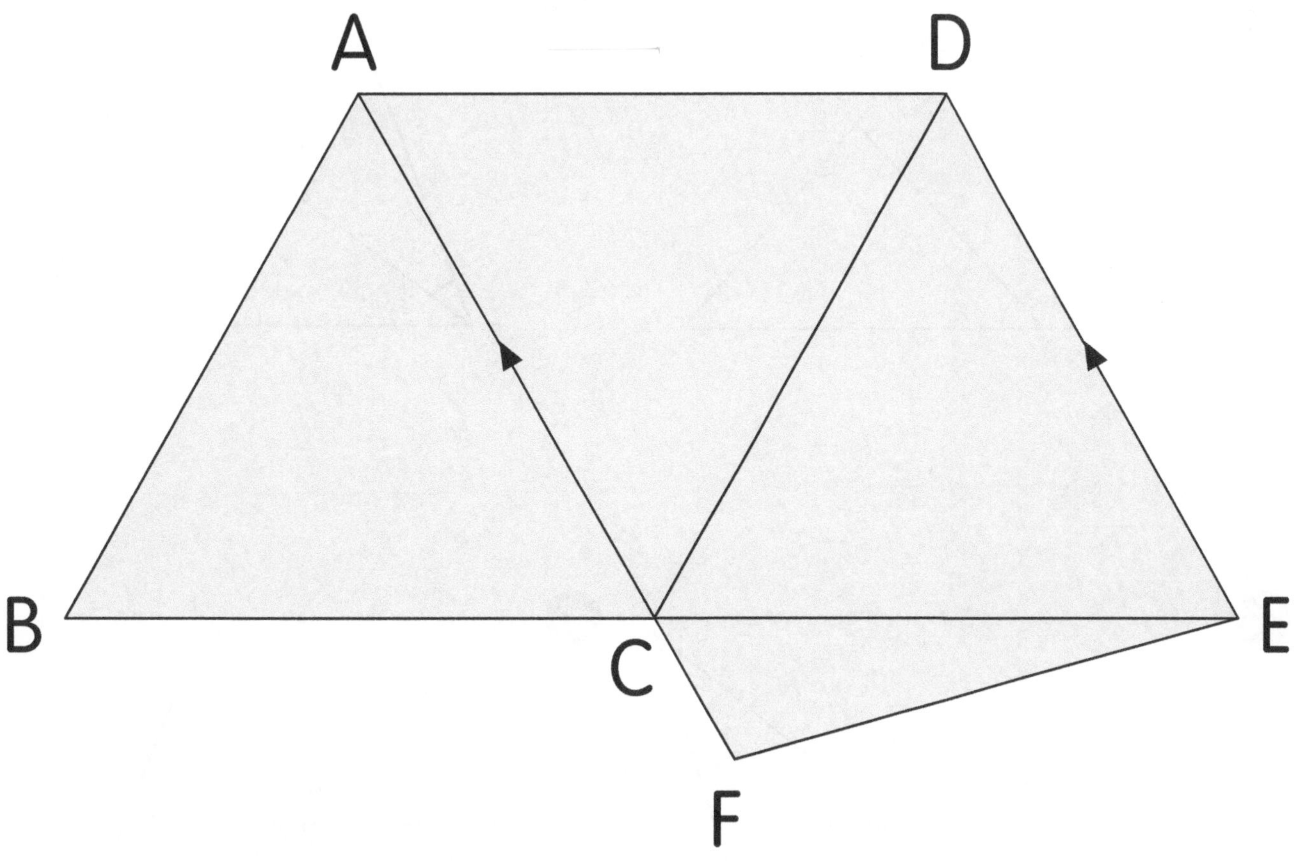

The shape above is not drawn to scale. ABCD is a rhombus and CFED is a trapezium in which DE // AF. BE and AF are straight lines. Using '+', '=', '180°' or '360°', state the relationship between the angles in each set.

For example, in **a**, ∠ABC = ∠ADC.

a ∠ABC and ∠ADC

b ∠ACB and ∠ECF

c ∠AFE and ∠DEF

d ∠ACB and ∠BCF

e ∠CAD and ∠ACD

f ∠ACB, ∠ACD and ∠DCE

g ∠BCD, ∠DCF and ∠BCF

Unit 2: Angles in Shapes and Diagrams

Let's Practise! (Pupil Textbook 6A, pp 33 and 34)

20

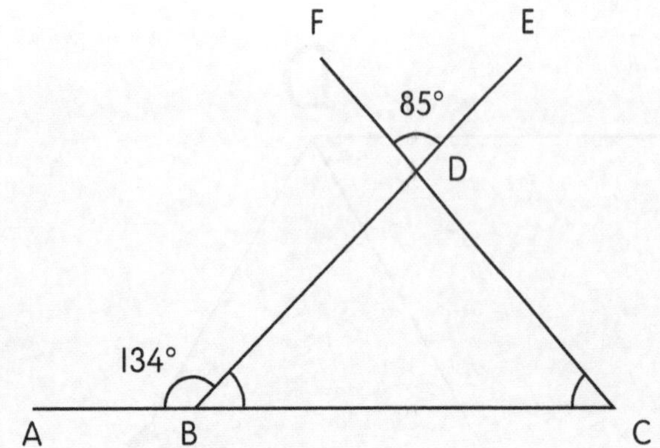

21

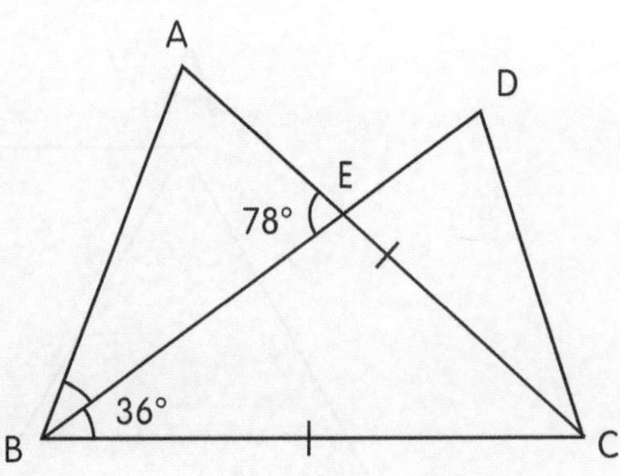

22

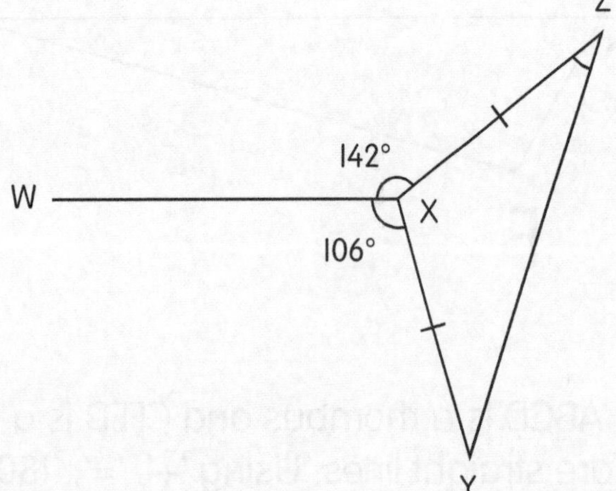

23

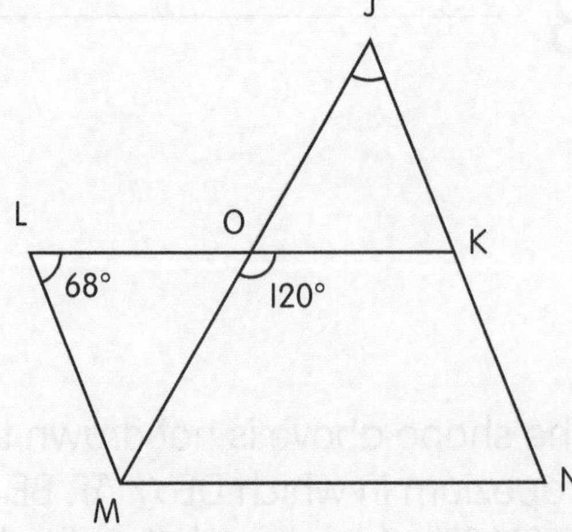

24

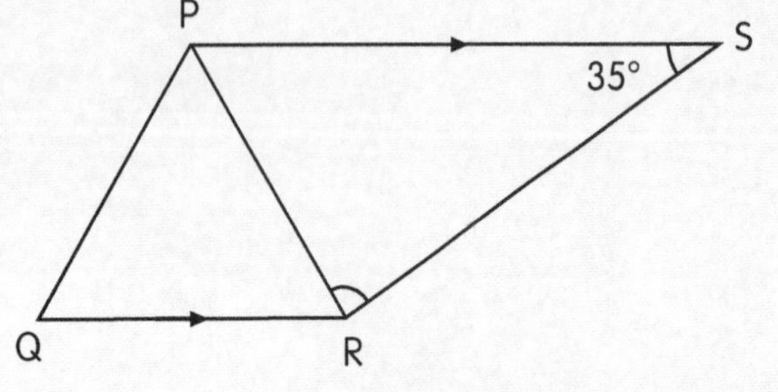

25

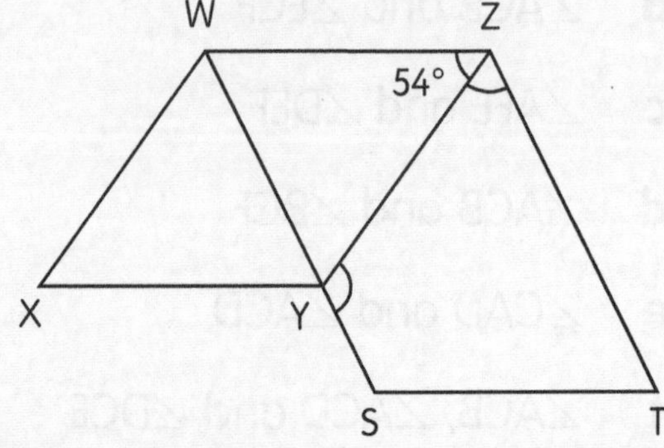

Unit 3: Nets

Let's Learn (Pupil Textbook 6A, p43)

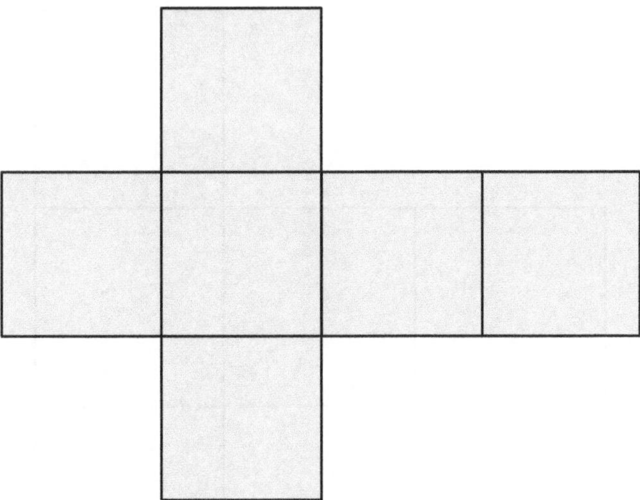

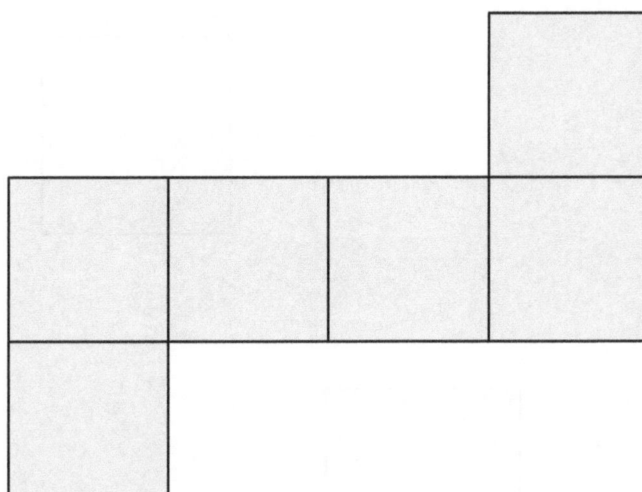

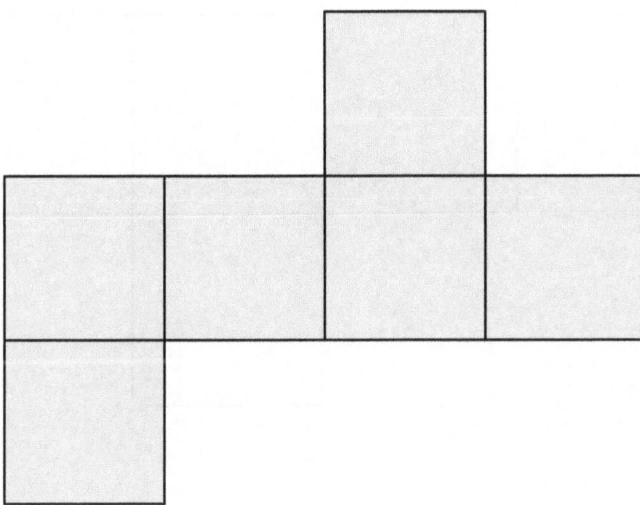

Unit 3: Nets

Activity (Pupil Textbook 6A, p 44)

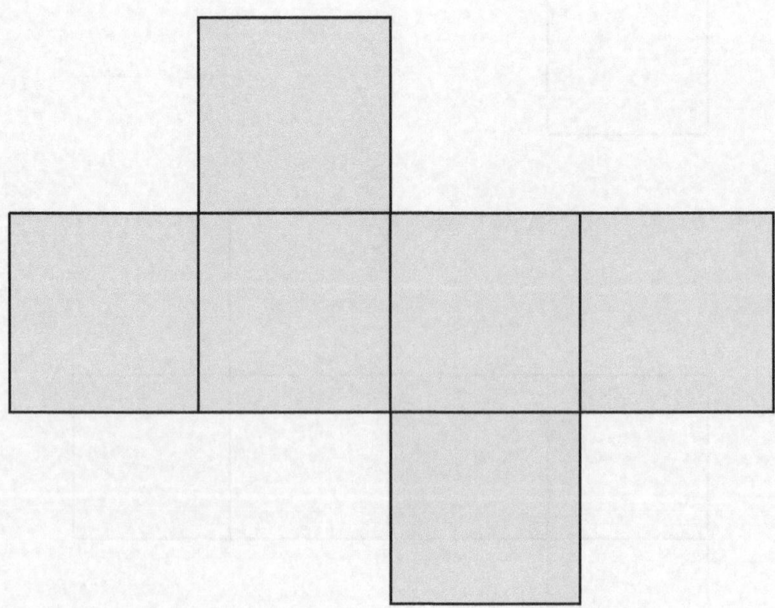

Unit 3: Nets

Let's Learn! (Pupil Textbook 6A, p 44),
Activity (Pupil Textbook 6A, p 44)

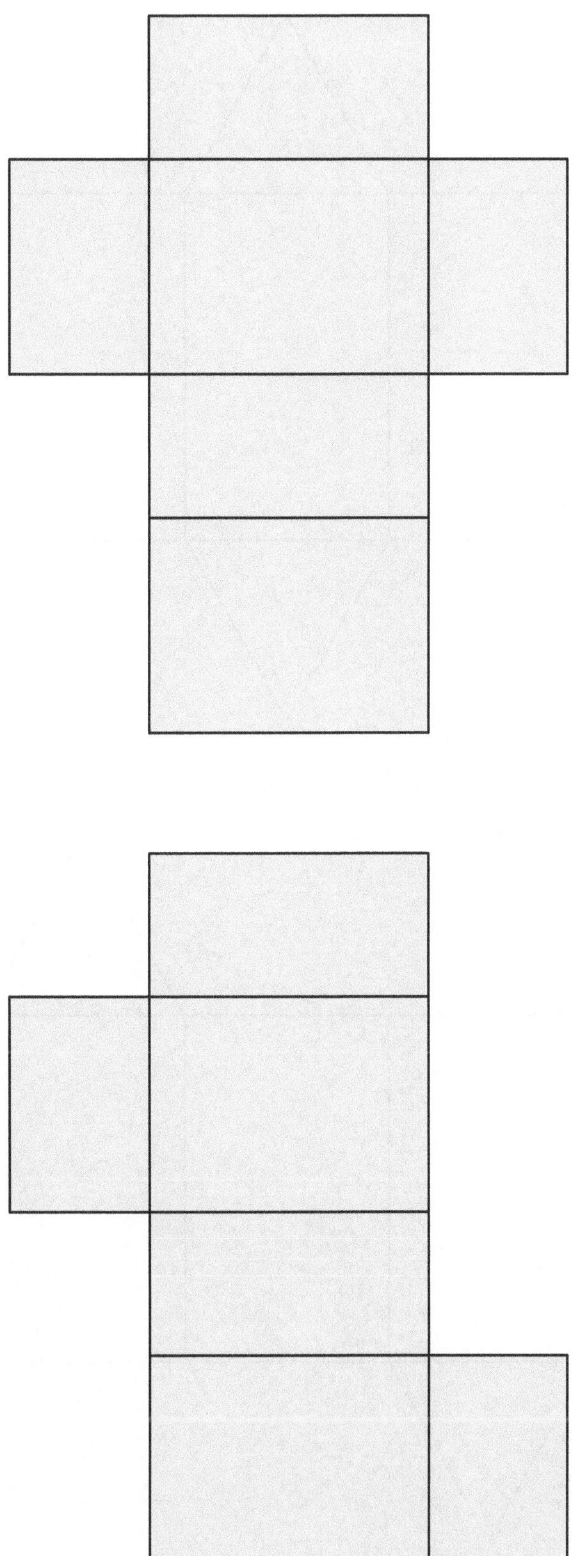

Unit 3: Nets

Let's Learn! (Pupil Textbook 6A, p 45),
Activity (Pupil Textbook 6A, p 46)

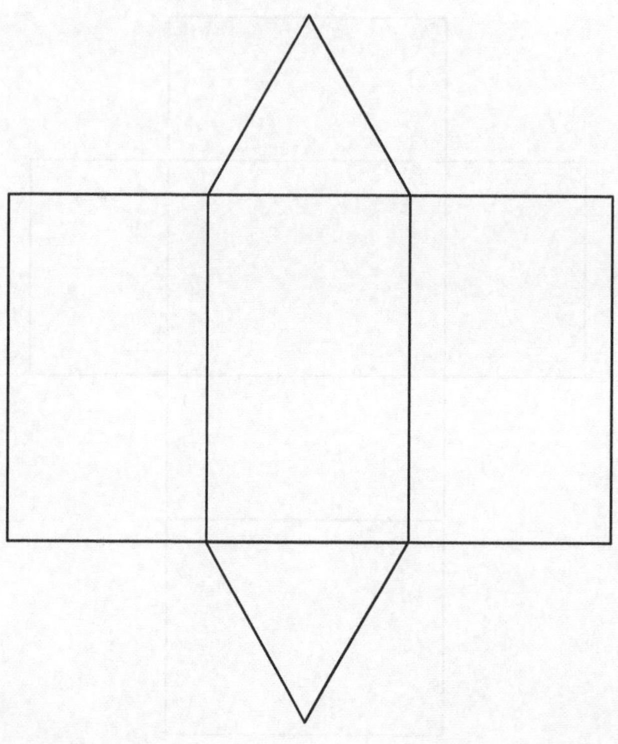

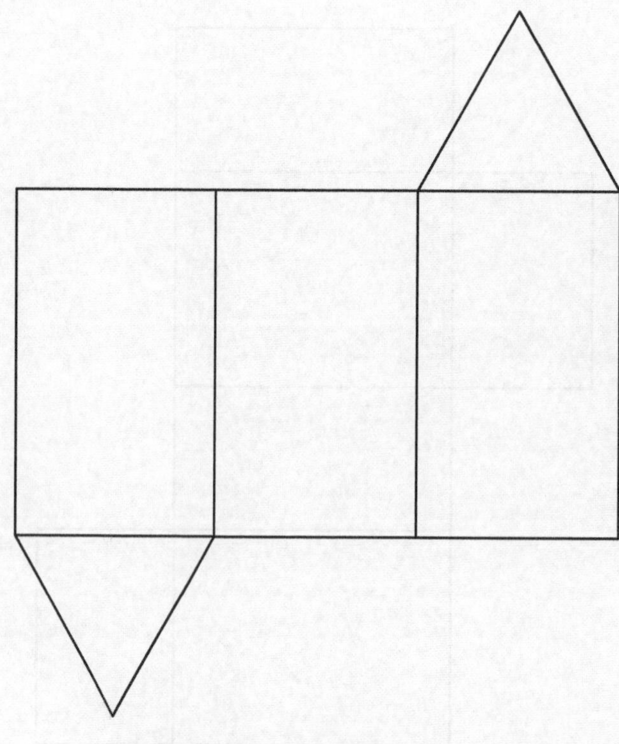

Unit 3: Nets

Let's Learn! (Pupil Textbook 6A, p 45),
Activity (Pupil Textbook 6A, p 46)

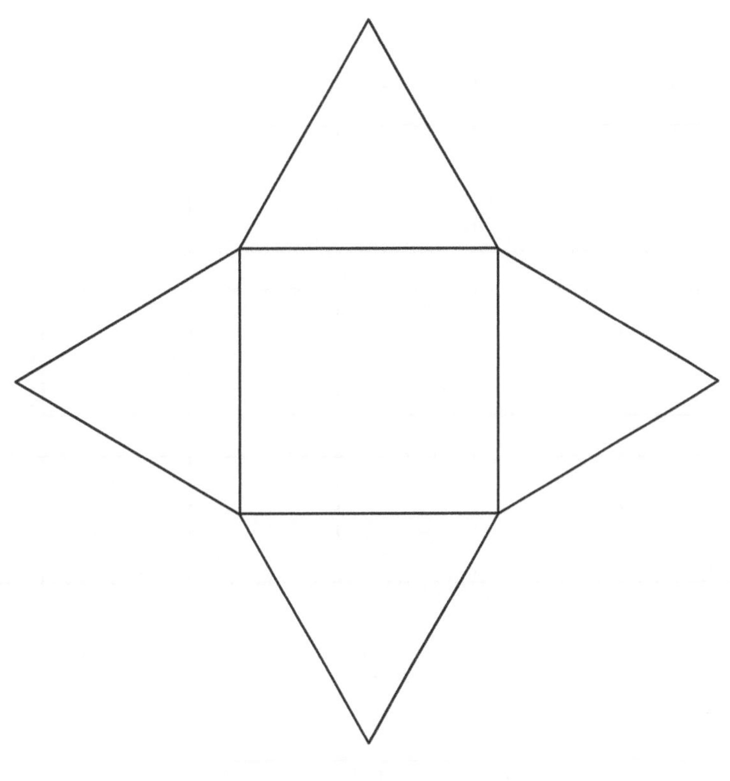

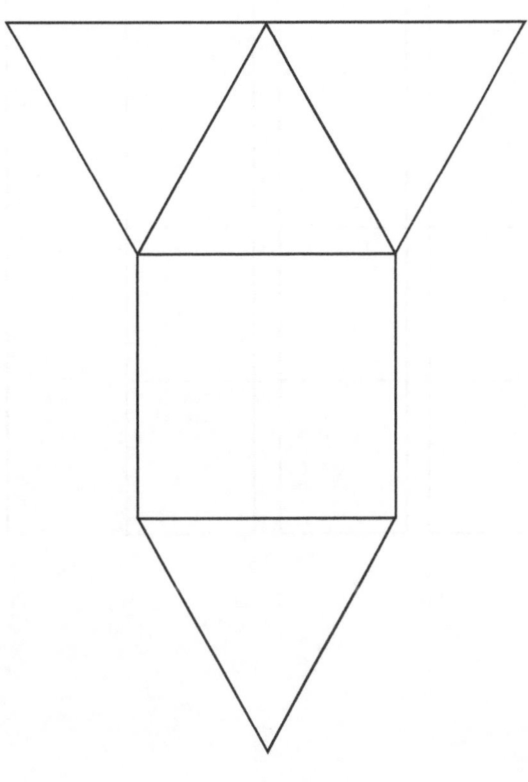

Unit 4: Fractions

Activity (Pupil Textbook 6A, pp 56, 59 and 62)

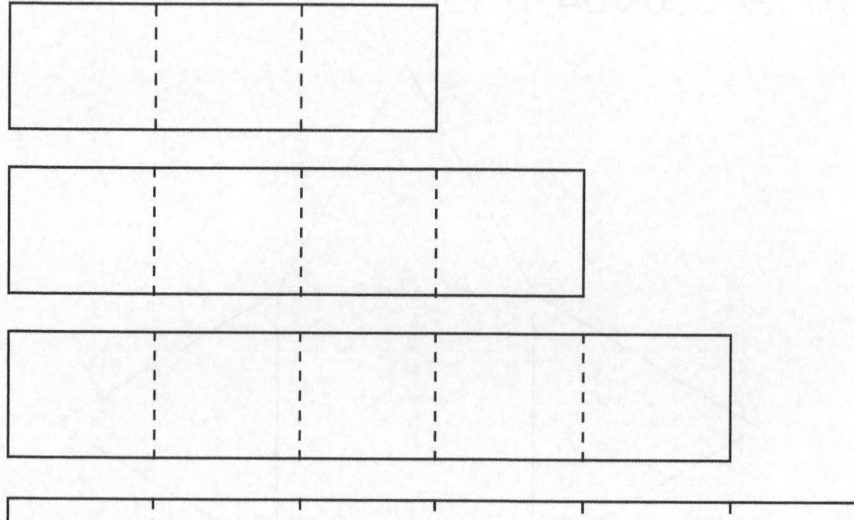

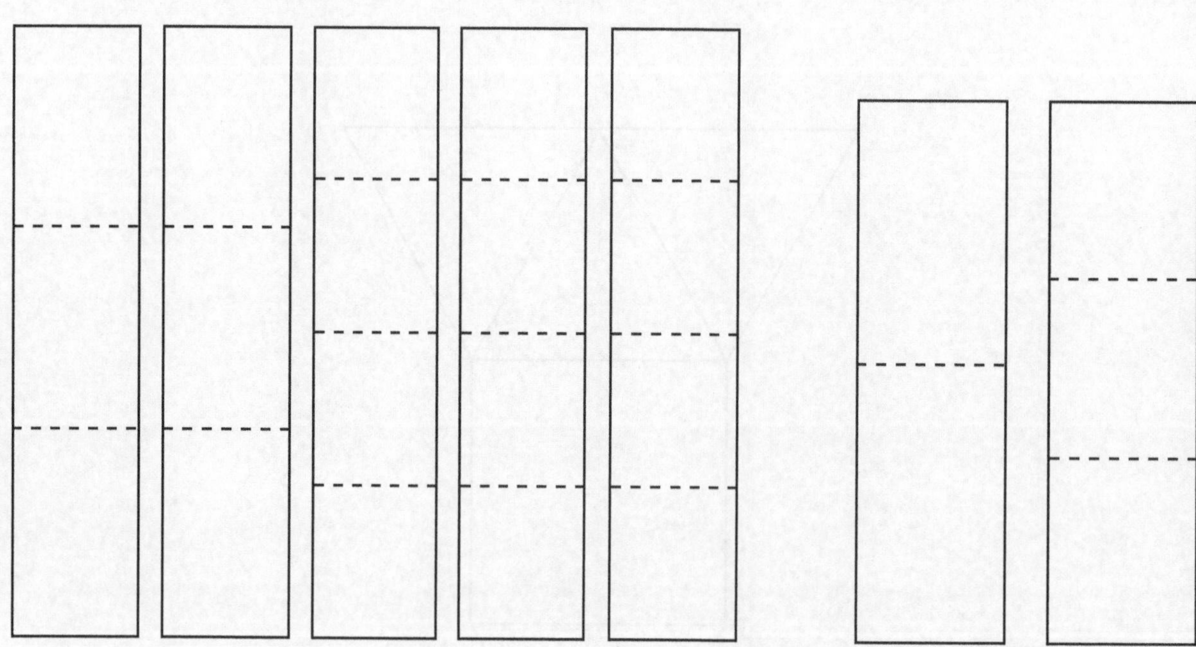

Unit 5: Ratio

Activity (Pupil Textbook 6A, p 100)

Group	A	B	C	D	E	F	G
Number of green beans	3						
Number of red beans	2						

Square grid paper

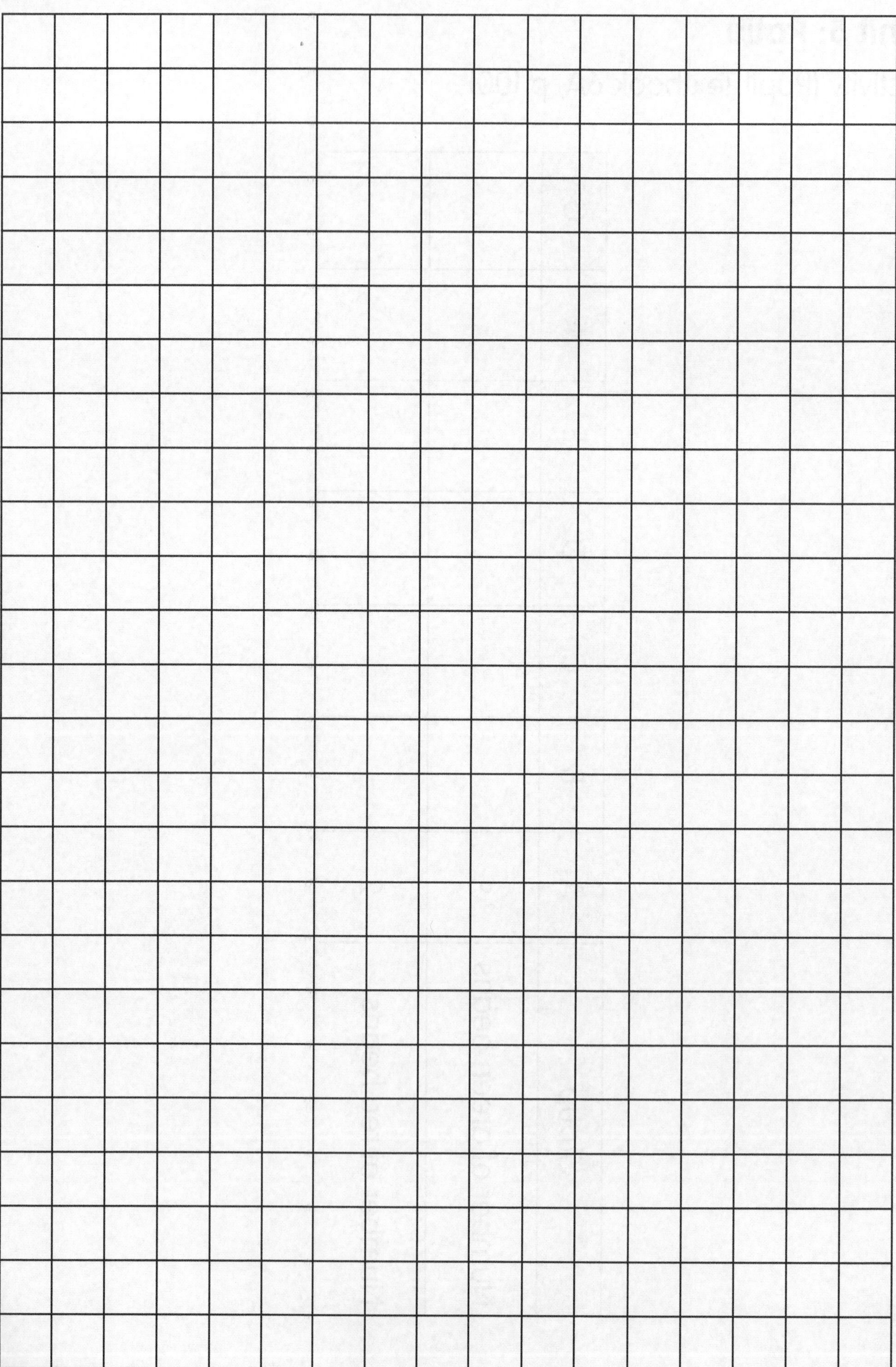